HEINEMANN MODULAR MATHEMATICS
for
LONDON AS AND A-LEVEL

Statis

Greg Attwood

1 Mathemati
  statistics
2 Collection
3 Graphical r
4 Methods fc

Review exercise

5 Probability
6 Random va
7 Discrete dis
8 Continuous

Review exercise

Examination ty

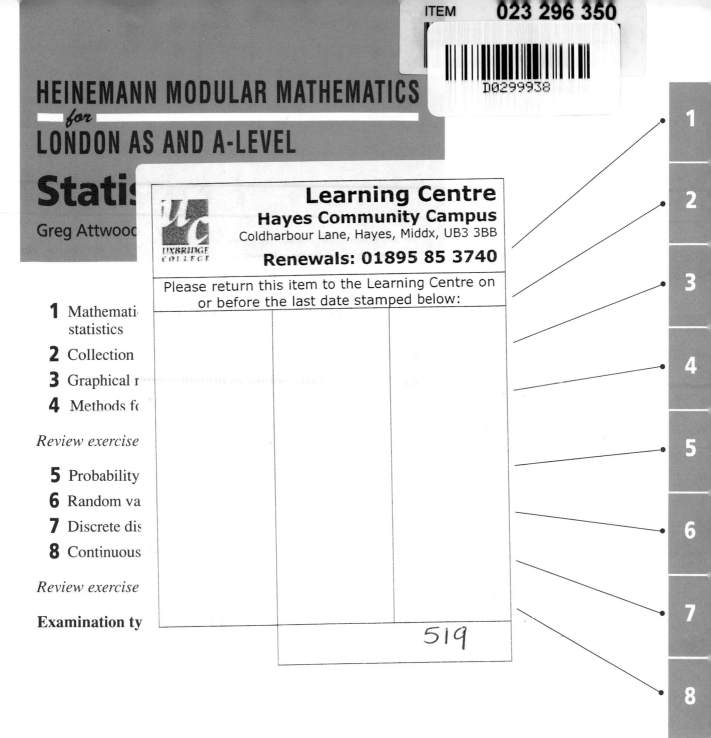
1
2
3
4
5
6
7
8

Heinemann Educational Publishers
Halley Court, Jordan Hill, Oxford OX2 8EJ
a division of Reed Educational & Professional Publishing Ltd

OXFORD   MELBOURNE   AUCKLAND
JOHANNESBURG   BLANTYRE   GABORONE
IBADAN   PORTSMOUTH (NH) USA   CHICAGO

First published 1994

99 00 01 02 20 19 18 17 16 15 14

ISBN 0 435 51811 9

Original design by Geoffrey Wadsley; additional design work by Jim Turner

Typeset and illustrated by TecSet Limited, Wallington, Surrey.

Printed in Great Britain by The Bath Press, Bath

Acknowledgements:

The publisher's and author's thanks are due to the University of London
Examinations and Assessment Council (ULEAC) for permission to reproduce
questions from past examination papers. These are marked with an [L].
   The answers have been provided by the authors and are not the responsibility
of the examining board.

The publishers would also like to thank the University of London Examinations
and Assessment Council (ULEAC) for permission to reproduce the following
mathematical tables:
Table 1 Binomial cumulative distribution function,
Table 2 Poisson cumulative distribution function,
Table 3 The Normal distribution function,
Table 4 Percentage points of the Normal distribution.

About this book

This book is designed to provide you with the best preparation possible for your London Modular Mathematics T1 examination. The series authors are examiners and exam moderators themselves and have a good understanding of the exam board's requirements.

Finding your way around

To help to find your way around when you are studying and revising use the:

- **edge marks** (shown on the front page) – these help you to get to the right chapter quickly;
- **contents list** – this lists the headings that identify key syllabus ideas covered in the book so you can turn straight to them;
- **index** – if you need to find a topic the **bold** number shows where to find the main entry on a topic.

Remembering key ideas

We have provided clear explanations of the key ideas and techniques you need throughout the book. Key ideas you need to remember are listed in a **summary of key points** at the end of each chapter and marked like this in the chapters:

■ $$IQR = Q_3 - Q_1$$

Exercises and exam questions

In this book questions are carefully graded so they increase in difficulty and gradually bring you up to exam standard.

- **past exam questions** are marked with an L;
- **review exercises** on pages 84 and 226 help you practise answering questions from several areas of mathematics at once, as in the real exam;
- **exam style practice paper** – this is designed to help you prepare for the exam itself;
- **answers** are included at the end of the book – use them to check your work.

Contents

Mathematical modelling in probability and statistics

1.1 What is a model?

Many people travel to work each day by train. These trains are frequently powered by electricity. They all run on a metal track and they each have a driver. You may have played with a toy train set when you were younger. The toy train would have been much smaller than the *real* train but it would have been made to look very similar to it. It too might have been powered by electricity but from a battery within the engine rather than through an extra rail by the track. The toy train probably ran on a plastic track not a metal one like a real train and might also have had a small plastic driver but this driver could not alter the speed or stop the train like the driver of a real train. Your toy train was a **model** of a real train. It was like the real train in many ways but did not have *all* the features of the real thing.

It is important to remember that a model is not the *same* as the more complicated object in the real world which it has been created to represent. When a model is created just *some aspects* of the real object are reproduced. No attempt is made to replicate the real object in every detail. A model will be a *simplification* of the real thing, it will be both *quicker and cheaper* to produce than the real one and can help us to *improve our understanding* of the real-world object. For example, a model train and track can be used to discover the effect on the train of a buckling of the track. Using a model in this way can help us to deal with problems which might arise in the real world without the expense and risk of testing them on a real train!

1.2 Mathematical modelling

In the same way that a model train can help to solve problems in the real world so a **mathematical model** can be used to find solutions to problems without the need to construct a physical model.

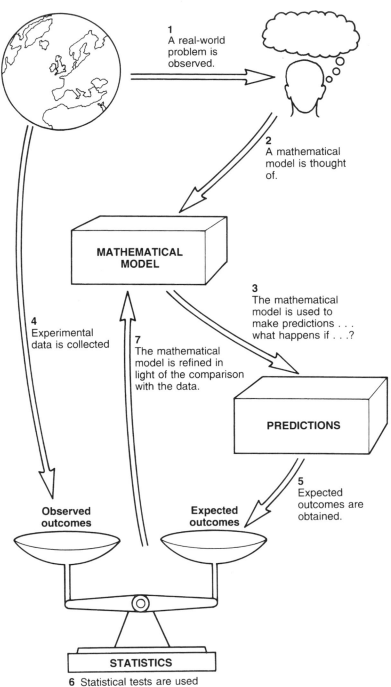

1 A real-world problem is observed.

2 A mathematical model is thought of.

MATHEMATICAL MODEL

3 The mathematical model is used to make predictions . . . what happens if . . .?

4 Experimental data is collected

7 The mathematical model is refined in light of the comparison with the data.

PREDICTIONS

5 Expected outcomes are obtained.

Observed outcomes

Expected outcomes

STATISTICS

6 Statistical tests are used to see how well the mathematical model works.

Mathematical models can be used to describe a wide variety of problems but when an element of *randomness* is involved the models require the use of **probability**. Consider the following problems:

"Will a coin land heads or tails when it is tossed or might it land on its edge?"

"How many rain drops will land on the window of your room in the next 5 minutes?"

"What are your chances of scoring a bull's eye with a single dart?"

These are the sorts of problems a probability model might be used to find an answer to.

The processes involved in the creation of a mathematical model are illustrated opposite:

Starting from a real-world problem (**1**), a mathematical model is devised (**2**) and this is used to make predictions about the expected behaviour of the real-world problem (**3**). Some experimental data is also collected about the real-world problem (**4**) and this is used to list observed outcomes which are then compared with the expected outcomes predicted by the mathematical model (**5**). **Statistical** concepts are then used (**6**) to test whether the mathematical model describes the real-world problem well or not. (Some of these tests are dealt with in the book for the T2 syllabus.)

It may then be necessary to **refine** the mathematical model (**7**) to produce a better model of the real-world problem by repeating steps **3** to **5**.

As you can see, **statistics** plays a crucial role in judging how well the mathematical model describes the real-world problem. It is for this reason that a knowledge of statistics is of such importance in carrying out practical work in the sciences or social sciences.

Throughout this book, but particularly in chapter 7, there are references to the modelling process described in the diagram opposite which shows how modelling fits into the subjects of probability and statistics.

Collection of data

2

2.1 Defining types of data

Every day we are faced with a variety of statistics produced from data collected by different agencies:

"The latest Audit Bureau of Circulation's figures for July to December 1993 show the *Times Higher Education Supplement's* circulation up 12.5 per cent on the same period in 1992 and 21.8 per cent up on 1991." – *THES* March 4 1994.

"Colleges in the Northern Region are expecting an increase of 5.9 per cent in full-time equivalent enrolments (FTEs) between 1992–93 and 1993–94." – *FEFC Northern Region News*, March 1994.

"He produces some good statistics: 400 000 acres, land the size of Surrey, are now covered in lawns rolling out like fitted carpet, harvesting more than 55 million tons of grass cuttings a year." – *Radio Times*, 9 April 1994.

But what is data? One dictionary defines data as "a series of observations, measurements or facts". So to obtain data we have to observe or measure something. This something is known as a **variate**. For example, shoe size, weight, and nationality are all variates as we can obtain a series of observations or measurements for each of them:

Variate	*Measurement or observation*
Shoe size	6, $6\frac{1}{2}$, 7, $7\frac{1}{2}$
Weight	8.21 kg, 7.9 kg, 0.5 kg
Nationality	British, French, German

Considering these variates and their measurements or observations reveals important differences between them. Shoe size and weight are both variates whose measurements are *numerical* but the observations on nationality are *non-numerical*. So shoe size and weight are both called **quantitative** variates as their measurements take the form of **numbers** (such as size $7\frac{1}{2}$) or **quantities** (such as 8.21 kg). Nationality is called a **qualitative** variate as numerical values cannot be assigned to it in the way that they can with shoe size or weight. With nationality and other qualitative variates it is necessary to use **non-numerical descriptors** (such as British) to represent the different possible observations within the variate.

Although now generally used as a singular noun, data is properly a plural and throughout this book it is used in this way, for example: 'these data'.

Example 1

For each of the following variates state whether they are **quantitative** or **qualitative** and give three possible measurements or observations of the variate:

(a) height   (b) eye colour   (c) age
(d) distance from college   (e) town of birth

(a) Height is a **quantitative** variate and three possible values are 72 inches, 6 feet 2 inches, and 1.76 metres.

(b) Eye colour is a **qualitative** variate and three possible observations are blue, green, and hazel.

(c) Age is a **quantitative** variate and three possible values are 9 months, 2 years, and 4 years 7 months.

(d) Distance from college is a **quantitative** variate and three possible values are $\frac{3}{4}$ mile, $2\frac{1}{2}$ miles and 4.2 kilometres.

(e) Town of birth is a **qualitative** variate and three possible observations are Derby, Bath, and Whitby.

Although the variates shoe size and weight are both quantitative variates as both are given numerical values, there is a difference in the way in which measurements on these two quantitative variates are recorded. When you buy a pair of shoes you can ask for a size 5 or $5\frac{1}{2}$, but *not* for a size 6.27. But when you measure someone's weight you can record it as 92.509 kg (if your scales are that accurate) even though that person may say they weigh $92\frac{1}{2}$ kg.

Weight is called a **continuous** variate as it can take any value within a given range. Shoe size is called a **discrete** variate as it can only take particular values. These values are discrete (meaning separate) from one another, so the variate is not continuous – it changes in steps.

You need to be able to distinguish between these different types of variates as the type of variate influences the method you can use to analyse data.

Example 2

State whether each of the following variates is **discrete** or **continuous**:

(a) time   (b) cost in £ and p   (c) volume   (d) height
(e) number of children in family.

(a) Time is **continuous**.

(b) Cost in £ and p is **discrete**.

(c) Volume is **continuous**.

(d) Height is **continuous**.

(e) Number of children in a family is **discrete**.

2.2 Populations and sampling

So far we have concentrated on defining different types of data. Let us now consider the heights of three students chosen at random from year 13 in a sixth form college. The students are John, Sandra and Tony and their heights, in inches, are 70 in, 64 in and 73 in. In statistical language the heights of John, Sandra and Tony are a *sample* of the heights of the *population* of year 13 students in the college. A **population** is a collection of individuals or items. You may be able to draw conclusions about a small population by considering each individual or item. For a large population you may not want to consider every individual. Instead you may draw conclusions about the whole population by considering a **sample** – a selection of individual members of the population. Notice that in statistics the word population refers to data in general and not just to people. So we can have a population of year 13 students, female cyclists, potatoes, two-inch nails, and so on.

In some situations a population may be of **finite** size. For example, the number of students in a sixth form college is finite because it is possible to give each student an individual number and know exactly how many students there are. In some situations we consider a population to be of **infinite** size as it is impossible for us to know exactly how many members there are in that population. Such an example might be the number of rabbits on the North Yorkshire moors – however hard we try it will not be possible to number them individually. A third type of population is of **countably infinite** size where we know that the population is infinite but we *can* count and number the individual members of that population. For example, the number of throws of a dice needed to obtain a six produces a countably infinite population. We may obtain a six on the first throw or the second or the twentieth, but we might need to go on throwing for ever.

In practice populations are often too large to work with data on each member, although it might be argued that a population of year 13 students in a sixth form college does not fall into this category. In this case each student *could* be identified individually and observations or measurements could be taken on every one. Then the total number of measurements would be known and we would have taken a census. Censuses are dealt with in Book T2.

In most situations, due to considerations of time and cost it is necessary to take observations or measurements from a selection of individual members of the population. These individual members are known as **sampling units**. For example, John, Sandra and Tony are three of the sampling units making up the population of year 13 students in the sixth form college. In some circumstances a sampling unit may contain several elements. For example, if the sampling unit is a household containing several individuals then each individual is known as a **sampling element**. However, if each sampling unit contains one and only one element (such as Sandra) then a sampling unit and an element from the population are identical. In this book we use the term sampling unit to refer to an individual member of the population.

Once the sampling units within a population are individually named or numbered to form a list then this list of sampling units is known as a **sampling frame**. For example, the class register of all the students in year 13 at the sixth form college is a sampling frame. In this example the sampling frame and the population should be the same provided the class register is up to date and accurate.

In practice the sampling frame may not include all the sampling units in the population because it may not be possible to keep details of the population up to date. For example, if we specify individual voters as the sampling units a list of all registered voters could serve as the sampling frame. This frame, however, is unlikely to contain all the voters in the population as it is impossible to update the list daily. So it is important to note that many sampling frames will contain some inadequacies of this type, but usually the difference between the population and the sampling frame is small enough to allow the sample drawn from the sampling frame to represent the population.

A sampling frame can take a variety of forms – list, index, map, file – but whatever its form, how well a sampling frame covers a population and its accuracy are important as the sampling frame is the basis of any sample drawn.

Example 3

Give an example of each of the following types of population

(a) finite   (b) infinite   (c) countably infinite.

(a) The number of students enrolled in The University of Teesside Business School in academic year 1994/95 is a finite population.

(b) The number of telephone calls made in a year throughout the world can be considered to be an infinite population.

(c) Toss a coin until a head appears and then count the number of times the coin was tossed. The number of times is a countably infinite population.

Example 4

Suggest possible sampling frames to enable samples to be obtained relating to:

(a) couples married in Cleveland in 1993

(b) fish caught at Scaling Dam in July 1993

(c) voting patterns in Devon.

(a) A possible sampling frame would be the list of marriages recorded by the Registrar in Cleveland in 1993.

(b) A list of anglers registered as having licences to fish on Scaling Dam in July 1993.

(c) The electoral register of voters in Devon would be a possible sampling frame.

2.3 Advantages and disadvantages of sampling

Section 2.2 introduced the terminology of sampling. This section looks at the advantages and disadvantages associated with sampling. First let us consider some of the advantages:

If it can be assumed that a population is infinite and well mixed then a sample will be *representative* of the whole population. Consider, for example, a large tank full of liquid known to contain millions of bacteria. It would be impossible to number the individual bacteria, but if the tank is well stirred and a sample of liquid is taken from it, then it would be reasonable to assume that the sample is representative of the liquid in the tank. The bacteria in the volume of liquid removed would represent the bacteria in the total volume of the tank, and conclusions drawn from the sample should also be true for the whole tank.

Sampling is generally *cheaper* than taking a census, although the cost per sampling unit studied will usually be greater than for a census. However, as sampling concentrates on gaining information about selected sampling units, then the *quality of information* gained about each sampling unit is often better.

Sampling is also advantageous in situations where testing items results in their destruction (for example, testing the lifetimes of light bulbs), and where checking every item on a production line makes the process uneconomical.

When using a sample rather than a census, data is generally more *readily available* for analysis and more quickly analysed.

Sampling also has some disadvantages:

One definition of statistics is that "statistics is the process of decision making in the face of uncertainty." The *uncertainty* associated with sampling can be looked upon as a disadvantage. This uncertainty can take two forms – natural variation and bias.

Natural variation is due to chance differences among the sampling units. These differences cannot be controlled or accounted for by the person taking the sample.

Bias can be defined as anything which occurs when taking a sample that prevents the sample from representing the population from which it is being taken. It can occur for a variety of reasons which are usually to do with the definition of the population or the method of selecting the sample. Bias can occur through:

■ *sampling from an incomplete sampling frame* – for example, a sample chosen from the telephone directory of a city cannot provide a good estimate of the proportion of the population of that city who smoke.

■ the introduction of *personal subjective choice* by the person taking the sample – for example, a child asked to take a random sample of shells from a beach may tend to choose the more eye-catching brightly coloured ones.

■ *non-response* where responses are only obtained from those who have a particular interest in the study being undertaken – for example, a postal questionnaire sent to motorists about the particular model of car they drive will be ignored by the majority. Those completing and returning it are likely to be those who have had a good experience of that model or a very poor experience of it.

■ *substituting convenient sample units* when those required are not easily available – for example, a sample which necessitates visits to households. The interviewer takes the next-door or nearest available household if there is no reply at the one chosen to be part of the sample.

Whatever the reasons for the presence of bias, it is worth noting that bias cannot be reduced by increasing the sample size, as every sample unit is likely to misrepresent the population in the same way.

2.4 Collecting sample data

Any sample of data you use should be a true (unbiased) representation of the population from which it is being drawn. For the purposes of this book and the T1 syllabus we shall assume that data has been obtained by the method of **simple random sampling**. If a population contains N sampling units and you require a sample of n of them, then a simple random sample is one such that every possible sample of size n has the same chance of being selected. In practice this is achieved by giving every member of the population an equal chance of selection, and using some form of random process (such as random numbers) to make the selection.

Details of simple random sampling and other methods of sampling are given in Book T2.

Exercise 2A

1 Which of the terms below apply to:
   (a) time spent on homework
   (b) number of eggs laid in a week by a hen
   (c) colour of hair?
   Quantitative Qualitative Discrete Continuous.

2 Explain briefly why:
   (a) wages earned per week is a quantitative and discrete variate

   (b) height in centimetres is a quantitative and continuous variate

   (c) type of fruit is a qualitative variate.

3 Write down:

   (a) three discrete variates

   (b) three continuous variates

   each associated with your school or college.

4 Explain whether these variates are discrete or continuous:

   (a) age in years

   (b) age to the nearest year.

5 For each of the following populations, state whether it is finite, infinite, or countably infinite:

   (a) the number of points at which a dart can enter a circular dart board

   (b) the number of items coming off a production line

   (c) the number of professional tennis players.

6 Suggest appropriate sampling units for populations associated with the following:

   (a) a library

   (b) a garage

   (c) a hospital.

7 A market research organisation wants to take a sample of:

   (a) students studying at the University of Teesside

   (b) owners of L-registered motor cars

   (c) professional golfers.

   Suggest a suitable sampling frame in each case.

8 A safety expert is interested in estimating the proportion of motor cars with illegal tyres. Discuss possible sampling units and sampling frames.

9 A factory manager wishes to investigate the life-time of batteries produced in the factory. A random sample of 25 batteries is taken every day for four consecutive weeks and each battery is tested to exhaustion. Comment on the advantages and disadvantages associated with this sampling scheme.

10 A forester wants to estimate for a large forest the total number of trees that have a trunk diameter exceeding

18 inches. A map of the forest is available. Discuss the problem of choosing appropriate sampling units and an appropriate frame.

SUMMARY OF KEY POINTS

1 A **quantitative** variate is one that has numerical values.

2 A **qualitative** variate is one involving non-numerical descriptors.

3 A **continuous** variate can take all possible values in a given range.

4 A **discrete** variate can only take particular values.

5 A **population** is a collection of individuals or items.

6 A **sample** is a selection of individual members or items from a population.

7 A **finite population** is one in which each member can be given an individual number.

8 An **infinite population** is one in which it is impossible to number each member.

9 A **countably infinite population** is one which is infinite in size, but each member can be given an individual number.

10 A **sampling unit** is an individual member of a population.

11 A **sampling frame** is a list of sampling units used in practice to represent a population. In some instances the two will be identical in others the sampling frame will represent the population as accurately as is possible.

12 In practice a **sample** is a collection of sampling units drawn from a sampling frame.

Graphical representation of sample data

3

Chapter 2 is about collecting data. This chapter is about summarising data once it has been collected. Two forms of summary are covered in this book, one graphical and the other numerical. This chapter covers graphical summaries. Numerical summaries are covered in Chapter 4.

Before considering some graphical summaries it is worth asking why we need to summarise data which has been collected. In simple terms it is because most samples of data are too large for us to handle in their raw form. If you left this data in its raw form you would be unlikely to recognise the important features which are revealed when the data has been summarised. One reason for taking a sample is to be able to make deductions about the population from which the sample has been taken. To do this you need to analyse the data you have collected. One way of doing this is by means of graphical and numerical summaries.

The purpose of these summaries is to condense data to reveal patterns and to enable comparisons to be made. Summarising data can lead to a loss of accuracy so that any calculations based on summarised data could be less accurate than calculations based on the raw data. You may already know some methods of summarising data. If so, this chapter will be useful revision.

3.1 Frequency distributions

This set of observations shows the number of times that each of the students in a year 13 class is late during a term.

0	7	6	4	10	1	8	9	10	9
3	9	6	2	8	1	2	1	2	3
7	8	1	8	7	1	10	6	2	5
7	1	8	1	3	4	1	1	4	5
7	1	0	10	4	7	2	5	3	7
0	5	0	7	7	2	9	1	7	8

Even after several minutes studying the data it is not easy to see any pattern or to be able to answer a question such as 'How many students were late on more than 6 occasions?' Condensing the data (grouping it into a smaller number of categories) makes it easier to understand. A frequency distribution does this for these data. It is produced by making a tally chart like this:

Times absent	Tally of number of students	Frequency	Cumulative frequency
0	‖ ‖	4	4
1	⊔⊔⊤ ⊔⊔⊤ ‖	11	15
2	⊔⊔⊤ ‖	6	21
3	‖‖‖	4	25
4	‖ ‖‖	4	29
5	‖‖ ‖	4	33
6	‖‖‖	3	36
7	⊔⊔⊤ ⊔⊔⊤	10	46
8	⊔⊔⊤ ‖	6	52
9	‖‖‖	4	56
10	‖‖‖	4	60
Total		60	

Each observation is represented by a tally mark placed against the appropriate category. A group of five observations is represented by ⊔⊔⊤ making it easier to add the tallies. The tally marks for each category are totalled to give the frequency for that category.

From the frequency distribution it is possible to see any patterns that emerge. For example, in this case there are those students who missed very few classes and those who tended to be more persistent absentees.

The **cumulative frequencies** for the **figures** in the table are obtained by adding the frequencies as we go down the column of frequencies:

4, 4 + 11, 4 + 11 + 6, and so on, giving 4, 15, 21 . . .

These show, for example, that there were 25 students who were absent on fewer than 4 occasions.

3.2 Cumulative frequency step polygon

It is sometimes useful to represent a cumulative frequency distribution graphically. You can do this by drawing **a cumulative frequency step polygon**. Look at the data on absences in the above table. You can see from the table that:

students could not be absent on fewer than zero occasions

4 students were never absent

15 students were absent on fewer than two occasions.

So the graph **steps** from 4 to 15 as there were no values between zero and one. Here is the cumulative frequency step polygon for the table:

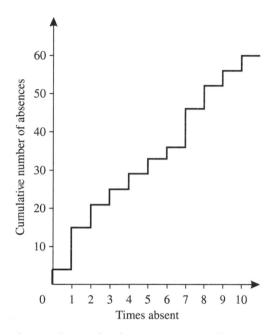

The use of such a polygon is shown on page 49.

3.3 Stem and leaf diagrams

Another way to order and present data is by means of a stem and leaf diagram. Here are some data:

60 51 53 42 45 42 51 65 62 50

And here is a stem and leaf diagram to represent these numbers:

stem ⟶ 4 | 2 5 2 ⟵ leaves

5 | 1 3 1 0

6 | 0 5 2

Each digit to the left of the vertical line is a stem. The digits on the right of the vertical line are the leaves associated with the stems. For the first row 4 2 5 2 the stem is 4 and the leaves are 2, 5 and 2. This row represents the numbers 42, 45 and 42. This stem and leaf diagram has been created by splitting each number into two parts in which the tens digit becomes the stem and the units digit the leaf.

Once the data have been ordered into stems and leaves it is usual to re-draw the diagram so that the leaves are in numerical order like this.

4	2 2 5
5	0 1 1 3
6	0 2 5

This allows the stem and leaf diagram to be used in calculations.

Sometimes the data being represented by a stem and leaf diagram is not integer data. The stem and leaf diagram is prepared in the same way, but a note is included on the diagram to ensure it is read correctly. For example, the following heights in centimetres:

4.2, 4.7, 5.1, 6.2, 5.3, 5.7, 5.9, 4.4, 5.9, 6.1, 5.9, 6.4, 5.2

can be shown on a stem and leaf diagram like this:

Height in cm   4 | 2 means 4.2

4	2 4 7
5	1 2 3 7 9 9 9
6	1 2 4

As you can see, only two significant figures can be represented on a stem and leaf diagram, so it may be necessary to round data to meet this constraint. For example, 7.27 and 8.322 would need to be rounded to 7.3 and 8.2 to allow them to be represented on a stem and leaf diagram.

In some diagrams a large number of leaves are associated with one stem. Then it is usual to use two lines for that stem to improve the display of the data.

Stem and leaf diagrams have the advantage over bar charts and similar representations that the shape of the distribution of the data can be seen without losing the detail of the original data. For example, in the height data there are clearly more observations between 5.0 and 5.9 cm than between 4.0 and 4.9 or between 6.0 and 6.9 as the number of leaves for the '5' stem is greatest. Each data value between 5.0 and 5.9 can still be read directly from the diagram: 5.1, 5.2 and so on.

Example 1

Over a period of time Mendit Ltd a motor repair company records the time, x minutes to the nearest minute, taken to carry out a particular type of repair. The values of x recorded for 51 repairs are given below. Construct a stem and leaf diagram for these data:

$$
\begin{array}{ccccccc}
33 & 38 & 34 & 46 & 42 & 36 & 41 \\
43 & 41 & 46 & 41 & 30 & 51 & 36 \\
37 & 33 & 24 & 36 & 31 & 31 & 24 \\
51 & 34 & 42 & 50 & 21 & 56 & 32 \\
34 & 34 & 46 & 43 & 62 & 34 & 32 \\
45 & 30 & 31 & 36 & 39 & 37 & 56 \\
31 & 47 & 40 & 40 & 55 & 42 & 30 \\
30 & 62
\end{array}
$$

Here is the unordered stem and leaf diagram produced by working down the columns. It is equally acceptable to work along the rows, since the ordered stem and leaf diagram will be the same for both.

Repair times $2 \mid 4$ means 24

Stem	Leaves	Count
2	4 1 4	(3)
3	3 7 4 1 0 8 3 4 4 0 4 1 6 6 0 1 9 6 1 4 7 6 2 2 0	(25)
4	3 5 1 7 6 2 6 0 6 1 3 0 2 2 1	(15)
5	1 0 5 1 6 6	(6)
6	2 2	(2)

Notice that it can help to improve the diagram by showing the number of leaves on each stem. These are shown in brackets. This is also a way of checking that all leaves have been accounted for.

Reordering and splitting the data into two parts for stems 3 and 4 gives:

Repair times		2 | 1 means 21
2	1 4 4	(3)
3	0 0 0 0 1 1 1 1 2 2 3 3 4 4 4 4 4	(17)
3	6 6 6 6 7 7 8 9	(8)
4	0 0 1 1 1 2 2 2 3 3	(10)
4	5 6 6 6 7	(5)
5	0 1 1 5 6 6	(6)
6	2 2	(2)

If direct comparison of two data sets is required, it can be achieved by placing the stem and leaf diagrams 'back to back' rather than keeping them as separate diagrams.

Example 2

There are 24 children in class A. Each child is given the same problem to solve. The time each child takes to solve it is recorded to the nearest tenth of a minute:

$$7.4 \quad 8.2 \quad 6.1 \quad 9.3 \quad 7.4 \quad 8.5 \quad 7.2 \quad 6.8$$
$$6.4 \quad 7.7 \quad 9.6 \quad 8.8 \quad 8.9 \quad 7.2 \quad 7.3 \quad 7.0$$
$$5.9 \quad 8.9 \quad 7.6 \quad 9.3 \quad 7.4 \quad 7.9 \quad 9.1 \quad 5.7$$

The 27 children in class B are also given the same problem and their times for solving it are:

$$8.2 \quad 7.3 \quad 6.9 \quad 5.5 \quad 6.1 \quad 9.3 \quad 8.1 \quad 7.2 \quad 7.7$$
$$6.7 \quad 7.6 \quad 8.4 \quad 8.8 \quad 5.8 \quad 6.9 \quad 8.2 \quad 9.5 \quad 9.1$$
$$5.4 \quad 6.4 \quad 7.7 \quad 5.2 \quad 7.1 \quad 6.6 \quad 5.9 \quad 6.7 \quad 6.0$$

Represent these data using a 'back to back' stem and leaf diagram. Use the diagram to compare the times of the two classes.

Here are unordered and ordered stem and leaf diagrams for the two classes.

Class A

Unordered   Ordered

Time to solve problem		5 | 9 means 5.9
5	9 7	(2)
6	1 8 4	(3)
7	4 4 2 7 2 3 0 6 4 9	(10)
8	2 5 8 9 9	(5)
9	3 6 3 1	(4)

Time to solve problem		5 | 7 means 5.7
5	7 9	(2)
6	1 4 8	(3)
7	0 2 2 3 4 4 4 6 7 9	(10)
8	2 5 8 9 9	(5)
9	1 3 3 6	(4)

Class B

Unordered	Ordered

Time to
solve problem   5|5 means 5.5

5	5 8 4 2 9	(5)
6	9 1 7 9 4 6 7 0	(8)
7	3 2 7 6 7 1	(6)
8	2 1 4 8 2	(5)
9	3 5 1	(3)

Time to
solve problem   5|2 means 5.2

5	2 4 5 8 9	(5)
6	0 1 4 6 7 7 9 9	(8)
7	1 2 3 6 7 7	(6)
8	1 2 2 4 8	(5)
9	1 3 5	(3)

The 'back to back' diagram can now be drawn.

Time to solve problem

	Class A		Class B		5|2 means 5.2
(2)	9 7	5	2 4 5 8 9	(5)	
(3)	8 4 1	6	0 1 4 6 7 7 9 9	(8)	
(10)	9 7 6 4 4 4 3 2 2 0	7	1 2 3 6 7 7	(6)	
(5)	9 9 8 5 2	8	1 2 2 4 8	(5)	
(4)	6 3 3 1	9	1 3 5	(3)	

This back to back diagram shows that the children in class B tend to
solve the problem in a shorter time than those in class A.

Exercise 3A

1 During the months of June and July a gardener noted the
temperature in °C each day at noon. The results are shown
below. Construct a frequency distribution for these data:

```
18  20  20  21  22  21  22  20
22  19  21  19  23  24  19  20
19  22  22  20  20  20  21  21
20  20  21  22  21  21  23  24
21  20  20  19  22  23  24  25
25  26  27  27  26  24  22  19
18  18  20  22  24  25  23  22
20  24  25  25  27
```

2 At the beginning of term a school held a disco. The next day
a random sample of 50 of those who attended were asked to
rate the disco on a five point scale A, B, C, D, E where A

represents maximum enjoyment and E minimum enjoyment. Their ratings are shown below. Construct a frequency distribution for these ratings:

```
A  C  E  C  C  E  A  C  B  C
E  C  B  B  A  B  C  B  D  D
D  B  D  B  B  B  C  B  C  C
E  B  B  B  D  A  B  A  B  B
C  D  C  E  B  D  C  C  D  D
```

3 For the data in question **1** draw a cumulative frequency step polygon.

4 The table below summarises the number of breakdowns on a stretch of motorway on 30 randomly selected days. Draw a cumulative frequency step polygon to represent these data:

Number of breakdowns	3	4	5	6	7	8	9	10	11
Number of days	3	4	2	5	3	6	3	1	3

5 In a germination experiment 200 rows of seeds with 10 seeds per row were incubated. The frequency distribution of the number of seeds which germinated per row is shown below. Draw a cumulative frequency step polygon to represent these data:

Number of seeds germinated	0	1	2	3	4	5	6	7	8	9	10
Frequency	4	10	16	28	34	44	32	16	10	6	0

6 The results of the GCSE mock examination in mathematics for Year 11 in 1993 at a school are shown below. Construct a stem and leaf diagram to represent these data:

42 54 80 48 73 50 59 45 84 49
67 47 70 78 77 67 55 88 42 59
54 41 69 65 41 86 80 89 44 68
82 41 71 42 85 84 51 69 89 72
72 46 85 40 78 67 66 52 42 89
86 41 62 51 73 50 41 58 44 69

7 A busy filling station records the number of motorists who buy diesel fuel for their cars each day. The number on 50 consecutive days is shown below. Construct a stem and leaf diagram to represent these data:

28 19 17 30 45 37 43 36 36 12
13 17 12 27 10 17 23 23   9 10
 9 14 15   8 26 30 26 22 19 20
28 19 32 21 23 26 34 16 17 18
33 26 28 31 30 22 21 21 15 19

8 A gardener is making a fence for his garden. He purchases a large number of pieces of wood, all of them longer than 100 cm in length. Each piece is then cut so that it is 100 cm long. The lengths of the 'off-cuts' in cm resulting from cutting the lengths to size are given below. Construct a stem and leaf diagram to represent these data:

5.2 6.6 4.3 8.3 5.1 7.5 8.6 7.1 7.8 2.2
6.6 5.8 3.5 7.5 6.1 3.8 2.5 2.7 8.8 4.8
3.5 4.3 6.1 5.6 5.2 8.8 6.4 6.4 3.8 8.1
8.9 3.5 7.6 3.1 7.2 3.4 7.8 8.4 4.7 7.7
7.5 6.8 7.5 8.3 6.2 6.7 5.2 3.7 8.6 5.2
7.3 2.5 4.7 7.6 2.7 5.1 5.2 3.2 3.2 6.4

9 The following data shows the playing times of the tracks on a selection of compact discs. Construct a stem and leaf diagram to represent these data:

4.33 8.02 4.47 5.11 5.05 3.17 5.06 3.42 3.33 3.41
8.46 3.25 4.41 5.19 3.36 4.25 3.26 4.48 6.20 6.33
5.15 6.25 8.19 5.03 7.41 6.28 7.17 9.12 6.53 4.19
2.57 6.45 7.31 5.41 5.13 6.16 7.51 6.28 8.58 7.05

10 The data below records the numbers of days a sample of patients had to wait before they were able to see their hospital consultant. Construct a stem and leaf diagram to represent these data:

55 46 36 49 20 59 48 54 35 34
31 44 52 46 33 52 51 22 43 47
29 28 29 57 17 38 25 10 38 16
39 44 15 57 25 14 51 38 17 49
56 19 45 51 21 37 44 19 45 21
29 52 28 32 57 35 53 25 42 14

11 At the same school described in question **6** the results of the GCSE mock examination in mathematics for year 11 in 1994 were as follows:

45 69 56 43 72 76 43 40 66 77
30 50 32 62 63 47 42 76 47 32
52 43 60 63 43 31 37 43 30 52
66 70 71 32 32 50 45 56 48 38
60 45 47 35 54 34 73 63 49 47
52 49 48 40 42

Use these data and that in question **6** to construct a 'back-to-back' stem and leaf diagram. Comment on your results.

12 Over a period of 40 school days the school shop recorded the number of packets of crisps bought each day by boys and girls at the school. The results were as follows:

Girls								Boys					
10	16	35	29	30	11	18		17	32	37	42	20	41	11
13	33	13	10	32	40	25		40	25	10	32	39	34	31
27	25	18	38	43	26	44		49	47	17	14	26	36	29
24	39	44	29	11	23	19		42	22	19	42	38	20	28
42	36	21	16	31	32	41		24	44	34	20	41	28	48
48	34	28	11	27				46	26	28	42	22	

Construct a 'back-to-back' stem and leaf diagram to represent these data. Comment on your results.

3.4 Grouped frequency distributions

When you need to summarise a large sample of data, the frequency distribution or stem and leaf diagram may not be appropriate. Instead you can use an alternative summary called a **grouped frequency distribution**. This involves tabulating the frequencies associated with *groups* of observations rather than single observations.

Here is a large sample of observations. It shows the number of visits to the doctor made by each of 150 patients during one year.

3	2	6	2	6	5	22	3	1	10
5	9	7	2	5	1	5	4	9	7
25	19	8	2	5	8	10	16	15	5
7	8	3	6	6	21	6	9	4	5
6	6	22	8	11	23	8	5	9	6
8	7	15	10	16	11	13	1	7	3
2	18	0	16	4	9	8	5	9	17
7	9	5	19	12	1	10	3	5	7
13	18	8	7	8	7	7	13	0	5
14	7	20	1	9	4	6	24	9	6
11	5	6	28	7	7	22	1	17	4
11	8	1	4	12	13	9	23	14	5
2	6	6	11	3	14	6	8	4	4
6	8	29	18	5	8	8	17	4	4
5	18	7	3	11	23	20	10	6	6

A frequency distribution for these data would give the table of 30 lines shown here. This is not a very useful summary.

Visits	Frequency
0	2
1	7
.	.
.	.
28	1
29	1

Only the start and end of the table are shown.

This table can be condensed even more to produce a grouped frequency distribution:

Visits	Frequency	Cumulative frequency
0–4	32	32
5–9	71	103
10–14	20	123
15–19	14	137
20–24	10	147
25–29	3	150
Total	150	

The cumulative frequency has been included as it will be needed in the next section which deals with the cumulative frequency polygon for grouped sample data.

Deciding on the number of groups and the width of the groups in a grouped frequency distribution is up to the person producing it. There are no definite rules to help make such decisions but here are two useful guidelines:

■ Aim to have as few groups as is reasonable; too many, and little advantage is gained over a frequency distribution; too few, and patterns in the data will not be revealed. Somewhere between 5 and 15 groups, with 10 being about right can be used as a 'rule of thumb'.

■ Use this 'rule of thumb' to estimate the class width:

$$\text{class width} = \frac{\text{largest value} - \text{smallest value}}{\text{number of groups}}$$

You need to use this rule of thumb sensibly. For example, if the largest value in a distribution is 579, the smallest value is 500 and 10 groups are required then

$$\text{class width} = \frac{579 - 500}{10} = 7.9$$

Rather than use 7.9 as the class width you might use 8, or more likely for ease of tabulation use 10. Using 10 as the width and starting at 500 (giving 500–509, 510–519) would give 8 groups rather than 10, but this still fits within the guideline of 5 to 15 groups. Remember, there are no hard rules, just 'rules of thumb' to be used with a little common sense.

Although the detail of the original set of 150 observations has been lost, the data reveals its patterns and allows summaries to be made. For example, the group containing the most observations is 5–9. Another summary is that two-thirds of the patients visited the doctor fewer than 10 times during the year.

Before moving on it is worth revising the terminology of grouped frequency distributions. The groups are more usually called **classes**. Here is the class 5–9:

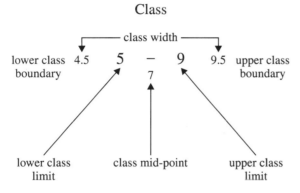

You need to remember all the terms shown in this diagram.

Example 3
Write down the class boundaries, mid-point and class width for each of the following classes:
(a) 8–12   (b) 2.5–3.4   (c) (−3)–(+3)

Class boundaries	Mid-point	Class width
(a) 7.5, 12.5	$\frac{1}{2}(7.5 + 12.5) = 10$	$12.5 - 7.5 = 5$
	or	
	$\frac{1}{2}(8 + 12) = 10$	
(b) 2.45, 3.45	2.95	1.00
(c) −3.5, 3.5	0	7

Example 4

The height x millimetres, to the nearest millimetre, of each of a number of seedlings was measured before each one was transplanted into an individual pot. The heights recorded for a sample of 50 seedlings were:

$$
\begin{array}{cccccccccc}
31 & 36 & 40 & 37 & 28 & 23 & 13 & 44 & 25 & 28 \\
46 & 33 & 33 & 31 & 42 & 32 & 53 & 30 & 24 & 35 \\
31 & 17 & 20 & 41 & 30 & 41 & 31 & 41 & 18 & 49 \\
46 & 39 & 29 & 27 & 39 & 26 & 43 & 21 & 31 & 35 \\
38 & 34 & 37 & 33 & 21 & 34 & 38 & 28 & 33 & 27
\end{array}
$$

Prepare a grouped frequency distribution for these data using equal class widths, the first class having a lower class boundary of 9.5 and mid-point of 12.

If the lower class boundary of the first class is 9.5, the lower class limit is 10. If the mid-point is 12 the upper class limit must be 14. So the grouped frequency distribution is:

Class	Frequency
10–14	1
15–19	2
20–24	5
25–29	8
30–34	14
35–39	9
40–44	7
45–49	3
50–54	1
Total	50

3.5 Cumulative frequency polygons for grouped data

In section 3.2 a cumulative frequency step polygon is used to represent the data in a frequency distribution. In a similar way the data in a grouped frequency distribution can be represented by a **cumulative frequency polygon**. In this situation the **cumulative frequencies** are plotted against the **upper class boundaries** of the corresponding classes. So for the data in section 3.4 relating to visits the plotted points are (4.5, 32), (9.5, 103), (14.5, 123) and so on. The polygon is shown opposite with the points joined by straight lines:

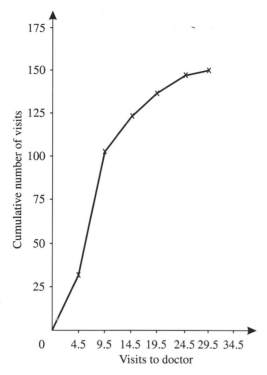

It is very important to stress that the upper class boundaries are used when plotting a cumulative frequency polygon. Ways of using cumulative frequency polgyons are described on page 51.

Example 5

This table summarises the weights in kilograms, to the nearest 100 grams, of 250 boys:

Weight (kg)	Number of boys
44.0–47.9	3
48.0–51.9	17
52.0–55.9	50
56.0–57.9	45
58.0–59.9	46
60.0–63.9	57
64.0–67.9	23
68.0–71.9	9

(a) Represent these data by means of a cumulative frequency polygon.

(b) Estimate the weight which is exceeded by 20% of the boys.

(a) The upper class boundaries and cumulative frequencies required to draw the polygon are:

Upper class boundaries	47.95	51.95	55.95	57.95	59.95	63.95	67.95	71.95
Cumulative frequencies	3	20	70	115	161	218	241	250

Here is the cumulative frequency polygon:

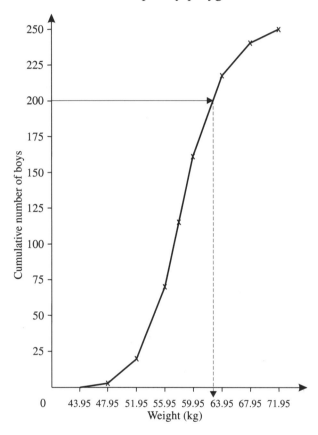

Notice that the polygon touches the horizontal axis at 43.95 as there are no boys below that boundary.

(b) 20% of 250 is 50 ∴ the weight corresponding to 200 boys needs to be estimated from the polygon. This is done by drawing a horizontal line from the cumulative frequency of 200 and where this intersects the polygon the corresponding value (indicated by the broken line) is read from the horizontal scale.

Thus from the cumulative frequency polygon the estimate is 62.75 kg. Hence to the nearest 100 g the estimate is 62.8 kg.

3.6 Histograms

Line diagrams and bar charts are usually drawn to represent frequency distributions. These diagrams use the height of any lines or bars to represent the frequencies and the distribution.

If the data available is for a **continuous variate** and it is summarised by **a grouped frequency distribution** then the data can be represented by means of a **histogram**.

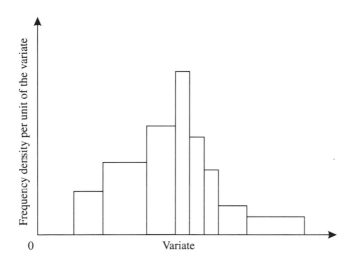

Although at a quick glance histograms look similar to bar charts there are two fundamental differences:

■   There are no gaps between the bars of a histogram

■   There is an important relationship between the area of a histogram bar and the frequency that it is representing.

For a histogram bar,

■   **Area $\propto$ Frequency**

and since the histogram consists of a series of bars, then for a histogram:

■   **Total area $\propto$ Total frequency**

This concept of area being proportional to frequency is important and distinguishes a histogram from a bar chart.

To calculate the height of each bar in a histogram use:

$$\text{Area} \propto \text{Frequency}$$

Thus: $$\text{Area} = \text{k} \times \text{Frequency}$$

where k is the constant of proportionality and can take any positive value. For simplicity and ease of calculation let k = 1.

Hence:

$$\text{Area} = \text{Frequency}$$

Therefore: $$\text{Height of bar} \times \text{class width} = \text{Frequency}$$

So: $$\text{Height of bar} = \frac{\text{Frequency}}{\text{class width}}$$

Even if all class widths are equal it is recommended that you use k = 1 so that the method used is consistent and the resulting histogram has an area which is always equal to the total frequency. This allows for easy reading and interpretation of histograms. When drawing a relative frequency histogram as shown on page 33, this method can help you to understand the use of area when calculating probabilities associated with continuous variates.

When calculating the height of the histogram bar you used the class width (i.e. upper class boundary – lower class boundary) and when plotting the histogram you also use these boundaries, thus ensuring that there are no gaps between the bars. Label the horizontal axis with the appropriate variate name and label the vertical axis 'Frequency density per unit of the variate' or more simply 'Frequency density'.

Example 6

A random sample of 250 children from a large school was taken. The height in centimetres, to the nearest cm, of each child was recorded and summarised in the table below. Represent the data by means of a histogram.

Height (cm)	130–134	135–139	140–144	145–149	150–154	155–159	160–164	165–169
Number of children	10	22	38	60	54	36	25	5

Estimate the number of children whose heights were between 142 cm and 153 cm.

Class	Number of children	Class width	Frequency density = $\dfrac{Frequency}{Class\ width}$
130–134	10	5	2.0
135–139	22	5	4.4
140–144	38	5	7.6
145–149	60	5	12.0
150–154	54	5	10.8
155–159	36	5	7.2
160–164	25	5	5.0
165–169	5	5	1.0

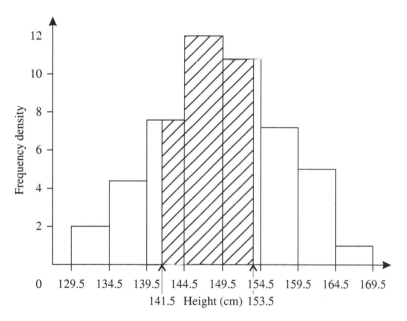

To estimate the number of children with heights between 142 cm and 153 cm, it is necessary to remember that the data is rounded up to the nearest whole number. So for estimating heights between 142 cm and 153 cm use 141.5 cm and 153.5 cm as height values when reading from the histogram.

Since Area = Frequency in this histogram then:

$$\text{Number of children} = (3 \times 7.6) + (5 \times 12) + (4 \times 10.8)$$
$$= 126$$

3.7 Relative frequency histograms

There are times when it is useful to draw a histogram based on relative frequencies rather than frequencies. An example of this is given in chapter 6 when introducing probability density functions. The method of drawing the histogram is similar to that used in Example 6 (see page 30) with relative frequencies replacing frequencies. Relative frequencies are obtained by expressing the frequencies as a proportion of the total frequency. So using the data in Example 6 the frequencies for the classes 130–134 and 135–139 are 10 and 22 respectively. Corresponding relative frequencies are:

$$\frac{10}{250} = 0.040 \text{ and } \frac{22}{250} = 0.088$$

Example 7

The length of time, to the nearest minute, of each consultation with the doctor of 300 patients is summarised in the following table.

Time (to nearest minute)	Number of consultations
2–3	30
4	96
5	48
6–7	84
8–10	27
11–15	15
Total	300

Represent the data by means of a relative frequency histogram.

Time	Number of consultations	Class width	Relative frequency	Relative frequency density
2–3	30	2	0.10	0.05
4	96	1	0.32	0.32
5	48	1	0.16	0.16
6–7	84	2	0.28	0.14
8–10	27	3	0.09	0.03
11–15	15	5	0.05	0.01
Total	300		1.00	

The area under this histogram is equal to 1.00 and this feature of a relative frequency histogram will prove useful later in the book.

Exercise 3B

1 Give the class boundaries, mid-point and class width for each of the following classes:
   (a) 6–7   (b) 0–2   (c) 5–14   (d) (−2)–(−8)
   (e) 1.50–1.75

2 The marks of 50 candidates in an examination are given below. Select suitable classes and prepare a grouped frequency distribution.

$$
\begin{array}{cccccccccc}
62 & 21 & 4 & 26 & 7 & 38 & 32 & 64 & 12 & 38 \\
45 & 6 & 33 & 55 & 62 & 48 & 49 & 7 & 9 & 41 \\
21 & 30 & 31 & 3 & 25 & 57 & 48 & 8 & 18 & 43 \\
72 & 23 & 5 & 8 & 37 & 31 & 31 & 39 & 65 & 53 \\
4 & 75 & 17 & 14 & 61 & 50 & 51 & 38 & 36 & 40
\end{array}
$$

3 Large quantities of data are often tabulated – collected together in tables. Describe two advantages and one disadvantage associated with tabulation.

4 A large number of people set out together on a fun run. The time taken by each of a sample of 50 of these people to

complete the run is recorded below. The times are given to the nearest minute.

```
61  83  62  96  66  61  92  87  69  91
82  62  80  86  97  72  78  68  88  63
85  63  73  99  66  82  61  86  63  73
65  89  95  61  72  89  92  76  75  77
75  88  87  91  84  73  67  76  82  79
```

Prepare a grouped frequency distribution for these data using equal class widths, the first class having a lower limit of 60 and mid-point of 62.

5 Draw a grouped frequency polygon to represent the data in question **2**.

6 A footwear store recorded the number of pairs of shoes sold on 52 consecutive Fridays. Here are the results:

```
60  62  94  78  73  56  64  79
54  68  66  68  71  76  67  73
67  83  87  90  93  58  46  77
37  60  74  62  40  56  59  80
69  70  69  70  70  47  54  49
63  66  66  47  51  57  53  77
68  61  98  98
```

Construct a grouped frequency distribution for these data. Draw a grouped frequency polygon to represent your distribution.

7 A random sample of 50 electric bulbs were tested. Their life-times to the nearest hour are given below. Construct a grouped frequency distribution for these data. Draw a grouped frequency polygon to represent your distribution.

```
730  681  710  682  660  695  717  680  700  732
738  707  692  708  701  663  695  726  676  696
697  722  698  699  689  676  715  714  717  721
696  690  716  662  697  696  710  684  692  705
689  724  694  699  703  682  656  702  694  671
```

8 The heights to the nearest centimetre of a group of students are summarised below. Draw a histogram to illustrate these data.

Height (cm)	120–129	130–139	140–149	150–159	160–169	170–179	180–189
Number of students	2	7	20	41	63	38	9

9 As part of his routine examination a vet weighs to the nearest pound every dog he sees in his surgery. The following table shows the distribution of weights for a random sample of 150 dogs. Represent these data by means of a histogram.

Weight (pounds)	25–29	30–34	35–39	40–44	45–49	50–54	55–59	60 64	65–69	70–74
Number of dogs	2	6	17	24	35	27	19	13	5	2

10 The distribution by age of 2000 patients attending a clinic for rheumatic diseases during 1985 is shown below. Draw a histogram to illustrate these data.

Age (years)	0–4	5–14	15–19	20–34	35–49	50–64	65–74	75–89
Frequency	10	32	30	270	300	405	338	615

11 The following table shows the time to the nearest minute a group of school children spent reading during a particular day. Represent these data by a histogram.

Time (to nearest minute)	Number of children
10–19	8
20–24	15
25–29	25
30–39	18
40–49	12
50–64	7
65–89	5

[L]

12 Telephone calls arriving at a switchboard are answered by the telephonist. The following table shows the time, to the nearest second, recorded for the telephonist to answer the calls received during one day. Represent these data by a histogram. Give a reason to justify the use of a histogram to represent these data.

Time to answer (to nearest second)	Number of calls
10–19	20
20–24	20
25–29	15
30	14
31–34	16
35–39	10
40–59	10

[L]

13 A psychologist recorded the time, to the nearest minute, for each child in a group of children to complete a particular task. Represent these data by a histogram. Estimate the number of children who completed the task in between 10 and 14 minutes.

Time (to nearest minute)	Number of children
2–4	1
5–6	7
7–8	24
9	37
10	57
11–12	69
13–15	39
16–19	6

SUMMARY OF KEY POINTS

1 For a **stem and leaf diagram** each row represents a **stem** and is indicated by the number to the left of the vertical line. The digits to the right of the vertical line are the **leaves** associated with the stem.

2 A **grouped frequency distribution** consists of several **classes** and their associated **class frequencies**.

   For the **class 5–9** for example the

lower class boundary	is	4.5
lower class limit	is	5
upper class limit	is	9
upper class boundary	is	9.5
class width	is	$9.5 - 4.5 = 5$
class mid-point	is	$\frac{1}{2}(4.5 + 9.5) = 7$

3 When plotting a **cumulative frequency polygon** cumulative frequencies are **plotted** against corresponding **upper class boundaries**.

4 When drawing a **histogram**, for each histogram bar the area is directly proportional to the frequency that it is representing:

   Area $\propto$ Frequency

and since the histogram consists of a series of bars, then for a histogram:

Total Area ∝ Total Frequency

5   The **height** of a histogram bar is found by dividing the class frequency by the class width.

6   Histograms are plotted using class boundaries.

Methods for summarising sample data

4

Having considered data collection and the graphical and tabular representation of data it is now important to explore numerical methods for ordering and presenting data. Chapter 3 considered several graphical ways of representing data (e.g. bar charts, histograms, etc.) so you might anticipate that there will be several numerical measures which can be used to summarise sample data. Some of them are single numbers used to represent a sample of data, others are used to indicate the spread of the data. The first are known as **measures of location** since they act as a *focus* for the data such that they can be used as single values to represent the whole data set. The second are known as **measures of dispersion** and are used to represent the *spread* or *variation* within the data since it is unlikely that all the values in a data set will be the same.

4.1 Measures of location

There are several measures of location but the three most commonly used ones are – the **mode**, the **median** and the **arithmetic mean**. For each of these measures it is necessary to have a definition together with an explanation of how it is evaluated in practice. This evaluation will be considered for a set of raw data, a frequency distribution and a grouped frequency distribution.

The mode

Consider the following set of raw data which shows the number of errors made by each of 11 secretarial students when typing the same report as part of their assessment:

$$4 \quad 6 \quad 7 \quad 5 \quad 9 \quad 10 \quad 6 \quad 6 \quad 4 \quad 7 \quad 8$$

The simplest measure used to represent these data is the **mode** which is defined as follows:

■ **The MODE is that value of a variate which occurs most frequently.**

In the data above you can see that the value which occurs most frequently is 6 and this is the **modal** value for these data. The mode is not always unique since some data sets may have more than one mode. For example, if a twelfth student had taken the assessment and made 4 errors then the values 4 and 6 would both have been modal values, each occurring three times. Sometimes a data set does not have a modal value and this is illustrated by the following data:

$$3 \quad 4 \quad 5 \quad 4 \quad 5 \quad 5 \quad 3 \quad 4 \quad 3$$

In this data set, each value occurs the same number of times.

The following data refers to the number of children in each of a random sample of twenty-three families. In this case the data is summarised using a frequency distribution:

Number of children	0	1	2	3	4	5
Number of families	2	5	9	4	2	1

From this distribution you can see that the modal number of children in a family is 2 since it occurs most frequently, i.e. 9 out of 23 families contain two children. It is important to make sure that you realise which is the mode (2 children) and which is the modal frequency (9 families).

In the case of a grouped frequency distribution the mode is not a particularly useful measure of location. Although there are ways of estimating the mode from a grouped frequency distribution, in this book we will restrict ourselves to using the **modal class** which is the class corresponding to the highest frequency.

The following grouped frequency distribution was used on page 24 of Chapter 3 and summarises the visits to the doctor of a random sample of 150 patients:

Visits	Frequency
0–4	32
5–9	71
10–14	20
15–19	14
20–24	10
25–29	3
Total	150

For this distribution the modal class is 5–9 corresponding to the highest frequency of 71.

It is easy to appreciate that there are some advantages to be gained by using the mode to represent data since:

– it is easy to calculate
– it is not affected by any extreme value in the data set.

For example, if one of the students had performed very badly in the typing assessment on page 39 and made 32 errors, then this extreme value would not have affected the value of the mode. Unfortunately this ease of calculation is offset by the fact that the mode is not a value which has useful mathematical properties and whilst this may not seem important at this stage it will become important later in the book.

The median

The obvious advantage of using the mode to represent a set of data is the fact that it is the most frequently occurring value of the variate and since it occurs most often it is likely to be a fair representative value. Having stated that this advantage is offset by other features then we need to consider an alternative measure. Perhaps the next obvious choice is one that is in the *middle* of the data – the **median**. Before defining the median it is necessary to re-arrange the data in ascending order of magnitude. Thus the reordered data relating to the typing errors of the original eleven students on page 39 is:

$$4 \quad 4 \quad 5 \quad 6 \quad 6 \quad \mathbf{6} \quad 7 \quad 7 \quad 8 \quad 9 \quad 10$$

The definition of the median is then as follows:

■ **The MEDIAN is the middle value of an ordered set of data.**

For the above data set, containing an *odd* number of observations it is easy to see that the middle value or median is 6 (as indicated in bold type). Note that there are five values above the median and five values below it.

In general, if there are n observations, the median is the value corresponding to the $\frac{1}{2}(n+1)$th observation. Thus in this case $n = 11$ and $\frac{1}{2}(n+1) = 6$ and the sixth value is 6.

In the situation where there are an even number of observations the median is evaluated by taking half the sum of the two central values. If the 4 errors made by a twelfth student are included, the data above becomes

$$4 \quad 4 \quad 4 \quad 5 \quad 6 \quad 6 \quad 6 \quad 7 \quad 7 \quad 8 \quad 9 \quad 10$$

and the median for these data is half the sum of the sixth and seventh values. Hence:

$$\text{the median} = \frac{6 + 6}{2} = 6.$$

If we use $\frac{1}{2}(n + 1)$, then in this case:

$$\tfrac{1}{2}(n + 1) = \tfrac{1}{2}(12 + 1) = 6\tfrac{1}{2}$$

implying a value between the sixth and seventh observations.

When considering frequency distributions in Chapter 3 cumulative frequencies were introduced and these can now be used to find the median when data is summarised in a frequency distribution. Thus for the data relating to the number of children in families the table, including cumulative frequencies, is as follows:

Number of children	0	1	2	3	4	5
Number of families	2	5	9	4	2	1
Cumulative number of families	2	7	16	20	22	23

The table is a summary of the 23 ordered observations

$$0 \quad 0 \quad 1 \quad 1 \quad 1 \quad 1 \quad 1 \dots \dots 4 \quad 4 \quad 5$$

and the median could be found as shown above. However, for large data sets like this, the procedure would be tedious and it is easier to use the cumulative frequencies. Here n is 23 and so the median value corresponds to the $\frac{1}{2}(23 + 1)$th observation, i.e. the 12th. For these data this must be 2, since the table shows that the seventh value is 1 and the sixteenth value is 2 with all intermediate values being 2 and hence the twelfth value, the median, is equal to 2. Perhaps a 'health warning' is needed at this point. The median is **NOT** $2\frac{1}{2}$ as is often suggested by students who wrongly calculate the median number of children; in this case

$$0, 1, 2, 3, 4, 5, \text{ i.e. } \tfrac{1}{2}(2 + 3) = 2\tfrac{1}{2}$$

This warning is introduced to try to remind you to look carefully at your final answer once you have made your evaluation. A similar warning will be issued in the next section when calculating the arithmetic mean!

You will remember that in Chapter 3 when using data which has been summarised by a grouped frequency distribution the detail of the original observations was lost. This implies that any value of the median obtained from such a distribution can only be an *estimate* of the median of the original data before it was summarised. Consider the following two methods of obtaining estimates of the median. The first method of estimation is by interpolation and the second method is a graphical method which is explained on page 48. Consider again the table relating to visits to the doctor:

Visits	Frequency	Cumulative frequency
0–4	32	32
5–9	71	103
10–14	20	123
15–19	14	137
20–24	10	147
25–29	3	150

Since there are 150 observations the median value will be that corresponding to the $\frac{1}{2}(150 + 1) = 75.5$th observation, i.e. half the sum of the 75th and 76th observations. Unfortunately, because of the tabular nature of these data the values of the 75th and 76th observations are not known. However, it is known that they both lie in the class 5–9 since the first 32 observations are in the class 0–4 and the next 71 observations (including the 75th and 76th) are in the class 5–9, the **median class**. Since, as defined earlier, the median is the middle value this implies that 50% of the values are less than or equal to the median. Thus when estimating the median for a grouped frequency distribution $\frac{1}{2}n$ is used rather than $\frac{1}{2}(n + 1)$.

To obtain an estimate of the median let b represent the *lower class boundary* of the median class (i.e. 4.5), f represent the sum of all the frequencies *below b* (i.e. 32), f_c represent the *frequency of the median class* (i.e. 71) and c represent the *width of the median class* (i.e. 5). Then, by interpolation, the median is given by:

$$\text{Median} = b + \left(\frac{\frac{1}{2}n - f}{f_c} \right) \times c$$

Thus for these data:

$$\text{Median} = 4.5 + \left\{ \frac{75 - 32}{71} \right\} \times 5$$

$$= 7.53$$

It is important to remember that when using interpolation in this way the lower class boundary is used. It is also important to recognise that 'visits' is a discrete variate which in this situation has been treated as if it was continuous. Whilst this is not ideal it is the best solution available and, as was stated earlier, it is only an estimate.

Again it is easy to appreciate that the median shares the advantages of the mode in that:

– it is relatively easy to calculate or estimate
– it too is unaffected by extreme values since by its definition it is in the middle of the data.

Unfortunately it also shares the same disadvantage – it does not have useful mathematical properties and this leads to its restricted use.

Quantiles

The concept of dividing the data into two equal parts can be extended to dividing the data into however many equal parts you wish. The values obtained in such situations are known as **quantiles**. The most commonly used quantiles are the **quartiles** which divide the data into four equal parts. Thus we have the following definition:

■ **The QUARTILES of an ordered set of data are such that 25% of the observations are less than or equal to the first quartile (Q_1), 50% are less than or equal to the second quartile (Q_2) and 75% are less than or equal to the third quartile (Q_3).**

When evaluating the quartiles for raw data or a frequency distribution it is necessary to have a procedure which allows you to implement the above definition as accurately and meaningfully as possible. There are several approaches to this problem but the following is recommended.

Consider the n ordered observations y_1, y_2, y_3, ..., y_n. To find Q_1, first evaluate $\frac{1}{4}n$.

If $\frac{1}{4}n$ is an integer, say r, then

$$Q_1 = \tfrac{1}{2}(y_r + y_{r+1})$$

If $\frac{1}{4}n$ is not an integer but lies between the integers r and $r + 1$, then

$$Q_1 = y_{r+1}$$

Similarly, to find Q_3, first evaluate $\frac{3}{4}n$ and then proceed as for Q_1.

It is worth remembering at this point that the median is Q_2 and that if you evaluate $\frac{1}{2}(n+1)$ you can then proceed as follows.

If $\frac{1}{2}(n+1)$ is an integer, say r, then

$$Q_2 = y_r$$

but if $\frac{1}{2}(n+1)$ is not an integer but lies between r and $r+1$, then

$$Q_2 = \tfrac{1}{2}(y_r + y_{r+1})$$

If these procedures are applied to the data on the typing errors (4, 4, 5, 6, 6, 6, 7, 7, 8, 9, 10) then $Q_1 = 5$, $Q_2 = 6$ and $Q_3 = 8$.

For the frequency distribution relating to the number of children in the family, $n = 23$. So:

$$\frac{1}{4}(23) = 5.75 \Rightarrow Q_1 \text{ corresponds to the 6th observation} \quad \therefore Q_1 = 1$$
$$\frac{1}{2}(23+1) = 12 \Rightarrow Q_2 \text{ corresponds to the 12th observation} \quad \therefore Q_2 = 2$$
$$\frac{3}{4}(23) = 17.25 \Rightarrow Q_3 \text{ corresponds to the 18th observation} \quad \therefore Q_3 = 3$$

To estimate the quartiles of a grouped frequency distribution the method of interpolation used to obtain the median is again used, but in this case using $\frac{1}{4}n$ and $\frac{3}{4}n$. For the data on visits to the doctor the quartiles are estimated as follows:

$$\text{Lower quartile} = Q_1 = b + \frac{(\frac{1}{4}n - f)}{f_c} \times c$$

where f, f_c and c now refer to the class containing the lower quartile.

$$\therefore \qquad Q_1 = 4.5 + \frac{(37.5 - 32)}{71} \times 5 = 4.89$$

Similarly $\qquad Q_3 = 9.5 + \frac{(112.5 - 103)}{20} \times 5 = 11.88$

Two other sets of quantiles which are often used are the **deciles** $(D_1, D_2, ..., D_9)$ and the **percentiles** $(P_1, P_2, ..., P_{99})$ which divide the data into 10 and 100 equal parts respectively.

Evaluation of the deciles and percentiles from raw data or frequency data uses the same approach as for the quartiles with $\frac{1}{4}n$ being replaced by $\frac{1}{10}n$ and $\frac{1}{100}n$ respectively. Thus for the data relating to the number of children in the family the third decile, D_3 is the value corresponding to $\frac{3}{10}(23) = 6.9$ i.e. the 7th observation. Thus $D_3 = 1$.

Similarly the 89th percentile, P_{89}, corresponds to $\frac{89}{100}(23) = 20.47$.

i.e. the 21st value. Thus $P_{89} = 4$.

For grouped frequency distributions the approach used is the same as for the median and quartiles. Thus for the data on visits to the doctor the 6th decile and 85th percentile are estimated as follows.

$$D_6 = 4.5 + \left(\frac{\frac{6}{10}(150) - 32}{71} \right) \times 5 = 8.58$$

$$P_{85} = 14.5 + \left(\frac{\frac{85}{100}(150) - 123}{14} \right) \times 5 = 16.11$$

Example 1

A group of 14 children were given a test in mathematics. Their marks out of 20 were as shown below:

8 18 10 14 18 11 13 16 13 14 13 17 15 8

Find: (a) the mode, (b) the median, (c) the upper quartile of these marks.

Re-arranging these data in ascending order of magnitude gives

8 8 10 11 13 13 13 14 14 15 16 17 18 18

(a) The mode is the value which occurs most frequently.

$$\therefore \qquad \text{Mode} = 13$$

(b) For the median:

$$\tfrac{1}{2}(n+1) = \tfrac{15}{2} = 7.5$$

Thus, using the seventh and eighth observations:

$$Q_2 = \tfrac{1}{2}(13 + 14) = 13.5$$

(c) For the upper quartile:

$$\tfrac{3}{4}n = \tfrac{3}{4}(14) = 10.5$$

Thus, using the 11th observation:

$$Q_3 = 16$$

Example 2

The following distribution shows the number of orders for groceries received each week in a particular year by a village shop.

Number of orders	18	19	20	21	22	23	24	25	26	27	28
Number of weeks	2	2	3	4	6	9	12	6	5	2	1

Find: (a) the mode, (b) the median and the quartiles, (c) the seventh decile.

Cumulative frequencies corresponding to the orders are:

2   4   7   11   17   26   38   44   49   51   52

(a) Mode = 24

(b) Since $n = 52$ then

$$\tfrac{1}{2}(n+1) = \tfrac{53}{2} = 26.5$$

Thus, you use the 26th and 27th observations:

$$\text{Median} = \tfrac{1}{2}(23 + 24) = 23.5$$

For Q_1:

$$\tfrac{1}{4}n = \tfrac{52}{4} = 13$$

Thus, you use the 13th and 14th observations:

$$Q_1 = \tfrac{1}{2}(22 + 22) = 22$$

For Q_3:

$$\tfrac{3}{4}n = 39$$

Thus, you use the 39th and 40th observations:

$$Q_3 = \tfrac{1}{2}(25 + 25) = 25$$

(c) For D_7:

$$\tfrac{7}{10}n = 36.4$$

Thus, you use the 37th observation:

$$D_7 = 24$$

Example 3

The lengths of a batch of 2000 rods were measured to the nearest centimetre. The measurements are summarised below.

Length (to nearest cm)	Number of rods	Cumulative number of rods
60–64	11	11
65–69	49	60
70–74	190	250
75–79	488	738
80–84	632	1370
85–89	470	1840
90–94	137	1977
95–99	23	2000
Total	2000	

Estimate: (a) the median and the quartiles, (b) the third decile, (c) the sixty-seventh percentile.

(a)
$$Q_2 = 79.5 + \left(\frac{\frac{1}{2}(2000) - 738}{632} \right) \times 5 = 81.57$$

$$Q_1 = 74.5 + \left(\frac{\frac{1}{4}(2000) - 250}{488} \right) \times 5 = 77.06$$

$$Q_3 = 84.5 + \left(\frac{\frac{3}{4}(2000) - 1370}{470} \right) \times 5 = 85.88$$

(b)
$$D_3 = 74.5 + \left(\frac{\frac{3}{10}(2000) - 250}{488} \right) \times 5 = 78.09$$

(c)
$$P_{67} = 79.5 + \left(\frac{\frac{67}{100}(2000) - 738}{632} \right) \times 5 = 84.26$$

Graphical methods and quartiles

In Chapter 3 graphical representation of data was considered and the cumulative frequency step polygon, the stem and leaf diagram and the cumulative frequency polygon were introduced. This section explores ways of using these diagrams to evaluate quartiles.

In section 3.2 the cumulative frequency step polygon for the following distribution was drawn:

Times absent	0	1	2	3	4	5	6	7	8	9	10
Frequency	4	11	6	4	4	4	3	10	6	4	4
Cumulative frequency	4	15	21	25	29	33	36	46	52	56	60

It is possible to use a cumulative frequency polygon to find the quartiles of the distribution. For example, if you wish to find the median and quartiles then proceed as follows. For this distribution the value of the median corresponds to the $\frac{1}{2}n = \frac{1}{2}(60) = 30$th observation. Thus a horizontal line is drawn at this point on the vertical axis and where this line intersects with the step polygon the value of the median is read from the horizontal axis. Similarly the quartiles are found using $\frac{1}{4}n$ and $\frac{3}{4}n$. If the horizontal line for a quartile is in line with one of the steps then you take as the quartile the value at the *mid-point of the step*. As can be seen from the following cumulative frequency step polygon, this is the case when finding Q_1 for the above frequency distribution.

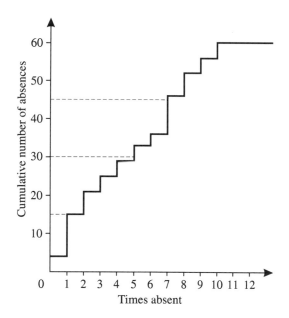

From the polygon:

$$Q_1 = 1\tfrac{1}{2} \qquad Q_2 = 5 \qquad Q_3 = 7$$

Although stem and leaf diagrams were only used in section 3.3 of Chapter 3 to summarise data, they can in fact be used to find quantiles, in particular the quartiles.

Consider the stem and leaf diagram for example 1 on page 17.

Repair times				2 $\mid$ 1 means 21
3	2	1 4 4		(3)
20	3	0 0 0 0 1 1 1 1 2 2 3 3 4 4 4 4 4		(17)
(8)	3	6 6 6 6 7 7 8 9		(8)
23	4	0 0 1 1 1 2 2 2 3 3 5		(11)
12	4	6 6 6 7		(4)
8	5	0 1 1 5 6 6		(6)
2	6	2 2		(2)

Notice that an additional column of information has been added to the left of the diagram. This is known as the **depth** column. The depth of a line indicates the number of leaves on that line or beyond it. The 20 on the second line down indicates that there are 20 leaves on that line or above it; the 12 on the third line from the bottom indicates that there are 12 leaves on that line or below it. The line with (8) on it contains the median and there are eight leaves on that line. To find the values of the quartiles from a stem and leaf diagram you use the same methods as before, counting the leaves from the top or bottom of the diagram until the appropriate values have been located. Thus for these data, proceed as follows.

For Q_1:

$$\tfrac{1}{4}n = \tfrac{51}{4} = 12.75 \Rightarrow 13\text{th observation}$$

$\therefore$
$$Q_1 = 32$$

For Q_2:

$$\tfrac{1}{2}(n+1) = 26 \Rightarrow 26\text{th observation}$$

$\therefore$
$$Q_2 = 37$$

For Q_3:

$$\tfrac{3}{4}n = 38.25 \Rightarrow 39\text{th observation}$$

$\therefore$
$$Q_3 = 45$$

Deciles and percentiles can be found similarly as before.

The graphical method for estimating quartiles for a grouped frequency distribution involves using a cumulative frequency polygon. The method of estimating the quartiles using this polygon is similar to that for the cumulative frequency step polygon. First evaluate $\frac{1}{4}n$, $\frac{1}{2}n$ and $\frac{3}{4}n$ and then draw horizontal lines from the corresponding cumulative frequencies on the vertical axis. The points at which these horizontal lines intersect the polygon indicate the values of the quartiles on the horizontal axis. The cumulative frequency polygon below corresponds to the data in example 5 of Chapter 3. The estimates of the quartiles are indicated by the broken lines such that:

$$Q_1 = 55.35 \qquad Q_2 = 58.35 \qquad Q_3 = 61.95$$

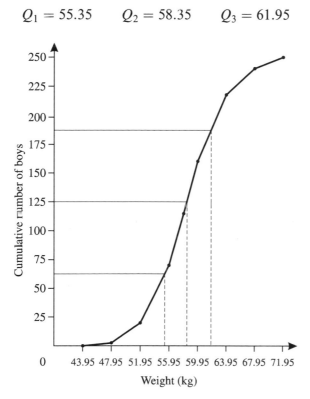

Now that you are familiar with the quantiles, and in particular the quartiles, it is possible to introduce another useful graphical method for representing data. This is known as a **box and whisker plot** or more commonly a **box plot**. The box is used to represent the central 50% of the data and the whiskers which extend from the box to the smallest and largest values give an indication of the overall spread of the data, as shown below:

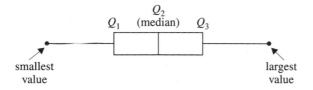

At this stage the box plot will be used simply as a means of representation. Later in this chapter its interpretation and use for comparisons will be considered. For the data on repair times it was found that $Q_1 = 32$, $Q_2 = 37$ and $Q_3 = 45$. The stem and leaf diagram shows that the smallest value is 21 and the largest value is 62. The box plot to represent these values is shown below:

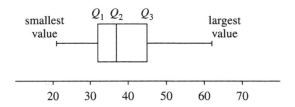

The mean

The third measure used to represent a data set is the arithmetic mean. You may be familiar with this measure from earlier studies and you may even use another name for it. The arithmetic mean is often referred to as the *average*, but from now on this measure will be referred to simply as the **mean** and defined as follows.

■ **The MEAN is the sum of all the observations divided by the total number of observations.**

At this point it may be helpful to revise earlier work on populations and samples. In Chapter 2, a population was defined as the collection of individual items or individuals from which samples are drawn in order to make inferences about that population. In practice populations are usually too large to be handled numerically and so samples are taken from them and these samples are used to represent the population. Thus rather than find the mean of a population you take a sample from the population, evaluate its mean and use it as an estimate of the mean of the population. However, it is important to remember that the population will have a mean value even if you are unable to evaluate it. The value of the population mean is denoted by the Greek symbol μ and any estimate of the mean you evaluate from a sample from the population is denoted by the symbol $\bar{x}$. The population mean, μ is known as a **parameter** of the population. Other parameters will be introduced later in this book and in *Book T2*. Consider the following illustration:

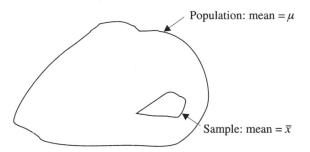

Since $\bar{x}$ is calculated from a sample in order to be able to make inferences about μ then it is essential that $\bar{x}$ is the *best representative value* of μ that can be obtained. In statistics, this best representative value is referred to as an *unbiased estimate* and although the proof is beyond the scope of this book it can be shown that the mean, $\bar{x}$, as defined earlier, is an unbiased estimate of μ. This implies that you can use the same method of evaluating the mean for both the population and a sample from that population. As will be seen later in this chapter it is not always the case that you can evaluate the population parameter and its estimate from a sample using the same method.

Consider the data on page 39 showing the errors made by each of 11 secretarial students:

$$4 \quad 6 \quad 7 \quad 5 \quad 9 \quad 10 \quad 6 \quad 6 \quad 4 \quad 7 \quad 8$$

Within the college at which these students are studying they may be the only secretarial students and they will then constitute the **population** of secretarial students at that college. For this population of students, the mean number of errors made is

$$\mu = \frac{4 + 6 + 7 + 5 + 9 + 10 + 6 + 6 + 4 + 7 + 8}{11} = \frac{72}{11} = 6.545$$

Rather than write out the sum of all the observations for each calculation as above you can introduce the $\sum$ notation (see page 96 in *Pure Mathematics 1* if you are unfamiliar with this notation) where $\sum$ implies the sum of all the observations. Thus if you have a set of n observations, $x_1, x_2, ..., x_n$, from a population then the mean of this population of observations is given by:

$$\mu = \frac{\sum_{i=1}^{n} x_i}{n}$$

If you were to take a **sample** of 4 students from the above population and they made 7, 9, 6, 4 errors respectively then the mean of this sample is given by:

$$\bar{x} = \frac{\sum x}{n}$$
$$= \frac{26}{4} = 6.5$$

Note that the $i = 1$ and n have been removed from $\sum$ for simplicity since we can only sum the observations available in the population or sample.

In the case of a frequency distribution you need to extend the above notation, since each value of the variate has a frequency associated with it. Thus x_1, x_2, ..., x_n have corresponding frequencies f_1, f_2, ..., f_n implying that x_1, occurred f_1 times etc. In this case the mean is found using:

$$\mu = \bar{x} = \frac{\sum fx}{\sum f}$$

Thus for the data relating to the sample of 23 families introduced earlier in this chapter the mean number of children per family is given by:

$$\bar{x} = \frac{(2 \times 0) + (5 \times 1) + (9 \times 2) + (4 \times 3) + (2 \times 4) + (1 \times 5)}{2 + 5 + 9 + 4 + 2 + 1}$$
$$= \frac{48}{23} = 2.09$$

Another 'health warning' is appropriate here! It is not unusual for students to give their answer as $\bar{x} = \frac{48}{6} = 8$ for this distribution, where the 6 comes from 0, 1, 2, 3, 4, 5, i.e. 6 values of the variate. First, it is totally wrong and second, it does not make sense. None of the families had 8 children, so 8 cannot possibly be a representative value for all 23 families. **Always check that your answer makes sense!**

The above calculation is often made easier using a simple table as shown below.

Number of children, x	Number of families, f	$f \times x$
0	2	0
1	5	5
2	9	18
3	4	12
4	2	8
5	1	5
Total	23	48

Hence:

$$\bar{x} = \frac{\sum fx}{\sum f}$$

$$= \frac{48}{23}$$

$$= 2.09$$

For raw data and data summarised by means of a frequency distribution the variate values, x_1, x_2, ..., x_n, are very obvious. This is *not* the case when data is summarised in a grouped frequency distribution. For example, what are the x_1, x_2, etc. for the data relating to the visits to the doctor? In Chapter 3 the term **class mid-point** was introduced. The class mid-point can be used to represent the class since you have no information as to how data is distributed within a class.

Thus for the class 0–4, use $\frac{1}{2}(0 + 4) = 2$ as the class mid-point and this becomes x_1 with a corresponding frequency of 32 associated with it. Once the mid-points of all the classes have been found you can then proceed as for a frequency distribution using the mid-points as x_1, x_2, ..., x_n. The calculation is easily carried out using a simple table as shown below:

Visits	Frequency, f	Class mid-point, x	$f \times x$
0–4	32	2	64
5–9	71	7	497
10–14	20	12	240
15–19	14	17	238
20–24	10	22	220
25–29	3	27	81
Total	150		1340

Hence:

$$\bar{x} = \frac{\sum fx}{\sum f}$$

$$= \frac{1340}{150}$$

$$= 8.93$$

At this point it is worth pausing to think about any advantages and disadvantages associated with the mean. There are two disadvantages to consider.

First, the mean is influenced by extreme values. If you have five observations as follows: 3, 4, 5, 6, 7, then the mean is found to be:

$$\bar{x} = \frac{3+4+5+6+7}{5}$$
$$= \tfrac{25}{5}$$
$$= 5$$

If the next observation is an extreme one, say 35, then

$$\bar{x} = \frac{25+35}{6}$$
$$= \tfrac{60}{6}$$
$$= 10$$

Thus it can be seen that the mean has been drawn towards the extreme value.

Second, and in this age of calculators perhaps not too big a disadvantage, the mean is not as easily calculated as the two earlier measures.

The advantages, however, tend to outweigh the disadvantages, the first being that all the values are used directly when calculating the mean. The second, and more important one, is that the mean has very important mathematical properties, which at this stage may not be obvious or seem important. Their importance should become clear in Chapter 8.

There are times when it is desirable to combine data sets and in such situations the mean of the combined data set can be obtained from the means of the individual data sets. This is done by weighting the mean of each data set according to the number of observations in each data set. For example, if the mean of a sample of 25 observations is 8.75 and the mean of a different sample of 30 observations is 9.28 then the mean of the combined sample is given by:

$$\bar{x} = \frac{(25 \times 8.75) + (30 \times 9.28)}{25 + 30}$$
$$= \tfrac{497.15}{55}$$
$$= 9.04$$

In general if there are k different samples with means $\bar{x}_1, \bar{x}_2, ..., \bar{x}_k$ respectively and the corresponding sample sizes are $n_1, n_2, ..., n_k$ then the mean of the combined samples is known as a **weighted mean** and is given by:

$$\bar{x} = \frac{n_1\bar{x}_1 + n_2\bar{x}_2 + ... + n_2 x_2 + ... + n_k\bar{x}_k n_k\bar{x}_k}{n_1 + n_2 + ... + n_k}$$

Note that this is very similar to

$$\bar{x} = \frac{\sum fx}{\sum f}.$$

An even more general form is given by:

$$\bar{x} = \frac{w_1 x_1 + w_2 x_2 + ... + w_k x_k}{w_1 + w_2 + ... + w_k}$$

where $x_1, x_2, ..., x_k$ are observations and $w_1, w_2, ..., w_k$ are appropriate weights.

Example 4

Over a period of 10 days a commuter timed, to the nearest minute, how long it took her to travel from home to her work. The following are her observations.

$$35 \quad 27 \quad 38 \quad 26 \quad 31 \quad 42 \quad 32 \quad 29 \quad 38 \quad 34$$

(a) Find the mean length of time it took her to travel to work.

At a later date she carried out the same process over a period of 15 days and found her mean time to be 36.4 minutes.

(b) Find the mean time for the combined sample of 25 observations.

(a)
$$\bar{x} = \frac{\sum x}{n}$$
$$= \frac{35 + 27 + ... + 34}{10}$$
$$= \frac{332}{10}$$
$$= 33.2 \text{ minutes}$$

(b)
$$\bar{x} = \frac{n_1 x_1 + n_2 x_2}{n_1 + n_2}$$
$$= \frac{332 + (15 \times 36.4)}{10 + 15}$$
$$= \frac{878}{25}$$
$$= 35.12 \text{ minutes}$$

Example 5

At the end of her statistics course, Diane sits two written papers, S1 and S2, and hands in a piece of coursework. Her marks out of 100 were 76 for S1 and 67 for S2 and she gained 81 marks for her coursework. Her overall percentage mark for the course is weighted so that the two written papers count for 40% each and the coursework counts for 20%. Find Diane's overall percentage mark.

$$\text{Diane's mark} = \frac{w_1 x_1 + w_2 x_2 + w_3 x_3}{w_1 + w_2 + w_3}$$

$$= \frac{(40 \times 76) + (40 \times 67) + (20 \times 81)}{40 + 40 + 20}$$

$$= \frac{7340}{100}$$

$$= 73.4\%$$

Example 6

A car park attendant counted the number of people in each car entering a car park between 7.30 am and 9.00 am and his results are summarised in the following frequency distribution:

Number of people	1	2	3	4	5
Number of cars	41	33	18	6	2

Calculate the mean number of people per car entering the car park.

Number of people, x	Number of cars, f	$f \times x$
1	41	41
2	33	66
3	18	54
4	6	24
5	2	10
Total	100	195

$$\text{Mean} = \bar{x} = \frac{\sum fx}{\sum f}$$

$$= \frac{195}{100}$$

$$= 1.95$$

Example 7

From a spot check of the speeds of vehicles on a motorway, the following grouped frequency distribution was obtained:

Speed (m.p.h.)	56–58	59–61	62–64	65–67	68–70	71–73	74–76
Number of vehicles	4	12	28	58	44	18	10

Find the average speed of the vehicles involved on this spot check.

Speed (m.p.h.)	Number of vehicles, f	Mid-point, x	fx
56–58	4	57	228
59–61	12	60	720
62–64	28	63	1764
65–67	58	66	3828
68–70	44	69	3036
71–73	18	72	1296
74–76	10	75	750
Total	174		11622

$$\therefore \quad \bar{x} = \frac{\sum fx}{\sum f}$$

$$= \frac{11622}{174}$$

$$= 66.79 \text{ m.p.h.}$$

You will no doubt have noticed that the arithmetic in Example 7 involved quite large numbers and whilst these are no problem with a modern calculator it is worth at this point giving some consideration to the reduction of this involved arithmetic. In statistics this is done using **coding**, whereby the original variate is transformed to a simpler one which eases the arithmetic. For example, if you wish to find the mean of the five observations 1001, 1002, 1003, 1004, 1005 then you could use:

$$\bar{x} = \frac{1001 + 1002 + 1003 + 1004 + 1005}{5}$$

$$= \frac{1015}{5}$$

$$= 1003$$

Alternatively, if you subtract 1000 from each observation you obtain the values 1, 2, 3, 4, 5 and the mean of these five values is 3. If you now add the 1000 which was originally subtracted then the value obtained is 1003, as above.

Consider the observations 1010, 1020, 1030, 1040, 1050. If you subtract 1000 from each of these observations you obtain the values 10, 20, 30, 40, 50. Dividing each value by 10 gives the values 1, 2, 3, 4, 5 and you already know that the mean of these values is 3. If you now multiply by 10 and add on 1000 the mean of the original observations is $(3 \times 10) + 1000 = 1030$. In general, if you have n observations x_1, x_2, ..., x_n and each observation is transformed or **coded** such that $y_1 = (x_1 - a)/b$, $y_2 = (x_2 - a)/b$, ..., $y_n = (x_n - a)/b$, (i.e. subtract a then divide by b) then $\bar{x} = b\bar{y} + a$

The effect of this coding is illustrated graphically below.

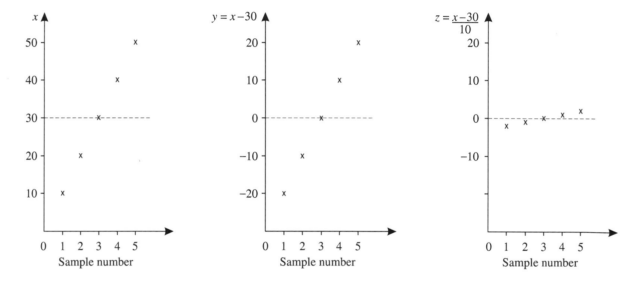

As can be seen the effect of subtracting a constant (i.e. $y = x - 30$) is the equivalent of moving the origin without affecting the spread of the data. The effect of dividing by a constant has the effect of reducing the spread of the data about this line of origin. This illustration may prove useful later in this chapter. In a practical situation it is necessary to choose suitable values for a and b in order to code the data using $y = (x - a)/b$. A simple rule-of-thumb is to let a take the x value corresponding to the modal frequency and to let b equal the class width. If the class widths are not all equal then use the smallest class width.

Example 8
Use the method of coding to estimate the mean of the grouped frequency distribution in example 7.

In this case, let $a = 66$ and $b = 3$, then, for example, when $x = 57$, $y = \frac{x-66}{3}$ gives $y = -3$.

The following table illustrates the way to carry out the calculation.

Speed (m.p.h.)	Number of vehicles, f	Mid-point, x	$y = \frac{x-66}{3}$	fy
56–58	4	57	−3	−12
59–61	12	60	−2	−24
62–64	28	63	−1	−28
65–67	58	66	0	0
68–70	44	69	1	44
71–73	18	72	2	36
74–76	10	75	3	30
Total	174			$\frac{-64+110}{46}$

$\therefore$
$$\bar{y} = \frac{\sum fy}{\sum f}$$
$$= \frac{46}{174}$$

$\therefore$
$$\bar{x} = b\bar{y} + a$$
$$= 3 \times \frac{46}{174} + 66$$
$$= 66.79 \text{ m.p.h.}$$

Note the simplification of the arithmetic – the only need for a calculator is to evaluate $\frac{46}{174}$, the rest is simple mental arithmetic. At this point it is worth issuing another 'health warning' relating to showing your working when answering examination questions. Entering numbers into your calculator, pressing the appropriate keys and writing down an answer scores full marks if the answer is *completely correct* to the required number of decimal places. The slightest error results in a score of zero marks. Showing your working at all stages will gain the method marks available and marks for accuracy will be lost at the stage the error is made – subsequent accuracy marks may well be awarded. For example if −24 above had appeared as −26 and thus

$$\bar{y} = \frac{44}{174} \Rightarrow \bar{x} = 66.76$$

then it is quite likely that all but one of the available marks would have been gained. An answer of 66.76 without working would have scored zero marks.

Before leaving this section it is necessary to consider two additional features associated with grouped frequency distributions. The first concerns *unequal class intervals*. In some circumstances data is grouped to reflect the uneven spread of the data being grouped. For example, if most of the data is in the range 0–50, but some lie in the range 50–250 then the classes used might be 0–9, 10–19, 20–29, 30–49, 50–74, 75–99, 100–149, 150–249. Unequal class widths such as these were easily dealt with when drawing histograms and they should not cause any problems when estimating the median or the mean since the same methods can be used with distributions with unequal intervals as are used with distributions with equal intervals.

The second feature relates to *open-ended classes*. These are classes appearing at the beginning or end of a distribution such that they do not have either a lower limit or an upper limit. For example, –9, 10–19, ..., 80–89, 90–, the first class implies any value less than or equal to 9 and the last class implies any value greater than or equal to 90. Although open-ended classes do not affect the estimation of the median, they do affect the drawing of histograms and the estimation of the mean. They are used when there is uncertainty about the least value or maximum value that could occur in a distribution and if an estimate for the mean of that distribution is required then the open-ended classes need to be closed. To do this needs a rule-of-thumb and the common one is to use 'twice the previous class interval'.

Thus for the class 90– you could use 90–109 since the interval of the class 80–89 is 10 (i.e. 89.5–79.5) and for 90–109 it is 20. It is not essential to use this rule-of-thumb since it may not always be appropriate. There are instances when you will know intuitively what value to use and this is perfectly acceptable. It is advisable that at some point you explain why you have used this value. For example, with –9 it may be that 0–9 is appropriate since you know that the variate cannot be negative.

Exercise 4A

1 For each of the sets of data given below find or estimate, as appropriate, the mode (or modal class) and the median.

(a) 4   10   15   8   3   8   9   7   6

(b)

Number	10	11	12	13	14	15
Frequency	4	6	13	18	7	5

(c)

Class	0–4	5–9	10–14	15–19	20–24	25–30
Frequency	2	6	7	9	8	4

2 For each of the sets of data given below find or estimate, as
appropriate, the quartiles.

(a) 3   8   8   2   2   7   9   10   7

(b)

Number	0	1	2	3	4	5	6	7	8	9	10
Frequency	1	1	4	8	12	14	7	6	4	2	1

(c)

Class	1–9	10–19	20–29	30–39	40–49	50–59	60–69
Frequency	3	6	12	18	10	4	2

3 For each of the sets of data given below find or estimate, as
appropriate, D_3 and D_9.

(a) 19   22   30   14   26   37   42   32   33   10

(b)

Number	10–12	13–15	16–18	19–21	22–24	25–27
Frequency	3	9	14	23	26	9

(c)

Number	0	1	2	3	4	5	6	7	8
Frequency	2	3	4	4	5	3	2	1	1

4 For each of the sets of data given below find or estimate, as
appropriate, P_{33} and P_{66}.

(a) 33   42   45   48   50   57   60   75   80   83

(b)

Number	10	11	12	13	14	15	16	17	18
Frequency	4	14	24	42	36	21	14	3	2

(c)

Class	11–20	21–30	31–40	41–50	51–60	61–70	71–80
Frequency	8	12	15	16	11	6	2

5 At a garage which did MOT car tests, the number of cars
tested each day, over a 14 day working period, was as
follows.

3   10   8   6   8   3   2   2   8   7   11   12   4

Find: (a) the mode, (b) the median, (c) the lower quartile, of these numbers.

6 Below is the frequency distribution which resulted when the height (in cm) of 50 tennis players was measured.

Height (cm)	170	172.5	175	177.5	180	182.5	185	187.5	190	192.5	195
Frequency	1	2	4	6	8	9	7	6	3	2	2

Find: (a) the mode, (b) the median and quartiles, (c) the third decile, of these data.

7 When checking the number of weeds growing in a field by using a 1 metre by 1 metre sampling frame, the frequency distribution was as summarised below.

Weeds per square metre	0	1	2	3	4	5	6	7	8
Frequency	4	15	27	20	18	10	4	1	1

Find: (a) the mode, (b) the median, (c) the upper quartile and the eighth decile, for these data.

8 The following grouped frequency distribution shows the number of items dispensed by a pharmacy over a period of time.

Number of items	Frequency	Cumulative frequency
0–4	1	1
5–9	9	10
10–14	30	40
15–19	52	92
20–24	64	156
25–29	41	197
30–34	17	214
35–39	14	228
40–44	5	233
45–49	2	235
Total	235	

Estimate: (a) the median and quartiles, (b) the ninth decile,
(c) the forty-third percentile, of the number of items dispensed
per day.

9 The grouped frequency distribution shown below gives the
speed of service of the top 50 performers in men's
professional tennis in 1992.

Service speed (m.p.h.)	90–94	95–99	100–104	105–109	110–114	115–119	120–124	125 129
Frequency	2	7	9	14	9	4	3	2

Estimate: (a) the median and lower quartile, (b) the third and
seventh deciles, (c) the thirty-ninth percentile, of these data.

10 Use the stem and leaf diagram given below to find the
median and the quartiles of these data:

                                                    1 | 1 means 11

```
1 | 1 5              (2)
2 | 2 4 6 6          (4)
3 | 2 5 6 7 7        (5)
4 | 0 0 1 4 6 8 8    (7)
5 | 0 1 1 5          (4)
6 | 2 4 4 7          (4)
7 | 8                (1)
8 | 2 2              (2)
```

11 When analysing the lengths of sentences, the number of
words per sentence in one paragraph were:

29   14   15   27   30   33   10   20   20   21

(a) Find the mean number of words per sentence.
(b) In another passage of the same book, over 16 sentences,
the mean was found to be 35.2 words per sentence. Find
the mean for the two passages combined.

12 A car dealer sells three different models made by the same
manufacturer. He sells
265 of model A at a mean price of £10 860,
352 of model B at a mean price of £12 580
150 of model C at a mean price of £18 250.

Find the mean price of all the cars sold during this period.

13 The number of general knowledge questions answered correctly during a test taken by 100 children is shown in the following frequency distribution:

Number of correct answers	1	2	3	4	5	6
Frequency	11	18	26	23	15	7

Calculate the mean number of correct answers.

14 The frequency distribution of the number of peas in a pod, for a sample of 90 pods, taken at random, from a new variety of pea is shown below.

Number of peas per pod	2	3	4	5	6	7	8
Frequency	5	8	10	11	19	27	10

Find the mean number of peas per pod for this sample.

15 For a selected group of people, an insurance company gave the following data:

Age	0–9	10–19	20–29	30–39	40–49	50–59	60–69	70–79
Number of deaths	2	12	55	95	71	42	16	7

Estimate the mean age of death.

16 The grouped frequency distribution for the life (in hours) of 200 electric light bulbs is given below.

Life (hours)	590–599	600–609	610–619	620–629	630–639	640–649	650–659	660–669
Frequency	4	9	23	41	81	29	9	4

Use a method of coding to estimate the mean life expectancy of a light bulb in this sample.

17 In an investigation of delays at a roadworks, the times spent
by a sample of commuters waiting to pass through the
roadworks were recorded to the nearest minute. Shown below
is part of a cumulative frequency table resulting from the
investigation.

Upper class boundary	2.5	4.5	7.5	8.5	9.5	10.5	12.5	15.5	20.5
Cumulative number of commuters	0	6	21	48	97	149	178	191	200

(a) For how many of the commuters was the time recorded
as 11 minutes or 12 minutes?

(b) Estimate: (i) the lower quartile, (ii) the 81st percentile, of
these waiting times.   [L]

4.2 Measures of dispersion

So far this chapter has been concerned with calculating or
estimating a single value to represent a set of data, for example,
the mode, the median or the mean. The outcome has usually been a
single value, such as the mean is equal to 12.72, although for
grouped frequency data the modal class was quoted rather than a
single value. This idea of using a range of values (for example,
modal class is 20–24) can now be expanded upon since it is essential
that you realise that although you can quote a single number to
represent data, the data itself will be spread about that number. It is
this measuring of the spread of data that will now be considered.

Ranges

The simplest measure which quantifies the spread of a data set is the
range which is easily and simply defined as follows.

■ **The RANGE of a set of data is the value obtained when the
smallest value is subtracted from the largest value.**

Example 9

Find the range of the following observations giving the number of absentees from the statistics class of 40 students over a period of ten days:

$$3 \quad 8 \quad 7 \quad 1 \quad 2 \quad 9 \quad 8 \quad 2 \quad 4 \quad 5$$

$$\text{Range} = \text{largest value} - \text{smallest value}$$
$$= 9 - 1$$
$$= 8$$

Although the range is easily calculated it does not lend itself to mathematical use and thus it tends to be used only with small data sets in conjunction with either the mode or the median.

This concept of range can be extended to the quantiles and in particular to the quartiles, giving the following definitions.

- **The INTERQUARTILE RANGE (IQR) is the value obtained when the lower quartile is subtracted from the upper quartile.**

$$\text{IQR} = Q_3 - Q_1$$

In some situations the **SEMI-INTERQUARTILE RANGE (SIQR)** is used where

$$\text{SIQR} = \tfrac{1}{2}(Q_3 - Q_1)$$

Example 10

For the data in example 9, find the upper and lower quartiles and hence the semi-interquartile range.

Re-arranging the data in ascending order of magnitude gives:

$$1 \quad 2 \quad 2 \quad 3 \quad 4 \quad 5 \quad 7 \quad 8 \quad 8 \quad 9$$

For Q_1 : $\tfrac{1}{4}n = \tfrac{10}{4} = 2.5 \Rightarrow$ 3rd observation

$\therefore$ $Q_1 = 2$

For Q_3 : $\tfrac{3}{4}n = 7.5 \Rightarrow$ 8th observation

$\therefore$ $Q_3 = 8$

$\therefore$ $\text{SIQR} = \tfrac{1}{2}(Q_3 - Q_1)$
$$= \tfrac{1}{2}(8 - 2)$$
$$= 3$$

Again the calculations are relatively easy but unfortunately the IQR and SIQR do not lend themselves to easy mathematical use. They arc based on the central 50% of the data and are thus not influenced by extreme values and are often used when data contains extreme values, or has open-ended classes or is not symmetrical. This property of symmetry will be discussed in section 4.3. In these situations it is not unusual to use the median and the SIQR (or IQR) to summarise a data set.

Variance and standard deviation

The fact that in the previous section reference was made to the lack of mathematical properties of the range and inter-quartile range suggests that there is a measure of spread or dispersion which does have suitable mathematical properties. This measure is known as the **standard deviation**. This section is concerned solely with its calculation or estimation. Its usefulness, through its mathematical properties, will be considered in Chapter 8. The one measure of location, previously considered, that is useful mathematically is the mean and evaluation of the variance of a set of data is based on the mean of that data; μ for a population or $\bar{x}$ for a sample. Rather than use the range of a data set you can consider the deviations of a set of observations about their mean. Since the mean is the representative value of the data and is a *focus* for the data, then it is only to be expected that some of the observations will be smaller than the mean and some will be larger.

Consider a **population** consisting of the following values:

$$2 \quad 3 \quad 7 \quad 4 \quad 9$$

The mean, μ, is 5 and the individual deviations of the observations from the mean are:

$$-3 \quad -2 \quad 2 \quad -1 \quad 4$$

Note that the sum of these deviations is zero. This is always true, as is shown below.

Let $x_1, x_2, ..., x_n$ represent a population of n observations and μ the mean of the population. The deviations from the mean are then $(x_1 - \mu), (x_2 - \mu), ..., (x_n - \mu)$.

The sum of these deviations is given by

$$\begin{aligned}
\sum(x - \mu) &= \sum x - \sum \mu \\
&= \sum x - n\mu \\
&= \sum x - n\frac{\sum x}{n} \\
&= 0
\end{aligned}$$

To overcome this situation the variance is based on the sum of the deviations squared, a fact which may be difficult to understand at this stage. Thus we use $(x_1 - \mu)^2$, ..., $(x_n - \mu)^2$. Another very difficult feature associated with variance needs to be introduced at this point and whilst some attempt will be made to justify this feature, it will be necessary to wait until Book T2 before a proof can be given. Having obtained the squared deviations, the variance of a population is based on the sum of these squared deviations. Since you are dealing with a population then a Greek symbol, σ^2, is used to denote the population variance and its definition is then as follows:

■ **The VARIANCE of a population of observations x_1, x_2, ..., x_n is the mean of the sum of the squared deviations from their mean, μ.**

i.e.
$$\sigma^2 = \frac{\sum (x - \mu)^2}{n}$$

For a population summarised by a frequency distribution the definition reflects the fact that each observation has a corresponding frequency and thus in this situation

$$\sigma^2 = \frac{\sum f(x - \mu)^2}{\sum f}$$

For a grouped frequency distribution the same definition is used but it must be remembered that the mid-points of the classes are used as the x-values in the calculation.

Whilst the above formulae define the variance, in practice it is usual to use a more computationally-friendly form for the variance. Thus it can be shown that:

$$\sigma^2 = \frac{\sum (x - \mu)^2}{n}$$

$$= \frac{\sum x^2}{n} - \mu^2$$

or
$$\sigma^2 = \frac{\sum f(x - \mu)^2}{\sum f}$$

$$= \frac{\sum f x^2}{\sum f} - \mu^2$$

Having defined variance in this way it is important to note that it is measured in terms of x^2 and not x. Thus whatever the units of x, then variance is measured in (units)^2. To overcome the difficulty of interpreting a measure of spread expressed in (units)^2 a measure is used called the **standard deviation**. This is a measure of spread or variability which has the same units as the original observations and is defined as follows:

■   **The STANDARD DEVIATION is the positive square root of the variance.**

Thus
$$\sigma = \sqrt{\frac{\sum (x - \mu)^2}{n}}$$

$$= \sqrt{\frac{\sum x^2}{n} - \mu^2}$$

or
$$\sigma = \sqrt{\frac{\sum f(x - \mu)^2}{\sum f}}$$

$$= \sqrt{\frac{\sum fx^2}{\sum f} - \mu^2}$$

Both variance and standard deviation are measures which you might find difficult to come to terms with after such simple measures as, for example, the mode or the mean. However, it is important that you understand how to evaluate them in order to use them in Chapter 8, where the link between μ and σ^2 will be made.

Example 11

Consider the **population** of values defined earlier on page 69:

$$2 \quad 3 \quad 7 \quad 4 \quad 9$$

Find the mean and the variance of this population.

$$\mu = \frac{\sum x}{n}$$

$$= \frac{25}{5}$$

$$= 5$$

x	$(x - \mu)$	$(x - \mu)^2$	x^2
2	−3	9	4
3	−2	4	9
7	2	4	49
4	−1	1	16
9	4	16	81
25		34	159

$\therefore$

$$\sigma^2 = \frac{\sum(x-\mu)^2}{n}$$
$$= \frac{34}{5}$$
$$= 6.8$$

or

$$\sigma^2 = \frac{\sum x^2}{n} - \mu^2$$
$$= \frac{159}{5} - (5)^2$$
$$= 6.8$$

It should be noted that using $\sum(x-\mu)^2$ is not generally recommended since in most situations μ is not an integer and thus rounding errors are introduced.

Example 12

Each member of an athletics club was asked to monitor the distance run in training during a particular week. The table below summarises the results. Estimate the mean and the standard deviation of this **population** of athletes.

Distance (to nearest km)	Number of athletes, f	Mid-point, x	fx	fx²
31–40	10	35.5	355	12602.5
41–45	15	43	645	27735
46–50	20	48	960	46080
51–55	70	53	3710	196630
56–57	64	56.5	3616	204304
58–60	24	59	1416	83544
61–70	20	65.5	1310	85805
71–90	10	80.5	805	64802.5
	233		12817	721503

$$\mu = \frac{12817}{233} = 55.009$$

$$\sigma^2 = \frac{721503}{233} - \left(\frac{12817}{233}\right)^2 = 70.6351$$

$\therefore$
$$\sigma = 8.404$$

You will have noticed that so far within this section much emphasis has been placed on *population data*. In practice, however, most data is sample data and you need to know how to evaluate the variance for sample data. In the section on the mean on page 53 it was stated that $\bar{x}$, the sample mean, was the best (i.e. unbiased) estimator of μ the population mean and you could evaluate both μ and $\bar{x}$ using

$\sum x / n$. Unfortunately, to find the variance of a sample of observations it is not possible to use the same method as for a population, as the value of μ is not known. If μ is replaced by $\bar{x}$ in $\frac{\sum (x-\mu)^2}{n}$ then it can be shown that $\frac{\sum (x-\bar{x})^2}{n}$ is not the most accurate or best (unbiased) estimator of σ^2, the population variance. In the same way that the value of the population mean μ, was estimated from a sample and was denoted by $\bar{x}$, so the value of σ^2, is estimated by s^2. To obtain the most accurate (or unbiased) estimate of σ^2, the population variance, use

$$s^2 = \frac{\sum (x - \bar{x})^2}{n - 1}$$

Note that μ has been replaced by $\bar{x}$ and the divisor n by $n - 1$. Since we do not know μ it does not seem unreasonable to replace it by $\bar{x}$, but why do we divide by $n - 1$ and not n? The mathematical proof is given in Book T2 but a simple explanation is as follows. Since, as was shown earlier, $\sum (x - \mu) = 0$ then so is $\sum (x - \bar{x})$ and this implies that if you know $(n - 1)$ of the $(x - \bar{x})$ values then you can easily obtain the other one since their sum is zero. This means that you are only free to choose $(n - 1)$ of the deviations before the other becomes fixed and thus we divide by $(n - 1)$ rather than n. Thus:

$$s^2 = \frac{\sum (x - \bar{x})^2}{n - 1}$$

$$= \frac{1}{n - 1} \left\{ \sum x^2 - \frac{(\sum x)^2}{n} \right\}$$

and

$$s^2 = \frac{\sum f(x - \bar{x})^2}{\sum f - 1}$$

$$= \frac{1}{\sum f - 1} \left\{ \sum fx^2 - \frac{(\sum fx)^2}{\sum f} \right\}$$

with the standard deviation, s, being the positive square root of s^2.

Example 13

The following table summarises the distance, to the nearest mile, travelled to work by a random sample of commuters.

Distance (miles)	Number of commuters
0–9	15
10–19	38
20–29	22
30–39	15
40–49	8
50–59	2
Total	100

Estimate the mean and the standard deviation of this distribution.

Distance	Number of commuters, f	Mid-point, x	$y = \dfrac{x - 14.5}{10}$	fy	fy^2
0–9	15	4.5	−1	−15	15
10–19	38	14.5	0	0	0
20–29	22	24.5	1	22	22
30–39	15	34.5	2	30	60
40–49	8	44.5	3	24	72
50–59	2	54.5	4	8	32
	100			$\dfrac{-15 + 84}{69}$	201

$\therefore$

$$\bar{y} = \frac{\sum fy}{\sum f}$$

$$= \frac{69}{100}$$

$$= 0.69$$

$$s_y^2 = \frac{1}{\sum f - 1}\left\{\sum fy^2 - \frac{(\sum fy)^2}{\sum f}\right\}$$

$$= \frac{1}{99}\left\{201 - \frac{(69)^2}{100}\right\} = 1.5494$$

$\therefore$

$$s_y = \sqrt{1.5494}$$

$$= 1.24$$

You will have noticed that this example has been solved using coding, such that $y = (x - 14.5)/10$. You now need to reverse the effect of this coding in order to obtain answers in terms of the original data. Thus:

$$\bar{x} = 10\bar{y} + 14.5$$
$$= (10 \times 0.69) + 14.5 = 21.4$$

As you will remember from earlier in the chapter, subtracting a constant from the data does not affect the spread of the data, but division by a constant does. Thus you can ignore the 14.5 when converting s_y to s_x but you must remember to multiply by 10.

Hence $\qquad\qquad s_x = 10s_y = 12.4$

Without coding:

$$\sum fx = 2140 \qquad \text{and} \qquad \sum fx^2 = 61135$$

$$\therefore \qquad\qquad \bar{x} = \tfrac{2140}{100} = 21.4$$

and

$$s_x^2 = \tfrac{1}{99}\left\{61135 - \tfrac{(2140)^2}{100}\right\} = 154.9394$$

$$\therefore \qquad\qquad s_x = \sqrt{154.9394} = 12.4$$

4.3 Interpretation

Before leaving this chapter, it is worth giving some consideration to ways in which the measures of location and dispersion can be interpreted and used. Each of the measures has been defined and in most cases their definition can be thought of as part of their interpretation. For example, the mode is the most frequently occurring value, so that if you were considering buying shoes for a large shoe shop then knowing the modal shoe size would enable you to cater for many of the customers. People with very small feet or very large ones, would not be too pleased but in any distribution they would find themselves in the first or last (possibly open-ended) class. Similarly, the quartiles indicate that there is 50% of data between Q_1 and Q_3 and thus definition and interpretation are obviously linked.

Whilst the mean and standard deviation or the median and semi-interquartile range can be used to measure location and dispersion within a data set, they can also be used to measure dispersion between data sets. Consider the following data sets:

$$x:\quad 6\quad 7\quad 8\quad 9\quad 10\quad 11\quad 12$$

$$y:\quad 56\quad 57\quad 58\quad 59\quad 60\quad 61\quad 62$$

Treating these as *populations* you get:

$$\mu_x = 9 \qquad \sigma_x = 2$$
$$\mu_y = 59 \qquad \sigma_y = 2$$

and the percentage increase in x is:

$$\frac{12 - 6}{6} \times 100 = 100\%$$

and in y is:

$$\frac{62 - 56}{56} \times 100 = 10.7\%.$$

Thus x has a much greater percentage spread than y. To enable you to compare the **relative dispersion** between data sets, use the **coefficient of variation**, V, which is defined as:

$$V = \frac{100 \times \sigma}{\mu} \qquad \text{or} \qquad \frac{100 \times s}{\bar{x}}$$

For x, you get:

$$V = \frac{100 \times 2}{9} = 22.2\%$$

and for y:

$$V = \frac{100 \times 2}{59} = 3.4\%$$

Notice that V does not have units, but is a percentage and thus you can use it to make comparisons between data sets.

There are times however when the quartiles can be used to describe the *shape of a data set*. Consider the following three histograms representing three different distributions:

Each histogram has a different shape and a statistical name is given to each of them. The middle histogram has a line of symmetry through its central bar and hence it is known as a **symmetrical distribution**. One of the important facts about a symmetrical distribution is that the mode, median and mean are all equal. The other two distributions are not symmetrical and they are known as

skew distributions. The one on the left is **positive skew** (the tail of the distribution extends in the direction of the positive axis) and the one on the right is **negative skew**. For relatively simple distributions, such as those represented by these histograms the following rules-of-thumb can be applied:

positive skew: mode < median < mean.
negative skew: mean < median < mode.

An alternative method of indicating skewness is to use the quartiles. If the median (Q_2) is closer to the lower quartile (Q_1) than it is to the upper quartile (Q_3) then the distribution is positive skew; if the median is equidistant from the lower quartile and the upper quartile the distribution is symmetrical; if the median is closer to Q_3 than it is to Q_1 then the distribution is negative skew. The above are easily seen on a box plot as illustrated by the box plots shown below.

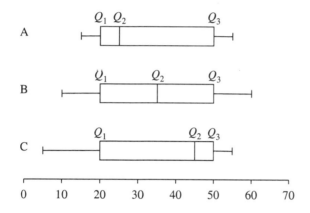

Thus: $\mathbf{A} \Rightarrow$ positive skew   since $Q_2 - Q_1 < Q_3 - Q_2$
$\mathbf{B} \Rightarrow$ symmetry   since $Q_2 - Q_1 = Q_3 - Q_2$
$\mathbf{C} \Rightarrow$ negative skew   since $Q_2 - Q_1 > Q_3 - Q_2$

A third method of assessing the skewness of a distribution is to evaluate:

$$\frac{3\,(\text{mean} - \text{median})}{\text{standard deviation}}$$

This method not only indicates the direction of the skewness but also quantifies it – the larger the value the more skewed is the data and the closer the value is to zero the more symmetrical is the distribution.

When data is skewed in either direction it is worth noting that rather than use the mean and standard deviation as appropriate measures of location and dispersion the median and semi-interquartile range are used, since as you will remember the mean is affected by extreme values and the median is not. Skew distributions tend to include extreme values. With this in mind we can measure relative dispersion by the **quartile coefficient of variation**, QV, where:

$$QV = \frac{100 \times \frac{1}{2}(Q_3 - Q_1)}{Q_2}$$

The expression 'extreme value' has been referred to several times already and in statistics such extreme values are often termed **outliers**. Although the treatment of outliers is beyond the scope of this book it is worth exploring a simple way of deciding whether or not a value is an outlier. Again this should be treated as a rule-of-thumb, although in Chapter 8 you will realise why it is useful. The rule requires the evaluation of $\frac{x-\mu}{\sigma}$ or $\frac{x-\bar{x}}{s}$ and then if the value obtained is greater than 2 or less than -2 the value x can be considered to be an outlier or extreme value.

Exercise 4B

1 For each set of data given below, find the range, interquartile range, and semi-interquartile range.
(a) 32 30 36 27 24 33 34 29
(b) 10 12 11 9 9 13 10 11 7 11 9 8
(c) 9 10 3 7 8 5 4 7 4 3 6 2

2 (a) Find the range of the following set of board game scores:
8 18 7 16 19 8 11 18 22 9 10 14 11 15 16 24
(b) For the same data find:
(i) the upper and lower quartiles
(ii) the interquartile range
(iii) the semi-interquartile range.

3 For each of the populations shown below calculate or estimate, as appropriate, the mean and the standard deviation:
(a) 12 10 8 20 6 13 7 9 25 15
(b)

Number	1	2	3	4	5	6
Frequency	3	7	10	14	8	2

(c)

Class	10–14	15–19	20–24	25–29	30–34
Frequency	2	8	14	10	6

4 For each of the following samples, estimate the mean and the standard deviation of the population:

(a) 17   16   15   22   13   20   13   18   24   18

(b)

Number	12	13	14	15	16	17	18
Frequency	90	150	240	290	160	70	0

(c)

Class	7– 10	11– 14	15– 18	19– 22	23– 26	27– 30
Frequency	1	3	9	15	14	8

5 A class of 6 children sat a test; the resulting marks, scored out of 10, were as follows:

$$4 \quad 5 \quad 6 \quad 8 \quad 4 \quad 9$$

Calculate the mean and the variance of this population.

6 Ten machines had to be fitted with new micro-chips. The time taken (in minutes) for each fitment was as follows:

$$51 \quad 49 \quad 56 \quad 60 \quad 52 \quad 58 \quad 49 \quad 56 \quad 52 \quad 57$$

Calculate the mean time taken and the variance of this population.

7 Each student in a small Higher Education College sat the same examination. The marks were recorded and the following grouped frequency distribution produced:

Mark	Frequency
1–20	8
21–30	30
31–40	90
41–50	103
51–60	79
61–70	64
71–80	21
81–90	5

Estimate the mean and the standard deviation of these marks for this population.

8   A health clinic wished to check the daily milk consumption of its 160 clients. Each client recorded their intake of milk (in ml) during a given day. The results were summarised as follows:

Milk intake (ml)	Number of clients
0–24	2
25–49	6
50–99	42
100–149	56
150–199	22
200–299	22
300–499	10

Estimate the mean and the standard deviation of the milk intake of this population.

9   A student visits a shop frequently. On twenty random occasions she recorded the queue length (the number of people queueing) at the check-out. The results were as follows:

Queue length	4	5	6	7	8	9
Number of visits	2	3	7	6	0	2

Estimate the mean and the standard deviation of the queue length at this shop.

10   The table below summarises the weights, to the nearest kilogram, of a random sample of forty Highland cattle.

Weight (kg)	Frequency
400–449	4
450–499	7
500–549	6
550–599	13
600–649	9
650–699	1

Estimate the mean and the standard deviation of the weights
for this distribution.

11 The numbers of errors, x, on each of 200 pages of typescript
was monitored. The results when summarised showed that:

$$\sum x = 920 \qquad \sum x^2 = 5032$$

Calculate the mean and the standard deviation of the number
of errors per page. [L]

12 The stem and leaf diagram below represents data collected for
the number of insects caught in an insect trap each day for 4
weeks.

		0 | 1 means 1

0	1 1 2	(3)
1	2 3 5 5 5 6	(6)
2	2 2 3 5 8 8	(6)
3	4 4 4 4 5 7 7 9	(8)
4	2 6 7 7 8	(5)

(a) Draw a box and whisker plot for the data.

(b) Using your plot to help you, comment on the skewness of
the distribution.

13 The number of birds visiting a bird table was counted each
minute for 15 minutes. The distribution was as follows:

9 4 7 5 3 8 6 5 8 10 5 6 5 8 10

Find the mode, median and mean of these data and use them
to comment on the skewness of this distribution.

14 Skewness can be quantitatively assessed by using

$$\frac{3\ (\text{mean} - \text{median})}{\text{standard deviation}}$$

Calculate this numerical measure of skewness for the
following distribution which shows ages of patients in a
hospital ward.

58 39 30 48 27 16 56 56 65 63

Comment on the skewness of this distribution.

SUMMARY OF KEY POINTS

1 The **mode** is that value of a variate which occurs most frequently.

2 The **median** is the middle value of an ordered set of data.

3 The **quartiles** of an ordered set of data are such that 25% of the observations are less than or equal to the first quartile (Q_1), 50% are less than or equal to the second quartile (Q_2) and 75% are less than or equal to the third quartile (Q_3).

4 The **mean** of a set of observations is the sum of all the observations divided by the total number of observations, i.e.

Thus $\qquad \mu = \bar{x} = \dfrac{\sum x}{n} \qquad$ or $\qquad \dfrac{\sum fx}{\sum f}$

5 The weighted mean is given by:

$$\bar{x} = \frac{w_1\bar{x}_1 + w_2\bar{x}_2 + \dots + w_k\bar{x}_k}{w_1 + w_2 + \dots + w_k}$$

6 The range of a data set is given by:

$$\text{Range} = \text{largest value} - \text{smallest value}$$

7 The interquartile range is given by:

$$\text{IQR} = Q_3 - Q_1$$

8 The semi-interquartile range is defined as:

$$\text{SIQR} = \tfrac{1}{2}(Q_3 - Q_1)$$

9 Variance of a population is defined as:

$$\sigma^2 = \frac{\sum(x - \mu)^2}{n} \qquad \text{or} \qquad \sigma^2 = \frac{\sum f(x - \mu)^2}{\sum f}$$

10 Unbiased estimator of the population variance is defined as:

$$s^2 = \frac{\sum(x - \bar{x})^2}{n - 1} \qquad \text{or} \qquad s^2 = \frac{\sum f(x - \bar{x})^2}{\sum f - 1}$$

11 The standard deviation is the positive square root of the variance.

12   For   positive skew: $Q_2 - Q_1 \; < \; Q_3 - Q_2$
         negative skew: $Q_2 - Q_1 \; > \; Q_3 - Q_2$
         symmetry: $Q_2 - Q_1 \; = \; Q_3 - Q_2$

Review exercise

1

1 The following figures show the number of goals scored during
   a tournament by sixty hockey clubs:

       0 4 6 3 4 5 1 3 2 4
       4 1 3 5 5 6 2 4 7 6
       3 6 7 0 1 7 4 1 5 3
       5 8 3 2 6 2 6 6 7 7
       3 5 2 5 5 3 8 4 6 4
       4 7 7 4 4 8 4 3 5 2

   (a) Construct a frequency distribution with an added
   cumulative frequency column for these data.
   (b) Draw a cumulative frequency step polygon to represent
   these data.

2 State whether the following variates are discrete or
   continuous giving reasons for your answers:
   (a) daily rainfall
   (b) growth rate of trees
   (c) the cost of meals
   (d) air temperature.

3 Give two reasons why a factory inspector might choose to
   test a sample of components rather than the whole
   population.

4 The mean height of a sample of 15 boys is 1.38 m and the
   mean height of a sample of 20 girls is 1.22 m. Find the mean
   height of the combined sample of boys and girls.   [L]

5 The stalk lengths (pedicels) of creeping buttercup were measured. These are the results.

Pedicel length (mm)	Frequency
1–10	7
11–20	25
21–30	63
31–40	52
41–50	36
51–60	27
61–70	9
71–80	12
81–90	1
Total	232

Draw a histogram to illustrate these data.

6 A questionnaire given to a class of students contained the following questions:

(a) What is your name?

(b) What is your weight?

(c) What is your height?

(d) Are you male or female?

(e) How many brothers and sisters do you have?

Which answers would be *qualitative* and which *quantitative*?

7 The grouped frequency distribution of the weights of 40 university students is as follows:

Weight (kg)	53–56	57–60	61–64	65–68	69–72	73–76	77–80
Frequency	2	3	4	11	9	6	5

Determine:

(a) the lower class boundary of the third class

(b) the upper class boundary of the fourth class

(c) the class width of the second class

(d) the lower class limit of the seventh class

(e) the class mid-point of the seventh class.

8 For each of the following populations state if they are finite, infinite, or countably infinite:

(a) the number of throws at darts before getting a double

(b) the number of students in your school or college

(c) the number of kangaroos in Australia

(d) the number of spins of a roulette-wheel before a given number comes up.

9 Sixty batteries were tested by continuously using them until they were exhausted. The results were summarised as follows:

Lifetime (hours)	5–5.9	6–6.9	7–7.9	8–8.9	9–9.9	10–10.9
Frequency	7	8	10	20	12	3

Represent these data by means of a cumulative frequency polygon.

From your graph estimate the median lifetime of the batteries.

10 Classes of students, from three different schools, sat the same examination paper. The mean scores for each school were 63, 48 and 72 percent. If the respective class sizes were 23, 30 and 15 students, find the mean mark for the three schools taken together.

11 A dairy farm records the milk yield, in litres, for each of its herd of 40 pedigree friesian cows. For one particular day the yields were as follows:

```
26  40  34  39  35  23  15  35  32  13
37  11  26  12  23  37  35  39  41  33
 5  34  25   5   7  42  19  41  36  12
34  25  39  23  29  24  36  25  39  33
```

Construct a stem and leaf diagram to represent these data. Find the median value.

12 For a sample survey of the lengths of beech-tree leaves suggest:

(a) a suitable sampling unit

(b) a suitable sampling frame.

13 In a series of Intelligence Tests, 40 adults between the ages of sixty and seventy-five were each given two different tests [AH1 and AH2]. The results were as shown on the next page.

	AH1			
34	32	48	42	41
16	37	30	44	41
59	62	12	36	24
50	44	56	18	44
47	23	34	40	41
50	21	40	25	25
34	23	26	32	37
34	28	54	30	30

	AH2			
25	34	40	28	45
16	18	29	24	25
34	18	32	25	51
19	40	9	44	14
26	50	18	23	36
34	10	16	23	17
26	31	38	19	23
22	44	17	34	37

Compare these data by construcing a back-to-back stem and leaf diagram. Comment on your results.

14 A marketing company always buys new cars on 1st August. Before making any purchases on 1st August 1994, they reviewed their fleet of cars. The following table shows the age, x, in years, of the cars in the fleet:

Age (x)	1	2	3	4	5	6	7	8	9	10	11
Number of cars (f)	14	20	16	14	12	8	6	4	3	2	1

Find:

(a) the mode

(b) the median and the quartiles

(c) the mean

of this distribution.

Draw a box plot to represent these data.

The distribution is positively skewed.

Use your calculations to justify this statement. [L]

15 Cartons of orange are filled by a machine. A sample of 10 cartons selected at random from the production contained the following quantities of orange (in ml).

201.2   205.0   209.1   202.3   204.6

206.4   210.1   201.9   203.7   207.3

Calculate unbiased estimates of the mean and variance of the population from which this sample was taken. [L]

16 The following table shows the time, to the nearest minute, spent writing during a particular day by a group of school children.

Time	Number of children
10–19	10
20–24	20
25–29	25
30–39	30
40–49	24
50–64	12
65–89	10

(a) Represent these data by a histogram.

(b) Comment on the shape of the distribution.   [L]

17 A study was done of the amount of pocket money received by English school children by taking 10 children from each class in a particular school.

State: (a) the sampling unit, (b) the sampling frame, (c) the population.

If the figures taken are used to represent the whole of England would the sample be unbiased?

18 In a knockout tennis competition 60 matches were played. The number of games played in each match were recorded. Copy and complete the following table.

Number of games	Frequency	Class width	Relative frequency	Relative frequency density
15–24	6			
25–34	12			
35–44	18			
45–54	15			
55–64	3			
65–84	6			
Total	60		1	

Illustrate these data by drawing a relative frequency histogram.

19 The table below summarizes data taken from the results of a promotion examination taken by 310 police constables.

Range of marks	0–9	10–19	20–29	30–39	40–49	50–59	60–69	70–79	80–100
Number of candidates	1	4	19	90	64	61	56	14	1

By calculation estimate:

(a) the mean and quartiles

(b) D_4 and D_7

(c) P_5 and P_{95}.

20 In a certain town an investigation was carried out into accidents in the home to children under 12 years of age. The numbers of reported accidents and the ages of the children concerned are summarised below:

Group	A	B	C	D	E	F
Age of child (years)	0 to < 2	2 to < 4	4 to < 6	6 to < 8	8 to < 10	10 to < 12
Number of accidents	42	52	28	20	18	16

(a) State the modal class.

(b) Calculate, to the nearest month, the mean age and the standard deviation of the distribution of ages.

(c) Draw a cumulative frequency polygon and from it estimate, to the nearest month, the median and the interquartile range for the ages of all children under 12 years of age concerned in reported accidents in the home.
State, giving a reason, whether you consider the mean, the mode or the median best represents the average age for accidents in the home to children under 12 years of age. [L]

21 The table on the next page summarises data relating to the lifetime of a random sample of 200 bulbs taken from the production line of a particular manufacturer.

Lifetime (to nearest hour)	Number of bulbs
700–719	10
720–729	14
730–739	16
740–749	21
750–754	35
755–759	41
760–764	38
765–769	15
770–779	7
780–799	3

(a) By calculation, estimate the median and quartiles of these lifetimes. Give your answers to 1 decimal place.

(b) One method of assessing the skewness of a distribution is to calculate

$$\frac{3\,(\text{mean} - \text{median})}{\text{standard deviation}}$$

Evaluate this, to 1 decimal place, for the above distribution.

(c) Use the quartiles to assess skewness and state whether or not you feel this result is compatible with your answer to (b). [L]

22 In a borehole the thicknesses, in mm, of the 25 strata are as shown in the table below:

Thicknesses of borehole strata

Thickness (mm)	0–	20–	30–	40–	50–	60–
Number of strata	2	5	9	8	1	0

Draw a histogram to illustrate these data. Construct a cumulative frequency table and draw a cumulative frequency polygon. Hence, or otherwise, estimate the median and the interquartile range for these data.

Find the proportion of the strata that are less than 28 mm thick. [L]

23 A sample of students sitting an entrance examination for the civil service has the following distribution of verbal reasoning (V.R.) scores.

V.R. score	80–99	100–109	110–119	120–129	130–139	140–149
Frequency	17	50	250	120	55	8

Using this data calculate the mean and standard deviation of this distribution.

24 A random sample of 51 people were asked to record the number of miles they travelled by car in a given week. The distances, to the nearest mile, are shown below.

```
67  76  85  42  93  48  93  46
52  72  77  53  41  48  86  78
56  80  70  70  66  62  54  85
60  58  43  58  74  41  52  74
52  82  78  47  66  50  67  87
78  86  94  63  72  63  44  47
57  68  81
```

(a) Construct a stem and leaf diagram to represent these data.

(b) Find the median and the quartiles of this distribution.

(c) Draw a box plot to represent these data.

Give one advantage of using (i) a stem and leaf diagram,
(ii) a box plot, to illustrate data such as that given above. [L]

25 A box of matches should contain 50 matches. A quality control department set up a test to check that the contents were satisfactory. A sample of 50 matchboxes gave the following results for the variable x (the number of matches in a box):

$$\sum x = 2514 \qquad \text{and} \qquad \sum x^2 = 126\,486$$

Calculate the mean and standard deviation of the variate x.

26 Explain briefly the difference between a census and a sample survey.

Give an example to illustrate the practical use of each method.

A school held an evening disco which was attended by 500 pupils. The disco organisers were keen to assess the success of the evening. Having decided to obtain information from those attending the disco, they were undecided whether to use a census or a sample survey.

Which method would you recommend them to use?

Give one advantage and one disadvantage associated with your recommendation. [L]

27 Explain briefly what you understand by the statement:

'A sample is chosen at random from a population.'

Describe briefly your method of selecting a random sample for a project.

The heights, in metres, of a random sample of 40 soldiers from a regiment were measured. The heights are summarised in the table below:

Height (m)	1.75–	1.80–	1.85–	1.90–	1.95–	2.00–	2.05–	2.10–	2.15–
Frequency	1	1	4	13	14	3	3	1	0

(a) Find the mean height and, to 3 significant figures, the standard deviation of this sample of heights.

(b) Draw on graph paper a cumulative frequency polygon for these data.

(c) Find the median height, Q_2, and the first and third quartiles, Q_1 and Q_3. Compare your values of $(Q_3 - Q_2)$ and $(Q_2 - Q_1)$ and explain what this tells you about the shape of the distribution in the table above.

(d) Find unbiased estimates of the mean and, to 2 significant figures, the variance of the heights of all soldiers in the regiment. [L]

28 A railway enthusiast simulates train journeys and records the number of minutes, x, to the nearest minute, trains are late according to the schedule being used. A random sample of 50 journeys gave the times listed on the next page.

17	5	3	10	4	3	10	5	2	14
3	14	5	5	21	9	22	36	14	34
22	4	23	6	8	15	41	23	13	7
6	13	33	8	5	34	26	17	8	43
24	14	23	4	19	5	23	13	12	10

(a) Construct a stem and leaf diagram to represent these data.

(b) Comment on the shape of the distribution produced by your diagram.

(c) Given that $\sum x = 738$ and $\sum x^2 = 16526$, calculate to 2 decimal places, unbiased estimates of the mean and the variance of the population from which this sample was drawn.

(d) Explain briefly the effect that grouping of these data would have had on your calculations in (c).   [1]

29 The following grouped frequency distribution summarises the values of orders taken by sales representatives employed by a company during one particular year.

Value of order (£)	Number of orders
0–	80
10–	120
20–	226
30–	135
50–	105
100–	40
150–	24
200–	12
500–	8
1000–	0

Let X represent the mid-point of each group.

(a) Using the coding $U = \frac{X-25}{5}$ show that $\sum fu = 4355$, where f represents the frequency in each group. Estimate the mean and standard deviation of the value of the orders.
(You may use $\sum fu^2 = 269\,975$.)

(b) Explain why these two measures might not be the best ones to use when analysing these data.

(c) Which alternative measures of location and spread would you recommend? [L]

30 The following grouped frequency distribution summarises the time, to the nearest minute, spent waiting by a sample of patients in a doctor's surgery.

Waiting time (to nearest minute)	Number of patients
3 or less	6
4–6	15
7–8	27
9	49
10	52
11–12	29
13–15	13
16 or more	9

The mean of the times was 9.63 minutes and the standard deviation was 3.03 minutes.

(a) Using interpolation, estimate the median and the semi-interquartile range of these data.

For a normal distribution the ratio of the semi-interquartile range to the standard deviation would be approximately 0.67.

(b) Calculate the corresponding value for the above data. Comment on your result.

For a normal distribution, 90% of times would be expected to lie in the interval

(mean ± 1.645 standard deviations).

(c) Find the theoretical limits for these data.

(d) Using appropriate percentiles, estimate comparable limits. Comment on your result. [L]

Probability

5

We live in a world full of uncertainty and describe this in many different ways.

> "I *should* be back by 10 pm."
> "John is *sure* to be in the team."
> "I *might* just scrape a pass in economics."

Each of these phrases expresses a degree of uncertainty. To deal with uncertainty mathematically you need to be able to express it as a number. You can do this by using a scale from 0 to 1 to describe the *chance* that something will happen. On this scale 0 represents a situation which is impossible and 1 represents something that is certain to happen. This number is called the **probability** that something will happen.

■ **Probability – If p is a probability then $0 \leqslant p \leqslant 1$**

In the situations described in the phrases above there is no obvious way for arriving at a value for the probability that each one will happen. You could ask someone involved in these incidents to estimate what they think the value of the probability will be. This would give you a **subjective probability** – one which depends on the judgement of the person making the estimate. This can be useful in such situations, but sometimes there are other ways of estimating a probability.

At the start of a cricket match two captains toss a coin to decide who should bat first. What is the probability that the coin will land heads up? The coin could land on its edge, but that is very unlikely, so you could argue that there are only two realistic possibilities – heads up and tails up. Both of these are **equally likely** so you could say that the probability of the coin landing heads up is 0.5 (halfway between 0 and 1 on the probability scale).

An alternative method for arriving at a value for this probability is to toss a coin a large number of times and calculate the ratio:

$$\frac{\text{number of times it lands heads}}{\text{number of tosses}}$$

This is called the **relative frequency** of the coin landing heads up because it is a measure *relative* to the total number of tosses. Plotting a graph of the relative frequency against the number of tosses gives something like this:

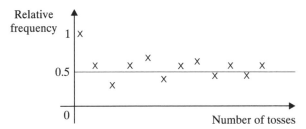

As the number of tosses increases the relative frequency gets closer and closer to a particular value – it tends to a limit. You could use this value as an estimate of the probability that the coin will land heads up.

So there are a variety of ways of arriving at a value for a probability. Most of the work on probability in this chapter assumes that the probabilities of different situations are already known and is about combining probabilities.

5.1 The terminology of probability

To introduce the terminology commonly used when studying probability imagine a school which has 100 students in its sixth form – 50 students study mathematics, 29 study biology and 13 study both subjects. A convenient method of summarising this information is to use a **Venn diagram**:

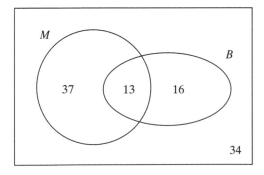

Notice how the 37 students who study mathematics but not biology and the 34 students who do not study either subject are represented.

Suppose you went into the sixth form common room one break and picked a student at random. What is the probability that this student studies mathematics? We call this process of walking into the room and selecting a student at random an **experiment**. An experiment must be capable of being repeated as many times as you like under essentially the same conditions. Though you cannot say for certain what the outcome of any one experiment will be, you can list all the possible outcomes and this list is called the **sample space**.

An **event** is a group or set of possible outcomes from such an experiment. Capital letters are usually used to label events, for example M for the event that the student selected studies mathematics. From the Venn diagram the probability that the student studies mathematics is:

$$\tfrac{37+13}{100} = \tfrac{1}{2}$$

This can be written $\qquad$ $P(M) = \tfrac{1}{2}$

In a similar way we can define the event B that the student studies biology and find that:

$$P(B) = \tfrac{29}{100}$$

The probability that the student studies *both* mathematics *and* biology can be written as

$$P(M \cap B) = \tfrac{13}{100}$$

The probability that the student studies mathematics *or* biology can be written as

$$P(M \cup B) = \tfrac{37+13+16}{100} = \tfrac{66}{100} = \tfrac{33}{50}$$

Notice that 'or' in mathematics includes the possibility of 'both'.

Other probabilities can easily be read off from the Venn diagram. For example the probability that the student *does not* study biology is:

$$P(B') = \tfrac{37+34}{100} = \tfrac{71}{100}$$

Notice that B' is the event *not B*.

Similarly the probability that the student studies biology but not mathematics is

$$P(B \cap M') = \tfrac{16}{100} = \tfrac{4}{25}$$

P(B') can also be found using the relationship:

$$P(B') = 1 - P(B)$$
$$= 1 - \frac{29}{100} = \frac{71}{100}$$

■ **Complementary probability** – If A' represents the event not A then $P(A') = 1 - P(A)$

5.2 Addition Rule

The above example shows that:

$$P(M \text{ or } B) = P(M) + P(B) - P(\text{both } M \text{ and } B)$$
$$\frac{66}{100} = \frac{50}{100} + \frac{29}{100} - \frac{13}{100}$$

Notice that the probability of the student studying mathematics and the probability of the student studying biology each include the probability of the student studying *both* mathematics and biology. To obtain the probability of studying mathematics *or* biology you only need to include this probability of *both* once, hence the extra case is subtracted.

So a general rule for events A and B is:

■ **Addition Rule** $P(A \cup B) = P(A) + P(B) - P(A \cap B)$

Example 1
In a mathematics test there are two questions on algebra. The probability of a student getting the first question correct is 0.6 and the probability of getting the second question correct is also 0.6 but the probability of getting both correct is 0.3. A student is recorded as having passed in algebra if either (or both) of the questions are correct. Find the probability that the student records a pass in algebra.

Let Q_1 represent the event "the student gets the first question correct" and
Q_2 represent the event "the student gets the second question correct."

The probability that a pass in algebra is recorded is

$$P(Q_1 \cup Q_2).$$

Now $P(Q_1 \cup Q_2) = P(Q_1) + P(Q_2) - P(Q_1 \cap Q_2)$
$$= 0.6 + 0.6 - 0.3$$
$$= 0.9$$

Exercise 5A

1 In a certain class of 30 primary school children there are 16 girls. There are 7 girls and 6 boys with fair hair. A pupil is selected at random to be a class captain. Find the probability that the class captain
   (a) is a girl whose hair is not fair
   (b) is a boy with fair hair
   (c) has not got fair hair
   (d) is a girl and has not got fair hair.

2 A card is selected at random from a normal set of 52 playing cards. Let Q be the event that the card is a queen and D the event that the card is a diamond. Find:
   (a) $P(Q \cap D)$ (b) $P(Q \cup D)$
   (c) $P(Q' \cup D)$ (d) $P(Q \cap D')$.
   Describe in words the probabilities:
   (e) $P(Q' \cap D) = \frac{12}{52} = \frac{3}{13}$ (f) $P(Q' \cap D') = \frac{36}{52} = \frac{9}{13}$.

3 An archer has two attempts to hit a target. The probability that his first arrow hits is 0.4 and the probability that the second arrow hits is 0.5. Given that the probability that he hits the target with both arrows is 0.25, find the probability that he misses the target with both arrows.

4 If A and B are two events and $P(A) = 0.6$, $P(B) = 0.3$ and $P(A \cup B) = 0.8$, find:
   (a) $P(A \cap B)$ (b) $P(A' \cap B)$ (c) $P(A \cap B')$
   (d) $P(A' \cap B')$ (e) $P(A \cup B')$ (f) $P(A' \cup B)$.

5 If S and T are two events and $P(T) = 0.4$, $P(S \cap T) = 0.15$ and $P(S' \cap T') = 0.5$, find:
   (a) $P(S \cap T')$ (b) $P(S)$ (c) $P(S \cup T)$
   (d) $P(S' \cap T)$ (e) $P(S' \cup T')$.

6 There are two events M and N and $P(M) = P(N) = 2P(M \cap N)$. Given that $P(M \cup N) = 0.6$, find:
   (a) $P(M \cap N)$ (b) $P(M)$ (c) $P(M' \cap N')$
   (d) $P(M \cap N')$.

7 A student going into the common room reads *Private Eye* with probability 0.75, *Private Eye* but not the *Daily Express*

with probability 0.65. The student reads neither with probability 0.20.

(a) Find the probability that the student reads both *Private Eye* and the *Daily Express.*

(b) Find the probability that the student reads the *Daily Express* but not *Private Eye.* [L]

8 Of the households in Edinburgh, 35% have a freezer and 60% have a colour TV set. Given that 25% of the households have both a freezer and a colour TV set, calculate the probability that a household has either a freezer or a colour TV set but not both. [L]

9 In a large group of people it is known that 10% have a hot breakfast, 20% have a hot lunch and 25% have a hot breakfast or a hot lunch. Find the probability that a person chosen at random from this group has a hot breakfast and a hot lunch. [L]

10 The carburettor for a particular motor car is manufactured at one of three factories X, Y, Z and then delivered to the main assembly line. Factory X supplies 45% of the total number of carburettors to the line, factory Y 30% and factory Z 25%. Of the carburettors manufactured at factory X, 2% are faulty and the corresponding percentages for factories Y and Z are 4% and 3% respectively.

Let X, Y and Z represent the events that a carburettor chosen at random from the assembly line was manufactured at factory X, Y or Z respectively and let F denote the event that this carburettor is faulty.

(a) Express in words the meaning of $Y \cap F'$ and of $Y \cup Z$.

(b) Calculate $P(X \cap F)$, $P(Y \cap F)$ and $P(Z \cap F)$.

(c) Sketch a Venn diagram to illustrate the events X, Y, Z and F. Include in your diagram the probabilities corresponding to the different regions within the diagram.

(d) Find the probability that a carburettor, selected at random from the main assembly line, is faulty. [L]

5.3 Multiplication Rule

Consider again the subjects studied by a school's sixth form students, which was summarised as follows:

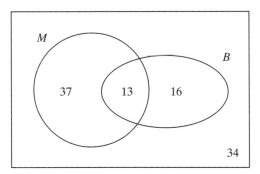

Suppose now that instead of going into the sixth form common room and selecting a student at random from the group of 100, you went into the biology department and selected a student at random from the 29 biologists. What is the probability that this student also studies mathematics?

The probability is written as:

$$P(M|B)$$

and read as:

"the probability of the student studying mathematics *given that* the student studies biology".

This is an example of a **conditional probability**:

the probability of M (the student studying mathematics) *conditional* upon the event B (the student studying biology) having already happened.

In this example

$$P(M|B) = \frac{13}{29}$$

as there are 13 of the 29 biology students who also study mathematics.

Notice that the 13 in the numerator represents the students in $\{M \cap B\}$ and the 29 in the denominator those in B. So this could be written as:

$$P(M|B) = \frac{P(M \cap B)}{P(B)} = \frac{\frac{13}{100}}{\frac{29}{100}} = \frac{13}{29}$$

which can also be written as:

$$P(M \cap B) = P(M|B) \times P(B)$$

Notice that we could write

$$P(M \cap B) = P(B|M) \times P(M)$$

(in this example that is $\frac{13}{100} = \frac{13}{50} \times \frac{50}{100}$)

The reordering of events in a conditional probability is sometimes useful in more complicated situations (see example 2(c) on page 103).

So for two events A and B:

■ **Multiplication Rule** $P(A \cap B) = P(A|B) \times P(B)$

Sometimes a dot · is used instead of $\times$ to represent times and in this case the multiplication rule is written

$$P(A \cap B) = P(A|B) \cdot P(B)$$

Tree diagrams

Consider a bag that contains 5 black and 3 yellow beads. A bead is selected at random from the bag and retained. A second bead is then selected from the remaining 7 beads. (This is an example of sampling without replacement and is discussed in more detail on page 110).

Let B_1 stand for the event "the first bead was black" and B_2 the event "the second bead was black", similarly the events Y_1 and Y_2 can be defined to stand for the first and second beads being yellow. The above events can be represented using a **tree diagram**:

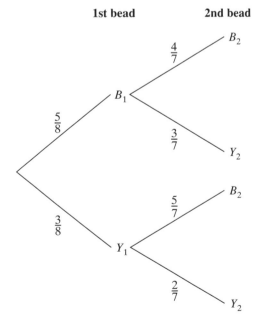

Probabilities are written along the branches. Notice that the probabilities on the second tier of branches are conditional probabilities, for example, $P(B_2 \mid B_1)$ is $\frac{4}{7}$. The probability that both beads are black:

$$P(B_1 \cap B_2)$$

is found using the multiplication rule as:

$$P(B_1 \cap B_2) = P(B_2|B_1) \times P(B_1) = \tfrac{4}{7} \times \tfrac{5}{8} = \tfrac{5}{14}$$

The probability that both beads are the *same* colour is:

$$P(B_1 \cap B_2) + P(Y_1 \cap Y_2) = \tfrac{5}{14} + \tfrac{3}{8} \times \tfrac{2}{7} = \tfrac{13}{28}$$

To understand why these probabilities are *added*, let $C = B_1 \cap B_2$ (i.e. the event both beads are black) and $D = Y_1 \cap Y_2$ (i.e. the event both beads are yellow). The probability that both beads are black *or* both are yellow is written as:

$$P(C \cup D).$$

Now by the addition rule this gives:

$$P(C \cup D) = P(C) + P(D) - P(C \cap D)$$

but the event $C \cap D$ is impossible (since both beads can not be black and yellow at the same time) so:

$$P(C \cap D) = 0$$

and the required probability is:

$$P(C) + P(D) = \tfrac{5}{14} + \tfrac{3}{28} = \tfrac{13}{28}$$

(This is an example of mutually exclusive events which are discussed on page 108.)

A useful rule for using tree diagrams is:

multiply *along* the branches and *add* between branches.

Example 2

A certain medical disease occurs in 1% of the population. A simple screening procedure is available and in 8 out of 10 cases where the patient has the disease, it produces a positive result. If the patient does not have the disease there is still a 0.05 chance that the test will give a positive result. Find the probability that a randomly selected individual:

(a) does not have the disease but gives a positive result in the screening test
(b) gives a positive result on the test.

Ann has taken the test and her result is positive.

(c) Find the probability that she has the disease.

Let C represent the event "the patient has the disease" and
S represent the event "the screening test gives a positive result".

A tree diagram of the information in the question gives:

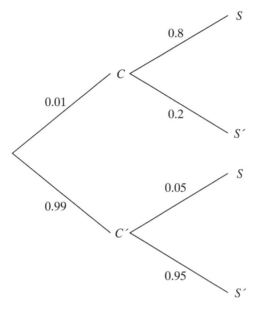

(a) The probability that the patient does not have the disease but gives a positive screening result is:

$$P(C' \cap S) = 0.99 \times 0.05$$
$$= 0.0495$$

(b) The probability that the patient gives a positive test result is:
$$P(S) = P(C \cap S) + P(C' \cap S)$$
$$= 0.01 \times 0.8 + 0.0495$$
$$= 0.0575$$

(c) The probability that Ann has the disease is:
$$P(C|S) = \frac{P(C \cap S)}{P(S)}$$
$$= \frac{0.01 \times 0.8}{0.0575}$$
$$= 0.139 \text{ (to 3 decimal places)}$$

Exercise 5B

1 A bag contains 6 red and 4 blue beads. A bead is picked out and retained and then a second bead is picked out. Find the probability that:
(a) both beads are red
(b) the beads are of different colours
(c) the second bead is red given that the first one is blue.

2 A teacher calculates that if a student regularly completes their homework the probability that they will pass the examination is 0.8 and that if the student does not do the homework the probability of passing is only 0.4. Given that only 75% of the students do their homework regularly, calculate the probability that a randomly selected student:
(a) does not do the homework regularly and passes the examination
(b) passes the examination.

3 A certain statistician's breakfast consists of either some cereal or toast (but not both) to eat and one drink from a choice of fruit juice, tea or coffee. If he has cereal to eat, the probability that he chooses coffee is $\frac{3}{5}$ and the probability he chooses tea is $\frac{3}{10}$. If he has toast to eat, the probability he chooses coffee is $\frac{2}{5}$ and the probability he chooses tea is $\frac{1}{5}$. Given that he has cereal with probability $\frac{3}{4}$:
(a) find the probability that on any particular day he has
   (i) fruit juice   (ii) cereal and coffee.
(b) Find his most popular breakfast combination.

4 Given that $P(A) = 0.7$, $P(B) = 0.4$ and $P(A \cup B) = 0.8$, find the following:
(a) $P(A \cap B)$ (b) $P(A|B)$ (c) $P(B|A)$ (d) $P(A|B')$.

5 Given $P(R|S) = 0.5$, $P(R|S') = 0.4$ and $P(S) = 0.6$, find:
(a) $P(R)$ (b) $P(S|R)$ (c) $P(S'|R)$ (d) $P(S'|R')$.

6 In year 11 of a certain school 55% of the pupils are boys. Of the boys 80% stay on into the sixth form but only 75% of the girls do.
(a) Find the probability that a randomly selected pupil from year 11 is a girl who stays on into the sixth form.

(b) Find the probability that a randomly chosen year 11 pupil will not stay on into the sixth form.

(c) Find the probability that a randomly selected sixth form pupil is a girl.

7 A bunch of 30 keys are either gold or silver in colour (but not both). There are 10 mortice lock keys and 20 yale lock keys. Of these 5 yale lock and 2 mortice lock keys are gold in colour. A key is selected at random.

(a) Find the probability that the key is silver in colour.

(b) Find the probability that the key is silver coloured and for a mortice lock.

I borrow this bunch of keys to open a yale lock.

(c) What is the probability that the correct key is silver?

8 Let A and B be events such that $P(A) = \frac{1}{4}$, $P(B) = \frac{1}{3}$ and $P(A \cup B) = \frac{5}{12}$.

(a) Find $P(A|B)$ and $P(A|B')$.

(b) Find $P(A|B)\,P(B) + P(A|B')\,P(B')$.

Comment on your result.   [L]

9 A teacher walks, cycles or drives to school with probabilities 0.1, 0.3 and 0.6 respectively. If she walks to school she has a probability of 0.35 of being late. The corresponding probabilities of being late if she cycles or drives to school are 0.1 and 0.55 respectively.

(a) Find the probability that she is late on any particular day.

(b) Given that she is late one day, find the probability that she walked.

(c) Given that she is not late one day, find the probability that she walked.

Give your answers to 3 decimal places.   [L]

10 State in words the meaning of the symbol $P(B|A)$, where A and B are two events.

A shop stocks tinned cat food of two makes A and B, and two sizes, large and small. Of the stock, 70% is of brand A, 30% is of brand B. Of the tins of brand A, 30% are small size whilst of the tins of brand B, 40% are small size. Using a tree diagram, or otherwise, find the probability that:

(a) a tin chosen at random from the stock will be of small size

(b) a small tin chosen at random from the stock will be of brand *A*. [L]

11 A boy always either walks to school or goes by bus. If one day he goes to school by bus, then the probability that he goes by bus the next day is $\frac{7}{10}$. If one day he walks to school, then the probability that he goes by bus the next day is $\frac{2}{5}$.

(a) Given that he walks to school on a particular Tuesday, draw a tree diagram and hence find the probability that he will go to school by bus on Thursday of that week.

(b) Given that the boy walks to school on both Tuesday and Thursday of that week, find the probability that he will also walk to school on Wednesday.

(You may assume that the boy will not be absent from school on Wednesday or Thursday of that week.) [L]

12 For married couples the probability that the husband has passed his driving test is $\frac{7}{10}$ and the probability that the wife has passed her driving test is $\frac{1}{2}$. The probability that the husband has passed, given that the wife has passed, is $\frac{14}{15}$. Find the probability that, for a randomly chosen married couple, the driving test will have been passed by:

(a) both of them

(b) only one of them

(c) neither of them.

If two married couples are chosen at random, find the probability that only one of the husbands and only one of the wives will have passed the driving test. [L]

5.4 Independent and mutually exclusive events

If you roll two fair dice, a yellow one and a red one, the possible outcomes could be represented by crosses in the following diagram:

Red die

		1	2	3	4	5	6
	1	x	x	x	x	x	x
	2	x	x	x	x	x	x
Yellow	3	x	x	x	x	x	x
die	4	x	x	x	x	x	x
	5	x	x	x	x	x	x
	6	x	x	x	x	x	x

The set of crosses inside the loop ⬭ represents the event Y, that the yellow die shows a six, and the set of crosses inside the rectangle ▯ represents the event R, that the red die shows a six. Since there are 36 possible outcomes (and they are all equally likely) then

$$P(Y) = \tfrac{1}{6}, \ P(R) = \tfrac{1}{6} \ \text{and} \ P(Y \cap R) = \tfrac{1}{36}.$$

Notice that in this situation the event Y is not going to influence the event R. So Y and R are **independent** events and the probability of Y *given that* R has happened will be the same as the probability of Y. This is written as:

$$P(Y|R) = P(Y)$$

Using the multiplication rule this gives:

$$P(Y \cap R) = P(Y) \times P(R)$$

and this is the usual definition for independent events. Notice that in this example $\tfrac{1}{36} = \tfrac{1}{6} \times \tfrac{1}{6}$.

■ **If two events A and B are independent**
  $P(A \cap B) = P(A) \times P(B).$

Now let E be the event that the number showing on the yellow die and the number showing on the red die are equal. This is indicated in the diagram opposite by ╲.

Let S represent the event that the sum of the number showing on the yellow die and the number showing on the red die is 7. This is indicated by 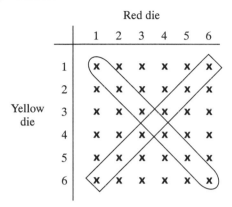 below.

Red die

From the diagram it is clear that:

$$P(E) = \tfrac{1}{6} \text{ and } P(S) = \tfrac{1}{6} \quad \text{but} \quad P(E \cap S) = 0$$

since if the numbers on the dice are equal then their sum can never be 7. So E and S are **mutually exclusive** events because they cannot both happen together.

- **If A and B are mutually exclusive events $P(A \cap B) = 0$.**

Notice that E and S are not independent events since $P(E) \times P(S) \neq P(E \cap S)$.

Example 3

In a certain group of 15 students, 5 have graphics calculators and 3 have a computer at home (one student has both). Two of the students drive themselves to college each day and neither of them has a graphics calculator nor a computer at home. A student is selected at random from the group.

(a) Find the probability that the student either drives to college or has a graphics calculator.
(b) Show that the events "the student has a graphics calculator" and "the student has a computer at home" are independent.

Let G represent the event "the student has a graphics calculator",
  H represent the event "the student has a computer at home"
  and
  D represent the event "the student drives to college each day".

The information in the question can be represented in a Venn diagram, as follows:

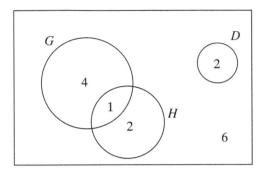

(a) The probability that the student either drives or has a graphics calculator is $P(G \cup D)$.

Notice that G and D are mutually exclusive events so $P(G \cap D) = 0$.

$\therefore \qquad\qquad P(G \cup D) = P(G) + P(D)$
$$= \tfrac{5}{15} + \tfrac{2}{15}$$
$$= \tfrac{7}{15}$$

(b) From the diagram:

$$P(G \cap H) = \tfrac{1}{15}, P(G) = \tfrac{5}{15} = \tfrac{1}{3} \text{ and } P(H) = \tfrac{3}{15} = \tfrac{1}{5}$$

Since $P(G) \times P(H) = P(G \cap H)$, the events G and H are independent.

The independence of two events is often connected with the *method* of sampling. The example on page 102 considered the selection of two beads from a bag containing 5 black and 3 yellow beads. In that example the first bead was *retained* before the second bead was selected. This is an example of **sampling without replacement**.

Consider again the tree diagram which represents the events in the example:

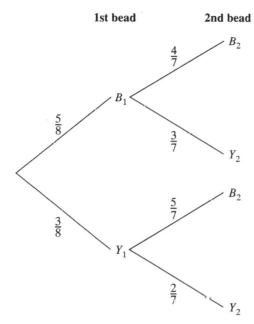

Notice that the events B_1 and B_2 (that the first and second beads were black) are *not* independent for

$$P(B_2|B_1) = \tfrac{4}{7}$$

but

$$P(B_2) = \tfrac{5}{8} \times \tfrac{4}{7} + \tfrac{3}{8} \times \tfrac{5}{7} = \tfrac{5}{8}$$

If the first bead is *replaced* before the next one is selected so that the total number of beads from which the selection is made remains the same, this is called **sampling with replacement** and results in the following tree diagram:

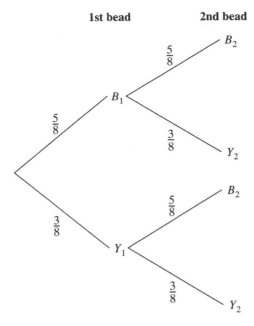

1st bead   2nd bead

The events B_1 and B_2 are now independent for

$$P(B_2) = \tfrac{5}{8} \times \tfrac{5}{8} + \tfrac{3}{8} \times \tfrac{5}{8} = \tfrac{5}{8}$$

and

$$P(B_1 \cap B_2) = \tfrac{5}{8} \times \tfrac{5}{8} = P(B_1) \times P(B_2)$$

Exercise 5C

1 Two archers each independently fire an arrow at a target. The probability that the first archer hits the target is 0.6 and the probability that the second archer hits the target is 0.7.
(a) Find the probability that they both hit the target.
(b) Find the probability that the target is hit by at least one of them.

2 In a game at a fair, contestants are given two darts and have to burst a balloon by throwing a dart to hit it. If they burst the balloon with the first dart the second dart is not used. Given that the probability of bursting the balloon with the first dart is 0.3 and, if the first time they miss, the probability of bursting it the second time is 0.4, find the probability that they burst the balloon.

3 Helen loves cuddly toys. The probability that her grandmother buys her a cuddly toy for her birthday is 0.8 and the probability that her grandfather buys her a cuddly toy is 0.7. Assuming that her grandparents do not liaise over the matter of birthday presents, find the probability that Helen receives a cuddly toy for her birthday.

4 A red and a yellow die are thrown and the events A, B and C are defined as follows:

$A =$ the yellow die shows a 5

$B =$ the sum of the scores of the two dice is 5

$C =$ the red die shows a 5.

(a) Find:

  (i) P(A)   (ii) P(B)   (iii) P(C)

  (iv) P($A \cap B$)   (v) P($B \cap C$)   (vi) P($A \cap C$).

(b) Which event is mutually exclusive to A?

(c) Which event is independent of A?

5 There are 15 books on a bookshelf. There are 10 books of fiction, 4 of which are hard-back. There are 6 hard-back books on the shelf, the other 9 are all paper-backs. One book is selected at random from the shelf.

(a) Find the probability that the book is a hard-back book of fiction.

(b) Find the probability that a hard-back book is selected.

(c) Find the probability that the book selected is a book of fiction.

(d) Find the probability that a paper-back is selected.

(e) Describe a pair of independent events.

6 The events A and B are independent and P(A) = 0.3 and P(B) = 0.5. Find:

(a) P($A \cup B$)   (b) P(A')   (c) P($A' \cap B$)

7 The events A and B have P(A) = 0.2, P(B) = 0.5 and P($A \cup B$) = 0.6. Find:

(a) P($A \cap B$)   (b) P($A|B$)   (c) P($B|A$).

8 A cubical die is relabelled so that it has 3 ones, 2 twos and 1 six. The die is rolled and R is the event that the number showing is 2 and Q is the event that the number showing is even. Find:

(a) $P(Q)$ (b) $P(R)$ (c) $P(Q')$ (d) $P(R')$

(e) $P(R \cap Q)$ (f) $P(R \cap Q')$ (g) $P(R' \cap Q)$.

(h) Write down a pair of mutually exclusive events.

9 A and B are two independent events such that $P(A) = \alpha$ and $P(A \cup B) = \beta$, $\beta > \alpha$. Show that:

$$\overset{\cdot}{P}(B) = \frac{\beta - \alpha}{1 - \alpha} \qquad \text{[L]}$$

10 A and B are two independent events such that $P(A) = 0.2$ and $P(B) = 0.15$.

Evaluate the following probabilities.

(a) $P(A|B)$

(b) $P(A \cap B)$

(c) $P(A \cup B)$. [L]

11 Seven identical balls are marked respectively with the numbers 1 to 7 inclusive. The number on each ball represents the score for that ball. The seven balls are then put into a bag. If 2 balls are chosen at random one after the other, find the probability of obtaining a total score of 11 or more:

(a) if the first ball is replaced

(b) if the first ball is not replaced.

If 2 balls are chosen at random one after the other from the 7 balls find, in case (a) and in case (b), the most probable total score for the 2 balls with its associated probability. [L]

12 State in words the relationship between two events E and F when:

(a) $P(E \cap F) = P(E).P(F)$

(b) $P(E \cap F) = 0$.

Given that $P(E) = \frac{1}{3}$, $P(F) = \frac{1}{2}$, $P(E' \cap F) = \frac{1}{2}$, find:

(c) the relationship between E and F

(d) the value of $P(E|F)$

(e) the value of $P(E' \cap F')$. [L]

13 An urn contains 3 red, 4 white and 5 blue discs. Three discs are selected at random from the urn. Find the probability that:

(a) all three discs are the same colour, if the selection is with replacement

(b) all three discs are of different colours, if the selection is without replacement. [L]

14 Show that, for any two events E and F:

$$P(E \cup F) = P(E) + P(F) - P(E \cap F).$$

Express in words the meaning of $P(E|F)$.

Given that E and F are independent events, express $P(E \cap F)$ in terms of $P(E)$ and $P(F)$, and show that E' and F are also independent.

In a college, 60 students are studying one or more of the three subjects Geography, French and English. Of these, 25 are studying Geography, 26 are studying French, 44 are studying English, 10 are studying Geography and French, 15 are studying French and English, and 16 are studying Geography and English.

Write down the probability that a student chosen at random from those studying English is also studying French.

Determine whether or not the events "studying Geography" and "studying French" are independent.

A student is chosen at random from all 60 students. Find the probability that the chosen student is studying all three subjects. [L]

5.5 Permutations

In a classroom there is a white board and a line of four holes for keeping the marker pens for use on the board. Usually four different coloured pens are in use: red (R), blue (B), black (K) and green(G). At the end of each lesson the pens are placed in the four holes. How many different *arrangements* are there for the pens?

Notice that the *order* is all important here as $RBKG$ and $RBGK$ are different arrangements. Sometimes a diagram can help in the visualization of the problem and aid in its solution. Imagine the four holes:

Hole 1   Hole 2   Hole 3   Hole 4

The first hole can be filled with any of the four coloured pens so there are 4 choices. The second hole could be filled with any of the remaining three colours so there are 3 choices for that hole and so on for the third and fourth holes.

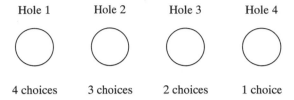

Hole 1	Hole 2	Hole 3	Hole 4
4 choices	3 choices	2 choices	1 choice

Now suppose that the first hole was filled with R, there are still 3 possibilities for the second hole (B, K or G), so each of the four possibilities for the first hole gives rise to 3 choices for the second so the first two holes could be filled in

$$4 \times 3 = 12 \text{ ways.}$$

Extending this argument through all the holes, there are:

$$4 \times 3 \times 2 \times 1 = 24 \text{ arrangements of the pens.}$$

The multiplication $4 \times 3 \times 2 \times 1$ can be written as 4! and is called **4 factorial**. This useful mathematical notation can be generalised as:

- $n! = n(n-1)(n-2)\ldots 1$

During a lesson on tree diagrams two different coloured pens are used, the first colour to draw the branches and the second colour to write the probabilities. How many different ways are there of drawing the tree diagram? In this example 2 colours are to be picked from a total of 4. Notice again that the order is important: blue branches with red probabilities is *different* from red branches with blue probabilities. The solution is found in the same way as before. There are 4 choices for the colour of the first pen (the branches) and 3 remaining for the second (the probabilities) so there are 4×3 possibilities. Picking two from a total of four, in this way, is taking a **permutation** of 2 from 4. This is written as: $^4P_2$ and is $4 \times 3 = 12$.

Notice two important features of a permutation: the key word *arrangements* and the importance of *order*.

If 3 different colours are used in the tree diagram and the third colour is used for writing the answers, then the number of different arrangements would be

$$^4P_3 = 4 \times 3 \times 2 = 24.$$

These examples can be used to illustrate a general formula for the number of permutations (different arrangements) of r objects from n different objects. This is:

$$^nP_r = \frac{n!}{(n-r)!}$$

■ **Permutations**   Number of permutations of r from n is
$$^nP_r = \frac{n!}{(n-r)!}$$

For example, the number of permutations of 3 objects from 5 different objects is:

$$^5P_3 = 5 \times 4 \times 3 \text{ or } \frac{5!}{(5-3)!} = 60.$$

Try to work out the number of arrangements and not to apply the formula blindly.

When the black and red pens were replaced only blue and green ones were available, so there were now 2 blue pens and 2 green pens. How many arrangements are there now?

Let the two blue pens be B_1 and B_2 and the two green pens be G_1 and G_2. There are now 4 *different* pens B_1, B_2, G_1 and G_2, and $4! = 24$ different arrangements. The arrangements are all listed below:

$B_1B_2G_1G_2$	$B_1G_1B_2G_2$	$B_1G_1G_2B_2$	$G_1G_2B_1B_2$	$G_1B_1G_2B_2$	$G_1B_1B_2G_2$
$B_1B_2G_2G_1$	$B_1G_2B_2G_1$	$B_1G_2G_1B_2$	$G_2G_1B_1B_2$	$G_2B_1G_1B_2$	$G_2B_1B_2G_1$
$B_2B_1G_1G_2$	$B_2G_1B_1G_2$	$B_2G_1G_2B_1$	$G_1G_2B_2B_1$	$G_1B_2G_2B_1$	$G_1B_2B_1G_2$
$B_2B_1G_2G_1$	$B_2G_2B_1G_1$	$B_2G_2G_1B_1$	$G_2G_1B_2B_1$	$G_2B_2G_1B_1$	$G_2B_2B_1G_1$

In reality of course there is no difference between the pens of the same colour so the subscripts can be removed. Notice that if the subscripts 1 and 2 are removed from the Gs then the top two rows are identical and so are the bottom two rows. So the total number of arrangements is reduced to

$$\frac{4!}{2} = 12$$

If the subscripts are then removed from the Bs then all four rows are identical and there are:

$$\frac{4!}{2 \times 2} = 6 \text{ arrangements.}$$

If the pens were then changed to 1 green and 3 blue pens we could group the arrangements into batches of $3! = 6$. For example, one batch would be:

$$GB_1B_2B_3 \quad GB_1B_3B_2 \quad GB_2B_3B_1 \quad GB_2B_1B_3 \quad GB_3B_1B_2 \quad GB_3B_2B_1$$

When the subscripts on the Bs are removed we are left with $\dfrac{4!}{3!} = 4$ arrangements.

This important idea can be generalised so that if there are k different types of objects with $n_1, n_2, n_3, \ldots n_k$ of each type then the number of arrangements of all the objects is

$$\frac{(n_1 + n_2 + n_3 + \ldots n_k)!}{n_1! n_2! n_3! \ldots n_k!}$$

For example, with 6 pens consisting of $3B$, $2G$ and $1R$ the number of arrangements would be

$$\frac{6!}{3!2!1!} = \frac{6 \times 5 \times 4}{2} = 60.$$

5.6 Combinations

Consider again the original set of 4 different coloured marker pens. In how many different ways can two pens be *selected*? Notice that there is no sense of order. It is not necessary to decide what to draw with the pens. They only have to be selected or *chosen*. This process splits the 4 pens into two groups: those that are chosen, which are labelled c and those that are not chosen, which are labelled c'. So the number of *selections* is the same as the number of ways of *arranging* 4 items of which there are $2c$s and $2c'$s. From the previous section this is:

$$\frac{4!}{2!2!} = 6.$$

The number of **combinations** of 2 objects from 4 is

$$\binom{4}{2} = \frac{4!}{2!2!} = 6.$$

Notice that the key words here are *select* or *choose* and that *order is not important*. The principle of splitting the objects into two groups: the chosen ones (c) and the rest (c'), is the important feature of a combination.

Suppose a general knowledge team of 4 is to be chosen from a class of 26 pupils. There will be $4c$s and $22c'$s and these can be arranged in

$$\frac{26!}{4!22!} \text{ ways.}$$

So the number of selections of 4 from 26 is

$$\binom{26}{4} = \frac{26!}{4!22!} = \frac{26 \times 25 \times 24 \times 23}{4!} = 14\,950.$$

So in general, to select r objects from n distinct objects there will be r labelled c and $n-r$ labelled c' so

$$\binom{n}{r} = \frac{n!}{r!(n-r)!}.$$

■ **Combinations**   Number of combinations of r from n is

$$\binom{n}{r} = \frac{n!}{r!(n-r)!}$$

(You may already have met the formula for $\binom{n}{r}$ when studying the binomial theorem in P1 and it will be used again in connection with the binomial distribution in chapter 7.)

Example 1
The letters of the word STATISTICS are jumbled and then arranged in a straight line.

(a) How many different arrangements are there?
(b) Find how many of these arrangements start and end with the letter S.
(c) Determine the probability of obtaining an arrangement in which the vowels are all together.

Peter has a set of 12 coloured felt tip pens. He selects 5 pens from his set.

(d) How many different selections could he make?

Peter chose blue, green, red, pink and yellow and planned to write the word STATISTICS using a different colour for each of the 5 different letters. He started with a red S but then noticed that the red and pink colours clashed and so decided that red and pink should not be adjacent.

(e) Find the number of different colourings that are still possible.

There are 10 letters in the word STATISTICS: 3Ss, 3Ts, 2Is and an A and a C.
(a) The number of arrangements is

$$\frac{10!}{3!3!2!1!1!} = 50\,400.$$

(b) If an arrangement has to start and end with S there are 8 letters left to be arranged. There are repeats of the letter T (3Ts) and the letter I (2Is) so the number of arrangements is

$$\frac{8!}{3!2!1!1!1!} = 3360.$$

(c) There are 3 vowels: A, I, I. These can be joined together to form a new "triple letter" AII. This can be done in

$$\frac{3!}{2!} = 3 \text{ ways.}$$

There are now 8 "letters": 3Ts, 3Ss, AII and C.

These can be arranged in

$$\frac{8!}{3!3!} \text{ ways}$$

but for each of these there are 3 possibilities for the "triple letter" so the number of arrangements with the vowels together is

$$\frac{8!}{3!3!} \times 3 = 3360.$$

The probability of obtaining such an arrangement is

$$\frac{3\,360}{50\,400} = \frac{1}{15} \text{ or } 0.06.$$

(d) Peter chooses 5 pens from a total of 12.

$$\binom{12}{5} = \frac{12!}{5!7!} = 792.$$

(e) Since the letter S is next to the letters T, I and C, the only letter which can be pink is the letter A.
Thus two colours are fixed (red and pink) and the remaining 3 can be arranged in any order, i.e.

$3! = 6$ different colourings are possible.

Exercise 5D

1 There are 5 competitors in a race.

(a) In how many different ways can they be assigned to the 5 lanes?

(b) How many different ways could the first three prizes be awarded?

2 A box of children's crayons has 6 different colours arranged in a line. Find the number of different ways they can be replaced in the box.

3 There are 8 questions on an examination paper.

(a) Assuming that a candidate answers all the questions, in any order, in how many different ways can this be done?

(b) Given that the candidate only answered 6 questions find the number of different arrangements of these 6 questions.

4 The digits of the number 12 354 are rearranged to give a different 5 digit number.

(a) How many different 5 digit numbers can be formed?

(b) One of these 5 digit numbers is chosen at random. Find the probability that it is even.

(c) Find how many of the 5 digit numbers from part (a) are greater than 30 000.

5 Repeat question 4 for the number 12 324.

6 (a) The letters of the word MODULE are jumbled up and 5 letters are then arranged in a line. Find the probability that they spell the word MODEL.

(b) The letters of the word MODELLING are jumbled and five letters are then arranged in a line. What is the probability that they spell the word MODEL this time?

7 The letters of the word EXAMINATION are jumbled and then arranged in a straight line.

(a) How many different arrangements are there?

(b) How many of these arrangements begin with the letter X?

(c) How many arrangements have the letter A at the beginning and the end?

(d) Determine the number of arrangements where no two vowels are next to each other.

8 The six letters of the word LONDON are written on six cards, one letter on each card. The cards are shuffled and placed in a line.

(a) Determine the number of different arrangements of the six letters.

(b) Find the probability of obtaining the word LONDON from the shuffled cards.

The cards are shuffled again and 4 cards are selected and placed in a line.

(c) Find the probability that all 4 letters are different?

9 A swimming team of 5 is to be selected from a squad of 8. How many possible teams are there?

10 A hockey team of 11 players is to be selected from a group of 20 students. Three of the students can only play in goal, the others can play in any of the remaining positions. How many different teams are possible?

11 In a group of 6 students, 4 are female and 2 are male. Determine how many committees of 3 members can be formed containing 1 male and 2 females. [L]

12 The four distinct points B_1, B_2, B_3 and B_4 lie on a straight line AB and the three distinct points C_1, C_2, C_3 lie on a second straight line AC. Given that none of the other seven points coincides with the point A, determine the number of different triangles that can be formed with vertices selected from

(a) the points B_1, B_2, B_3, B_4, C_1, C_2, C_3

(b) the points B_1, B_2, B_3, B_4, C_1, C_2, C_3 and A. [L]

13 From a class of 8 students it is decided to send a party of either 3 or 4 or 5 students to a meeting.

(a) Calculate the total number of different parties which could be formed.

(b) Find the number of these parties in which two specific students are always members. [L]

14 From the 6 letters of the word SUMMER, calculate:

(a) the number of different selections of 4 letters that can be made

(b) the number of different arrangements of 4 letters that can be made. [L]

15 Find the number of ways a committee of 4 people can be chosen from a group of 5 men and 7 women when it contains

(a) only people of the same sex

(b) people of both sexes and there are at least as many women as men. [L]

SUMMARY OF KEY POINTS

$$\text{P(event } A \text{ or event } B) = \text{P}(A \cup B)$$

$$\text{P(both events } A \text{ and } B) = \text{P}(A \cap B)$$

$$\text{P(not event } A) = \text{P}(A')$$

Complementary probability $\text{P}(A') = 1 - \text{P}(A)$

Addition Rule $$\text{P}(A \cup B) = \text{P}(A) + \text{P}(B) - \text{P}(A \cap B)$$

Conditional probability $$\text{P}(A \text{ given } B) = \text{P}(A|B) = \frac{\text{P}(A \cap B)}{\text{P}(B)}$$

Multiplication Rule $\text{P}(A \cap B) = \text{P}(A|B) \times \text{P}(B)$

A and B are **independent** events if

$$\text{P}(A \cap B) = \text{P}(A) \times \text{P}(B)$$

A and B are **mutually exclusive** events if

$$\text{P}(A \cap B) = 0$$

Permutations   Number of permutations of r from n is

$$^{n}\text{P}_r = \frac{n!}{(n-r)!}$$

Combinations   Number of combinations of r from n is

$$\binom{n}{r} = \frac{n!}{r!(n-r)!}$$

Random variables

6

Earlier in your mathematical studies you may have come across problems like this:

> "Mrs Brown bought 4 grapefruit and 2 melons from her grocer. A melon costs 60p more than a grapefruit and her total bill was £2.94. What was the cost of a grapefruit?"

A common approach to problems such as this is to introduce a **variable** x, which represents the cost in pence of a grapefruit, and then form an equation in x:

$$4x + 2(x + 60) = 294.$$

This equation can then be solved to obtain $x = 29$.

In this chapter you will be considering situations where the variable could take one of several possible values. It may not be possible to say for sure which value is going to arise in a particular situation but the aim is to be able to state how likely it is, that is the **probability** that a particular value will occur.

6.1 Types of random variables

A certain statistician decided to introduce an element of probability into the weekly pocket money he gave his son. The son rolled a fair die and whatever the value on the uppermost face of the die his father gave him that many pounds for his pocket money that week. Thus, a roll of 5 on the die meant that the boy received £5 pocket money that week. If $M =$ the value in pounds of the son's pocket money for next week then M is a **random variable**. Capital letters, like M, are used to describe random variables and a lower case letter, such as m is used to represent a particular value of the random variable.

Notice that the answer to "$M =$" will be a number but it is not possible to say what that number will be. However, in this example you know that M has to be one of the six numbers 1, 2, 3, 4, 5 or 6 (all the numbers on the faces of the die) and, since the die is fair, you can assign a probability, in this case $\frac{1}{6}$ every time, to each of these values. The set of all possible values of a random variable together with the associated probabilities is called a **probability distribution** and the function that describes how the probabilities are assigned is called the **probability function**. In the case of the pocket money, the probability function is:

$$p(m) = P(M = m) = \tfrac{1}{6} \qquad m = 1, 2, \ldots, 6$$

and the probability distribution is written as:

m:	1	2	3	4	5	6
$P(M = m)$:	$\frac{1}{6}$	$\frac{1}{6}$	$\frac{1}{6}$	$\frac{1}{6}$	$\frac{1}{6}$	$\frac{1}{6}$

Since the probability function describes how probability is assigned to *all* possible values then the sum of the p(m) values equals 1, in this case this is simply:

$$\sum_{m=1}^{6} \tfrac{1}{6} = 1$$

This important property of the probability function often provides a useful check that a probability distribution has been properly defined.

The statistician's son bought some new batteries for his walkman and they were advertised as giving between 5 and 8 hours of continuous play. Let $H =$ the number of hours these new batteries will last. H is another random variable. Notice that there is an important difference between M and H. The random variable M can take any *whole* number value (between 1 and 6) but $M = 5.43$ is not possible. The random variable M is called a **discrete random variable** – one which changes *by steps* and therefore only takes some values in the interval. On the other hand H could take *any* value (inside the advertised range of values, called the interval [5,8]). H is a **continuous random variable**. The probability distribution for a continuous random variable cannot be described in terms of a simple probability function. You cannot talk about the probability of a single value, for example, $P(H) = 7$, but rather a range of values, for example, $P(H \geqslant 7)$. This will be discussed in greater depth later in this chapter.

The important property of discrete random variables is summarised below.

■ If X is a **discrete random variable** with probability function p(x) then:

$$\sum_{\forall x} p(x) = 1$$

(The symbol $\forall x$ means for all values of x.)

Example 1

A tetrahedral die has the numbers 1, 2, 3 and 4 on its faces. The die is biased in such a way that the probability of the die landing on the number n is inversely proportional to n, for example:

$$P(3) = \frac{k}{3}$$

where k is a constant.

Find the probability distribution for X, the number the die lands on after a single roll.

The distribution of X will be:

x:	1	2	3	4
$p(x)$:	$\frac{k}{1}$	$\frac{k}{2}$	$\frac{k}{3}$	$\frac{k}{4}$

Since this is a probability distribution, $\sum p(x) = 1$.

$\therefore$
$$k(1 + \tfrac{1}{2} + \tfrac{1}{3} + \tfrac{1}{4}) = 1$$

i.e.
$$k\left(\tfrac{12+6+4+3}{12}\right) = 1$$

$\therefore$
$$k = \tfrac{12}{25}$$

So the probability distribution of X is:

x:	1	2	3	4
$p(x)$:	$\tfrac{12}{25}$	$\tfrac{6}{25}$	$\tfrac{4}{25}$	$\tfrac{3}{25}$

Exercise 6A

1 A discrete random variable X has the following probability distribution:

x:	1	2	3	4
$p(x)$:	$\tfrac{1}{3}$	$\tfrac{1}{3}$	k	$\tfrac{1}{4}$

where k is a constant.
   (a) Find the value of k.   (b) Find $P(X \leqslant 3)$.

2 The discrete random variable Y has the following probability distribution:

y:	-1	0	1
$p(y)$:	a	$\tfrac{1}{4}$	a

where a is a constant.

(a) Find the value of a. (b) Find $P(Y \geqslant 0)$.

3 State which of the following could describe discrete probability distributions and give the value of x when a probability distribution is defined.

(a)

a:	-2	-1	0	1	2
$p(a)$:	$\frac{1}{4}$	$\frac{1}{4}$	x	$\frac{1}{6}$	$\frac{1}{6}$

(b)

b:	0	$\frac{1}{2}$	1
$p(b)$:	0.4	x	0.4

(c)

c:	1	2	3	4
$p(c)$:	x	$\frac{2}{3}$	x	$\frac{1}{2}$

4 The random variable X has the following probability distribution:

x:	1	5	9
$p(x)$.	a	b	c

where a, b and c are constants.

It is known that $P(X < 4) = P(X > 4)$ and $P(X \leqslant 5) = 2P(X > 5)$. Find the values of a, b and c.

5 A cubical die is biased in such a way that the probability is proportional to the number showing, for example, $p(5) = 5k$, where k is a constant. Find the probability distribution for S, the score on the die.

6 Two tetrahedral dice have the numbers 1, 2, 3 and 4 on their faces. The dice are thrown together. Let $S =$ the sum of their two scores and let $D =$ the difference between their two scores.

(a) Show that $P(S = 6) = \frac{3}{16}$.

(b) Find the probability distribution for the random variable S.

(c) Show that $P(D = 1) = \frac{3}{8}$.

(d) Find the probability distribution for the random variable D.

7 Sam's pocket contains one £1 coin, one 50p coin and three 20p coins. He selects 2 coins at random to place in a collection box. The random variable X represents the amount, in pence, that he puts in the box.

(a) Show that $P(X = 70) = 0.3$.

(b) Find the probability distribution for X.

8 A fair coin is tossed repeatedly until a head appears or 3 tosses have been made. The random variable T represents the number of tosses.

(a) Show that $P(T = 2) = \frac{1}{4}$.

(b) Find the probability distribution of T.

The random variable H represents the number of heads.

(c) Find the probability distribution of H.

9 Some of the following could be random variables and some could not. If they could not explain why and if they could then state whether the random variable would be discrete or continuous.

(a) A bag contains 20 red, 20 blue and 10 yellow beads.

(i) Four beads are selected and $R =$ the number of red beads selected.

(ii) Four beads are selected and $F =$ the colour of the 4th bead selected.

(iii) Beads are selected until a blue bead is found and $B =$ the number of beads selected.

(b) A pupil is selected at random from a class.

(i) $E =$ the colour of their eyes.

(ii) $T =$ their body temperature in degrees Celsius.

(iii) $S =$ the number of letters in their surname.

(iv) $D =$ the distance in metres they can throw a tennis ball.

10 Decide whether a discrete or a continuous random variable can be used to describe the following.

(a) The height of a seedling in a biology experiment 14 days after planting.

(b) Your final mark in the T1 examination.

(c) The number of times the word "probability" occurs on a randomly selected page from this book.

(d) The time it would take you to run 100 m.

11 The discrete random variable X has probability function given by:

$$p(x) = \begin{cases} (\frac{1}{2})^x & x = 1, 2, 3, 4, 5 \\ C & x = 6 \\ 0 & \text{otherwise} \end{cases}$$

where C is a constant.

Determine the value of C. [L]

12 A darts player practises throwing a dart at the bull's-eye on a dart board. Independently for each throw, her probability of hitting the bull's-eye is 0.2. Let X be the number of throws she makes, up to and including her first success.

(a) Find the probability that she is successful for the first time on her third throw.

(b) Write down the distribution of X.

(c) Find the probability that she will have at least 3 failures before her first success. [L]

13 Six fuses, of which two are defective and four are good, are to be tested one after another in random order until both defective fuses are identified. Find the probability that the number of fuses that will be tested is:

(a) three

(b) four or fewer. [L]

6.2 Expectation for discrete random variables

In example 1, the probability distribution for the discrete random variable X, representing the score on a biased tetrahedral die, was found to be:

x:	1	2	3	4
$p(x)$:	$\frac{12}{25}$	$\frac{6}{25}$	$\frac{4}{25}$	$\frac{3}{25}$

Consider the following problem: if you were to throw the die 100 times then how many 3s would you expect to obtain? Since $P(X = 3) = \frac{4}{25}$ then 4 times in every 25 throws you would expect a 3 to occur. So, in 100 throws you might expect $100 \times \frac{4}{25} = 16$ occasions when a 3 occurs. In practice, of course, you may well not obtain exactly 16 threes. The 16 reflects the distribution of X which you are using as a model for this practical experiment. These 100 "theoretical" throws will give rise to the following expected frequency table:

x:	1	2	3	4
Expected frequency:	48	24	16	12

To find the mean for the population of x values, use $\mu = \dfrac{\sum fx}{\sum f}$ which gives

$$\frac{1 \times 48 + 2 \times 24 + 3 \times 16 + 4 \times 12}{100} = 1.92$$

A closer look at this calculation shows that the number of throws is irrelevant. If you treat the values of p(x) as frequencies you obtain the same result:

$$\frac{1 \times \frac{12}{25} + 2 \times \frac{6}{25} + 3 \times \frac{4}{25} + 4 \times \frac{3}{25}}{\sum \text{p}(x) \ (=1)} = \frac{48}{25} = 1.92$$

and this value is called the **mean of X** or **expected value of X**. The expected value of X is usually written as E(X) and sometimes the Greek letter mu, μ is used for the mean value of a random variable.

In general, for a discrete random variable X:

■ **Expected value of X**

$$\mu = \text{E}(X) = \sum_{\forall x} x\text{P}(X = x)$$

The **expectation of a *function* of a random variable** can be considered in a similar way. Suppose you again throw this biased tetrahedral die and instead of recording the score X, you record $2X - 1$. If you let this new variable be Y then you can ask, what is E(Y)? The distribution is:

x:	1	2	3	4
y:	1	3	5	7
p(y):	$\frac{12}{25}$	$\frac{6}{25}$	$\frac{4}{25}$	$\frac{3}{25}$

Notice how the probabilities relating to X are still being used, for example, P($Y = 7$) = P($X = 4$). Now

$$\begin{aligned} \text{E}(Y) &= 1 \times \tfrac{12}{25} + 3 \times \tfrac{6}{25} + 5 \times \tfrac{4}{25} + 7 \times \tfrac{3}{25} \\ &= \tfrac{71}{25} \\ &= 2.84 \end{aligned}$$

This is:

$$\sum y \mathrm{P}(Y = y) = \sum (2x - 1) \mathrm{P}(X = x)$$
$$= 2 \sum x \mathrm{P}(X = x) - \sum \mathrm{P}(X = x)$$
$$= 2 \mathrm{E}(X) - 1$$

This is equivalent to:

$$\mathrm{E}(2X - 1) = 2 \mathrm{E}(X) - 1$$

which is an example of a general result that will be dealt with in the next section.

You can also find $\mathrm{E}(X^2)$ in a similar way. The distribution is:

x:	1	2	3	4
x^2:	1	4	9	16
$\mathrm{p}(x^2) = \mathrm{p}(x)$:	$\frac{12}{25}$	$\frac{6}{25}$	$\frac{4}{25}$	$\frac{3}{25}$

and

$$\mathrm{E}(X^2) = \sum x^2 \mathrm{P}(X = x)$$
$$= 1^2 \times \tfrac{12}{25} + 2^2 \times \tfrac{6}{25} + 3^2 \times \tfrac{4}{25} + 4^2 \times \tfrac{3}{25}$$
$$= \tfrac{120}{25}$$
$$= 4.8$$

Notice that

$$\mathrm{E}(X^2) \neq [\mathrm{E}(X)]^2$$

In general, you can find the expected value of a function of a random variable $g(X)$ as follows:

■ $\mathrm{E}[g(X)] = \displaystyle\sum_{\forall x} g(x) \mathrm{P}(X = x)$

You can now find the **variance of a random variable** X, $\mathrm{Var}(X)$. In chapter 4, the population variance was defined as:

$$\frac{\sum f(x - \mu)^2}{\sum f}$$

which was equivalent to:

$$\frac{\sum f x^2}{\sum f} - \mu^2$$

So using the probabilities as frequencies again you have:

$$\mathrm{Var}(X) = \sum_{\forall x} (x - \mu)^2 \mathrm{P}(X = x)$$
$$= \sum_{\forall x} x^2 \mathrm{P}(X = x) - \mu^2$$

So for your tetrahedral die:

$$\mathrm{Var}(X) = 4.8 - (1.92)^2$$
$$= 1.1136$$

The Greek letter sigma, σ, is used to represent the **standard deviation** of a random variable and so you have:

$$\sigma^2 = \mathrm{Var}(X)$$

■ **Variance of X**

$$\mathrm{Var}(X) = \sum_{\forall x}(x - \mu)^2 \mathrm{P}(X = x)$$
$$= \sum_{\forall x} x^2 \mathrm{P}(X = x) - \mu^2$$

or
$$\sigma^2 = \mathrm{Var}(X) = \mathrm{E}(X^2) - \mu^2$$

Example 2

Two fair cubical dice are thrown: one is red and one is blue. The random variable M represents the score on the red die minus the score on the blue die.

(a) Find the distribution of M.
(b) Write down $\mathrm{E}(M)$.
(c) Find $\mathrm{Var}(M)$.

(a) You can represent the value of M in the following table:

Blue Red	1	2	3	4	5	6
1	0	−1	−2	−3	−4	−5
2	1	0	−1	−2	−3	−4
3	2	1	0	−1	−2	−3
4	3	2	1	0	−1	−2
5	4	3	2	1	0	−1
6	5	4	3	2	1	0

$\therefore$

m:	−5	−4	−3	−2	−1	0	1	2	3	4	5
$\mathrm{p}(m)$:	$\frac{1}{36}$	$\frac{2}{36}$	$\frac{3}{36}$	$\frac{4}{36}$	$\frac{5}{36}$	$\frac{6}{36}$	$\frac{5}{36}$	$\frac{4}{36}$	$\frac{3}{36}$	$\frac{2}{36}$	$\frac{1}{36}$

(b) By symmetry, $\mathrm{E}(M) = 0$.

(c) $\text{Var}(M) = \sum\limits_{m=-5}^{5} m^2 \text{P}(m) - 0^2$

$\qquad = 25 \times \frac{1}{36} + 16 \times \frac{2}{36} + 9 \times \frac{3}{36} + \ldots + 0 + 1 \times \frac{5}{36} + \ldots + 25 \times \frac{1}{36}$

$\qquad = \dfrac{(25 + 32 + 27 + 16 + 5) \times 2}{36}$

$\qquad = \frac{105}{18}$

$\qquad = \frac{35}{6}$

Exercise 6B

1 Find the mean and variance for each of the following distributions of X:

(a)

x:	1	2	3
p(x):	$\frac{1}{3}$	$\frac{1}{2}$	$\frac{1}{6}$

(b)

x:	-1	0	1
p(x):	$\frac{1}{4}$	$\frac{1}{2}$	$\frac{1}{4}$

(c)

x:	-2	-1	1	2
p(x):	$\frac{1}{3}$	$\frac{1}{3}$	$\frac{1}{6}$	$\frac{1}{6}$

2 Given that Y is the score when a single unbiased cubical die is rolled, find $\text{E}(Y)$ and $\text{Var}(Y)$.

3 Two fair cubical die are rolled and S is the sum of their scores.
  (a) Find the distribution of S.   (b) Write down $\text{E}(S)$.
  (c) Find $\text{Var}(S)$.

4 Two fair cubical die are rolled and D is the difference between their scores.
  (a) Show that $\text{P}(D = 3) = \frac{1}{6}$ and find the distribution of D.
  (b) Find $\text{E}(D)$.   (c) Find $\text{Var}(D)$.

5 A fair die is rolled and the random variable N represents the number showing. A square of side N is then drawn on a piece of paper.
  (a) Find the expected value of the area of this square.
  (b) Find the variance of the perimeter of this square.

6 A fair coin is tossed twice and the random variable H represents the number of heads recorded.
(a) Find the distribution of H. (b) Write down E(H).
(c) Calculate Var(H).

7 A fair coin is tossed repeatedly until a head appears or 3 tosses have been made. The random variable T represents the number of tosses of the coin.
(a) Show that the distribution of T is:

t:	1	2	3
p(t):	$\frac{1}{2}$	$\frac{1}{4}$	$\frac{1}{4}$

(b) Find the mean and standard deviation of T.

8 A statistically-minded parent is discussing pocket money with a young child. The parent has a £1 and a 50p coin. Both coins are spun and if a coin lands with heads uppermost the child can have it as pocket money, otherwise the parent keeps it. The child's parent is generous and, rather than disappointing the child, in the event of both coins landing tails the child will receive 50p. How much pocket money can the child expect to receive?

9 The random variable X has the following distribution:

x:	1	2	3
p(x):	a	b	a

where a and b are constants.
(a) Write down E(X).
(b) Given that Var(X) = 0.75, find the values of a and b.

10 At a fair a roll-a-penny stall can be played with 1p or 2p coins. If the coin lands inside a square (without touching the edges) the player receives the coin plus 2 other coins of the same value, otherwise the coin is lost. The probability of winning the prize with a 1p coin is $\frac{19}{40}$ and the probability for a 2p coin is $\frac{11}{40}$.
(a) Find the expected winnings for each coin.
(b) Would you play this game and why?
(c) The stall was eventually closed down by the management. Give a possible reason for this.

11 The random variable X has probability function

$$P(X = x) = \begin{cases} \frac{c}{x} & x = 1, 2, \ldots, 6 \\ 0 & \text{otherwise} \end{cases}$$

where c is a constant.

Find the value of:

(a) c

(b) $E(X)$

(c) $\text{Var}(X)$. [L]

12 A box A contains 9 red balls and one white ball. A box B contains 8 red balls and one white ball. A ball is to be taken at random from box A and put into box B, and then a ball is to be taken at random from box B. Find the probability that this ball from box B will be white.

Of the 2 balls drawn, one from A and one from B, let X denote the number that are white. Find the probability distribution of X.

Find the mean of X.

Find also, to 2 decimal places, the variance of X. [L]

13 A random variable R takes the integer value r with probability p(r), where:

$$\begin{aligned} p(r) &= kr^3 & r = 1, 2, 3, 4 \\ p(r) &= 0 & \text{otherwise.} \end{aligned}$$

Find:

(a) the value of k, and display the distribution on graph paper

(b) the mean and the variance of the distribution. [L]

6.3 Continuous random variables

Earlier in this chapter in section 6.1 you considered a continuous random variable $H = $ the number of hours some batteries would last. The manufacturer specified that the batteries would last between 5 and 8 hours but did not provide information about how the probability is distributed over this range of values. Since H can take any value in the interval [5,8] you need to use a *continuous* function to describe the distribution. This is called a **probability density function** (p.d.f.) and it is denoted by f(x). It is usual to define f(x) over the range $(-\infty, \infty)$ and so f(x) = 0 for values of $x < 5$ and $x > 8$.

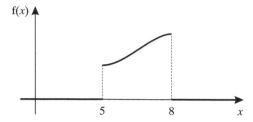

In chapter 3, you looked at the relative frequency histogram for consultation times at a doctor's surgery which were as follows:

Time (to nearest minute)	Number of consultations	Relative frequency
2–3	30	0.10
4	96	0.32
5	48	0.16
6–7	84	0.28
8–10	27	0.09
11–15	15	0.05
Total	300	1.00

These gave the following relative frequency histogram:

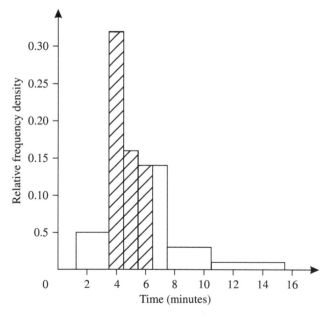

An important feature of a histogram like this is that the total area of the histogram is *equal to* 1. Furthermore the relative frequency is given by the area of the bar and not the height.

In chapter 5, you used the idea of relative frequency as a way of defining probability and you could use this relative frequency histogram to find the probability that a consultation lasts between 4 and 6 minutes by calculating the shaded area of the histogram ($3\frac{1}{2}$ to $6\frac{1}{2}$, since the data is given to the nearest minute) which gives:

$$0.32 + 0.16 + \tfrac{1}{2}(0.28) = 0.62$$

A probability density function, f(x), gives a "smooth" version of a relative frequency histogram and so f(x) will have two important properties:

f(x) $\geqslant 0$ $\forall x$ (this is equivalent to the result that probability $\geqslant 0$)

$$\int_{-\infty}^{\infty} f(x)\, dx = 1$$ or the area under the curve is 1
(compare $\sum p(x) = 1$).

The probability density function of a continuous random variable is providing a *model* of a relative frequency histogram and so to *calculate probabilities for a continuous random variable you need to find an area under the probability density function.*

- **If X is a continuous random variable with p.d.f. f(x)**

    (i) $$f(x) \geqslant 0 \;\; \forall x$$

    (ii) $$\int_{-\infty}^{\infty} f(x)\, dx = 1$$

    and $$P(a < X < b) = \int_{a}^{b} f(x)\, dx$$

The probability that a continuous random variable X lies between x and $x + \delta x$ will give an approximation to p(x) for a discrete distribution and from the diagram below you can see that this is approximately f(x) δx.

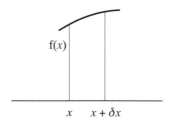

This leads to a useful parallel between results for discrete and continuous random variables. In the case of a discrete random variable:

$$\sum p(x) = 1$$

whereas for a continuous random variable:

$$\int f(x)\,dx = 1$$

So you can replace

$$\mathbf{p(x)\ by\ f(x)\ dx \quad and \quad \sum by \int .}$$

The mean μ for a *discrete* random variable X is given by:

$$\mu = E(X) = \sum_{\forall x} xp(x)$$

So for a *continuous* random variable X you can find the mean by replacing

$$\sum_{\forall x} \ by \int_{-\infty}^{\infty} \quad and \quad p(x)\ by\ f(x)\,dx$$

to obtain:

$$\mu = E(X) = \int_{-\infty}^{\infty} xf(x)\,dx$$

In the same way, the variance of the *discrete* random variable X is given by:

$$\sigma^2 = Var(X) = \sum_{\forall x} x^2 p(x) - \mu^2$$

So for a *continuous* random variable X you have:

$$\sigma^2 = Var(X) = \int_{-\infty}^{\infty} x^2 f(x)\,dx - \mu^2$$

■   **If X is a continuous random variable with p.d.f. f(x)**

$$\mu = E(X) = \int_{-\infty}^{\infty} xf(x)\,dx$$

$$\sigma^2 = Var(X) = \int_{-\infty}^{\infty} x^2 f(x)\,dx - \mu^2 = E(X^2) - E(X)^2$$

Example 3
A random variable X has p.d.f. f(x) given by:

$$f(x) = \begin{cases} kx & 0 \leqslant x \leqslant 1 \\ 0 & \text{otherwise} \end{cases}$$

where k is a positive constant.

Find: (a) k (b) $E(X)$ (c) $Var(X)$.

A sketch of the p.d.f. looks like this:

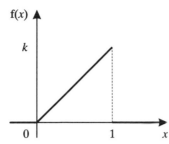

(a) To find k, use $\displaystyle\int_{-\infty}^{\infty} f(x)\,dx = 1$.

From the sketch this means finding the area of the triangle, so:

$$\tfrac{1}{2} \times 1 \times k = 1$$

$\Rightarrow$ $\qquad\qquad\qquad \tfrac{1}{2}k = 1$

i.e. $\qquad\qquad\qquad\quad k = 2$

(b) $$E(X) = \int_0^1 x.2x\,dx$$

$$= \left[\tfrac{2x^3}{3}\right]_0^1$$

$$= \tfrac{2}{3} - 0$$

$$= \tfrac{2}{3}$$

(c) $$E(X^2) = \int_0^1 x^2\,2x\,dx$$

$$= \left[\tfrac{2x^4}{4}\right]_0^1$$

$$= \tfrac{1}{2} - 0$$

$$= \tfrac{1}{2}$$

$\therefore$ $$\text{Var}(X) = \tfrac{1}{2} - \left(\tfrac{2}{3}\right)^2$$

$$= \tfrac{1}{18}$$

Notice the form in which a p.d.f. is usually defined. In this example the main range of interest was the interval [0,1] but $f(x)$ was defined for all real values of x. It is always worth drawing a sketch of the p.d.f. as this can often shorten the subsequent working.

Example 4

The continuous random variable Y has probability density function given by

$$f(y) = \begin{cases} \frac{3}{32}[4 - y^2] & -2 \leqslant y \leqslant 2 \\ 0 & \text{otherwise.} \end{cases}$$

(a) Find $E(Y)$.

(b) Show that $\text{Var}(Y) = \frac{4}{5}$.

(c) Find $P(Y > 1)$.

The p.d.f. is part of a parabola and can be sketched as:

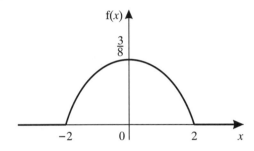

(a) By symmetry:
$$E(Y) = 0$$

(b)
$$\text{Var}(Y) = E(Y^2) - 0^2 = \frac{3}{32}\int_{-2}^{2} (4y^2 - y^4)\, dy$$

$$= \frac{3}{32}\left[\frac{4}{3}y^3 - \frac{1}{5}y^5\right]_{-2}^{2}$$

$$= \left(1 - \frac{3}{5}\right) - \left(-1 + \frac{3}{5}\right)$$

$$= \frac{4}{5}$$

(c)
$$P(Y > 1) = \frac{3}{32}\int_{1}^{2} (4 - y^2)\, dy$$

$$= \frac{3}{32}\left[4y - \frac{1}{3}y^3\right]_{1}^{2}$$

$$= \left(\frac{3}{4} - \frac{1}{4}\right) - \left(\frac{3}{8} - \frac{1}{32}\right)$$

$$= \frac{16 - 12 + 1}{32}$$

$$= \frac{5}{32}$$

Exercise 6C

1 A random variable X has p.d.f. f(x) given by:

$$f(x) = \begin{cases} k(1-x) & 0 \leqslant x \leqslant 1 \\ 0 & \text{otherwise} \end{cases}$$

where k is a positive constant.
(a) Find k.   (b) Find $E(X)$.
(c) Show that $\text{Var}(X) = \frac{1}{18}$.
(d) Find $P(X > \mu)$.

2 The random variable Y has p.d.f. given by:

$$f(y) = \begin{cases} \frac{1}{3} + \frac{1}{6}y & 0 \leqslant y \leqslant 2 \\ 0 & \text{otherwise.} \end{cases}$$

Find the following:
(a) $E(Y)$ (b) $\text{Var}(Y)$ (c) $P(Y < 1)$ (d) $P(Y > \mu)$.

3 The random variable X has p.d.f. given by:

$$f(x) = \begin{cases} 12x^2(1-x) & 0 \leqslant x \leqslant 1 \\ 0 & \text{otherwise.} \end{cases}$$

(a) Find $P(X < \frac{1}{2})$.   (b) Find $E(X)$.

4 The random variable X has p.d.f. given by:

$$f(x) = \begin{cases} \frac{3}{8}(1+x^2) & -1 \leqslant x \leqslant 1 \\ 0 & \text{otherwise.} \end{cases}$$

(a) Sketch the p.d.f. of X.   (b) Write down $E(X)$.
(c) Show that $\sigma^2 = 0.4$.   (d) Find $P(-\sigma < X < \sigma)$ to 2 d.p.

5 The random variable T has p.d.f. given by:

$$f(t) = \begin{cases} kt^3 & 0 \leqslant t \leqslant 2 \\ 0 & \text{otherwise} \end{cases}$$

where k is a positive constant.
(a) Find k.
(b) Show that $E(T) = 1.6$.
(c) Find $P(T < 1)$.

6 Describe which of the following could represent a p.d.f. and give a reason for your choice:

(a) $f(x) = \begin{cases} \frac{1}{5}x & -1 \leqslant x \leqslant 3 \\ 0 & \text{otherwise.} \end{cases}$

(b) $f(x) = \begin{cases} x^2 & 0 \leqslant x \leqslant 2 \\ 0 & \text{otherwise.} \end{cases}$

(c) $f(x) = \begin{cases} \frac{3}{2}(x-1)^2 & 0 \leqslant x \leqslant 2 \\ 0 & \text{otherwise.} \end{cases}$

7 The random variable X has probability density function:

$$f(x) = \begin{cases} 3x^k & 0 \leqslant x \leqslant 1 \\ 0 & \text{otherwise} \end{cases}$$

where k is a positive integer.
Find:

(a) the value of k

(b) the mean of X.   [L]

8 An agency rents out flats to holiday makers. The weekly rent, X tens of pounds, of the flats is a continuous random variable with probability density function given by:

$$f(x) = kx(18 - x) \qquad 6 \leqslant x \leqslant 15$$
$$f(x) = 0 \qquad\qquad \text{otherwise.}$$

(a) Show that $k = \frac{1}{648}$.

(b) Calculate, to the nearest penny, the mean weekly rent.

(c) To book a flat with the agency, a holiday maker must pay a deposit of 10% of the weekly rent of the flat. Find, to the nearest penny, the mean deposit paid.

(d) In order to cover the agency's costs, the mean deposit needs to be £14. It is decided that on any flat with a weekly rent of more than £120 an *extra* fixed deposit of £D must be paid. Calculate the value of D correct to 2 decimal places.   [L]

9 The queuing time, X minutes, of a traveller at the ticket office of a large railway station has probability density function, f, defined by:

$$f(x) = kx(100 - x^2) \qquad 0 \leqslant x \leqslant 10$$
$$f(x) = 0 \qquad\qquad\quad \text{otherwise.}$$

Find:

(a) the value of k

(b) the mean of the distribution

(c) the standard deviation of the distribution to 2 decimal places

(d) the probability that a traveller at the ticket office will have to queue for more than 2 minutes.

Given that 3 travellers go independently to the booking office, find, to 2 significant figures, the probability that one has to queue for less than one minute, one has to queue for between one and two minutes and one has to queue for more than two minutes. [L]

10 The continuous random variable Y has a probability density function:

$$f(y) = \begin{cases} \frac{1}{\pi} & -\frac{\pi}{2} \leqslant y \leqslant \frac{\pi}{2} \\ 0 & \text{otherwise.} \end{cases}$$

(a) Find the mean of Y.

(b) Find the variance of Y. [L]

6.4 Expectation of a linear combination of random variables

The concept of the expected value of X considered earlier in this chapter can be extended to deal with the expected value of a function of X and, depending on whether X is discrete or continuous, the following definitions are used:

$$E[g(X)] = \sum g(x)p(x) \qquad \text{or} \qquad \int g(x)f(x)\,dx$$

where $p(x)$ is the probability function for a discrete random variable and $f(x)$ is the probability density function for a continuous random variable.

There are certain properties of expected value and variance which are fairly easy to verify in specific cases and are particularly useful. They are:

■ If X is a **random variable** and a and b are constants

$$E(aX) = aE(X)$$
$$E(aX + b) = aE(X) + b$$
$$\text{Var}(aX) = a^2\text{Var}(X)$$
$$\text{Var}(aX + b) = a^2\text{Var}(X)$$

An example of the second result was considered on page 138 and a little thought should enable you to appreciate why the last result is true. The variance is a measure of spread relative to the mean so adding a constant value to all the values of X will not affect this measure of spread hence the "b" does not change the variance. The "a^2" is understandable if you remember that:

$$\text{Var}(X) = E(X^2) - E(X)^2$$

so if each value of X is multiplied by the value of a the variance will be multiplied by a^2.

Example 5
The random variable X has p.d.f. given by:

$$f(x) = \begin{cases} \frac{1}{2}x & 0 \leqslant x \leqslant 2 \\ 0 & \text{otherwise.} \end{cases}$$

(a) Find the mean and variance of X.

(b) Find $E(X^3)$.

(c) Write down $E(3X + 1)$ and $\text{Var}(3X + 1)$.

(a)
$$\mu = \int_0^2 x \tfrac{1}{2} x \, dx$$
$$= \left[\frac{x^3}{6} \right]_0^2$$
$$= \tfrac{4}{3}$$
$$\sigma^2 = \int_0^2 x^2 \tfrac{1}{2} x \, dx - \mu^2$$
$$= \left[\frac{x^4}{8} \right]_0^2 - \tfrac{16}{9}$$
$$= \tfrac{2}{9}$$

(b)
$$E(X^3) = \int_0^2 x^3 \tfrac{1}{2}x \, dx$$
$$= \left[\tfrac{x^5}{10} \right]_0^2$$
$$= 3.2$$

(c)
$$E(3X + 1) = 3 \times \tfrac{4}{3} + 1$$
$$= 5$$
$$Var(3X + 1) = 3^2 \times \tfrac{2}{9}$$
$$= 2$$

Linear combinations of two random variables

Consider a set of 5 cards. Three of the cards have the number zero on them and two have the number 1. Two cards are dealt without replacement from the set. Let X_1 and X_2 be the random variables representing the numbers on the first and second cards respectively. This situation can be represented using a tree diagram, as in chapter 5:

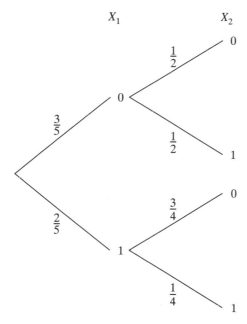

From this you can find:

$$P(X_2 = 0) = \tfrac{3}{5} \times \tfrac{1}{2} + \tfrac{2}{5} \times \tfrac{3}{4} = \tfrac{3}{5}$$

and

$$P(X_2 = 1) = 1 - P(X_2 = 0) = \tfrac{2}{5}$$

So the probability distributions for X_1 and X_2 are the same, namely:

x:	0	1
$p(x)$:	$\tfrac{3}{5}$	$\tfrac{2}{5}$

This result might, at first, seem somewhat surprising. Imagine the two cards laid out in a random arrangement on a table. Reading from left to right X_1 is the first card and X_2 is the second. Now walk round the table and stand on the other side. This time the first card is the one you previously labelled X_2 which demonstrates the symmetry of the situation. It is important to remember that although X_1 and X_2 have the same distribution they are not independent random variables. This should be clear from the way in which the experiment was set up as the value of X_2 depends upon the value of X_1.

In chapter 5 you saw that if two *events* A and B are independent, then:

$$P(A \cap B) = P(A) \times P(B).$$

In order to show the **independence of two random variables** X_1 and X_2 you need to show that *all* pairs of events involving X_1 and X_2 are independent. This means that:

$$P(\{X_1 = r\} \cap \{X_2 = s\}) = P(X_1 = r) \times P(X_2 = s)$$

for **every possible pair** of values (r, s).

Proving two random variables *are* independent is often a difficult task. To show that two random variables are *not* independent is usually easier as only a single counter example is required. In this case it is easily seen that:

$$P(\{X_1 = 0\} \cap \{X_2 = 0\}) = \tfrac{3}{10}$$

but

$$P(X_1 = 0) \times P(X_2 = 0) = \tfrac{9}{25}$$

so X_1 and X_2 are not independent random variables.

The distributions of X_1 and X_2 enable us to find:

$$
\begin{aligned}
E(X_1) &= E(X_2) \\
&= 0 \times \tfrac{3}{5} + 1 \times \tfrac{2}{5} \\
&= \tfrac{2}{5}
\end{aligned}
$$

and

$$\text{Var}(X_1) = \text{Var}(X_2)$$
$$= \left(0 + 1^2 \times \tfrac{2}{5}\right) - \tfrac{4}{25}$$
$$= \tfrac{6}{25}$$

From the tree diagram you can also find the distribution for the random variable $S = X_1 + X_2$ that is the sum of the numbers on the two cards:

s:	0	1	2
p(s):	$\tfrac{3}{10}$	$\tfrac{6}{10}$	$\tfrac{1}{10}$

From this:

$$E(S) = 0 \times \tfrac{3}{10} + 1 \times \tfrac{6}{10} + 2 \times \tfrac{1}{10}$$
$$= \tfrac{8}{10}$$
$$= \tfrac{4}{5}$$

and

$$\text{Var}(S) = \left(0 + 1^2 \times \tfrac{6}{10} + 2^2 \times \tfrac{1}{10}\right) - \tfrac{16}{25}$$
$$= \tfrac{9}{25}$$

Notice that:

$$E(X_1 + X_2) = E(X_1) + E(X_2)$$

but a similar result for $\text{Var}(X_1 + X_2)$ does not work.

Now repeat the above experiment but this time the cards are dealt *with* replacement and the random variables Y_1 and Y_2 represent the numbers on the first and second cards respectively. This time Y_1 and Y_2 *will* be independent and the tree diagram is as follows:

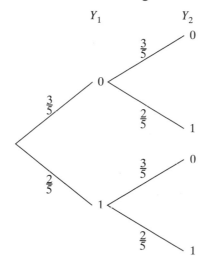

As before:

$$P(Y_2 = 0) = \tfrac{3}{5} \times \tfrac{3}{5} + \tfrac{2}{5} \times \tfrac{3}{5}$$
$$= \tfrac{3}{5}$$

and the distributions of Y_1 and Y_2 are identical and the same as in the previous experiment.

Now let T be the random variable representing the sum of the numbers on the two cards, i.e. $T = Y_1 + Y_2$. The distribution of T is as follows:

t:	0	1	2
$p(t)$:	$\tfrac{9}{25}$	$\tfrac{12}{25}$	$\tfrac{4}{25}$

From this:

$$E(T) = 0 + 1 \times \tfrac{12}{25} + 2 \times \tfrac{4}{25}$$
$$= \tfrac{20}{25}$$
$$= \tfrac{4}{5}$$

which is the same as $E(S)$, and

$$Var(T) = \left(0 + 1^2 \times \tfrac{12}{25} + 2^2 \times \tfrac{4}{25}\right) - \tfrac{16}{25}$$
$$= \tfrac{28-16}{25}$$
$$= \tfrac{12}{25}$$

This time $Var(Y_1 + Y_2)$ does equal $Var(Y_1) + Var(Y_2)$ as well as:

$$E(Y_1 + Y_2) = E(Y_1) + E(Y_2)$$

This example illustrates part of the following important results:

- If X and Y are **two random variables** and a and b are constants then:

$$E(aX \pm bY) = aE(X) \pm bE(Y)$$

$$Var(aX \pm bY) = a^2\, Var(X) + b^2\, Var(Y) \quad \text{(if } X \text{ and } Y \text{ are \textbf{independent})}$$

The variance formula often causes some confusion but it is easy to see why variances are always added. If X and Y are independent random variables, then:

$$
\begin{aligned}
Var(X - Y) &= Var[X + (-1)Y] \\
&= Var(X) + Var[(-1)Y] && \text{using } Var(X + Y) = Var(X) \\
& && + Var(Y) \text{ since } X \text{ and } Y \\
& && \text{are independent} \\
&= Var(X) + (-1)^2 Var(Y) && \text{using } Var(aY) = a^2 Var(Y) \\
&= Var(X) + Var(Y)
\end{aligned}
$$

It is also important to remember that the formula for the variance of a sum of two random variables only applies if the random variables are independent as illustrated in the above examples.

Example 6

The error in measuring the length of a desk is a random variable L with mean 1.0 cm and standard deviation 0.3 cm, whereas the error in measuring the width of the desk is a random variable W with mean 0.8 cm and standard deviation 0.2 cm. The random variables L and W are independent. One length and one width of the desk are measured and used to estimate the perimeter of the desk. Find the mean and standard deviation of the error in the value given for the perimeter.

The perimeter will have error $2W + 2L$.

$$\begin{aligned}
E(2W + 2L) &= 2E(W) + 2E(L) \\
&= 2 \times 0.8 + 2 \times 1.0 \\
&= 3.6 \, \text{cm} \\
\text{Var}(2W + 2L) &= 4\text{Var}(W) + 4\text{Var}(L) \\
&= 4 \times 0.04 + 4 \times 0.09 \\
&= 0.52
\end{aligned}$$

$\therefore \qquad$ Standard deviation $= 0.72 \, \text{cm} \, (2 \, \text{d.p.})$

Exercise 6D

1 The random variable Y has mean 2 and variance 9. Find the following:
   (a) $E(3Y + 1)$ (b) $E(2 - 3Y)$ (c) $\text{Var}(3Y + 1)$
   (d) $\text{Var}(2 - 3Y)$ (e) $E(Y^2)$ (f) $E(Y^2 - Y)$
   (g) $E[(Y - 1)(Y + 1)]$ (h) $E[(Y + 1)^2]$

2 The random variable X has mean μ and standard deviation σ. Find the following in terms of μ and σ:
   (a) $E(3X)$ (b) $E(2X + 3)$ (c) $E(3 - 2X)$
   (d) $\text{Var}(2X + 3)$ (e) $\text{Var}(3 - 2X)$ (f) $E(X^2)$
   (g) $E(X^2 + X)$ (h) $E[(X + 1)(X - 2)]$

3 The random variable T has mean 20 and standard deviation 5. It is required to scale T by using the transformation $S = aT + b$, where a and b are constants ($a > 0$), so that $E(S)$

and Var(S) satisfy specified values. Find the values of a and b in each of the following cases:

(a) $E(S) = 0$ and $Var(S) = 1$

(b) $E(S) = 100$ and $Var(S) = 225$

(c) $E(S) = 50$ and $Var(S) = 100$

(d) $E(S) = 5$ and $Var(S) = 25$

4 The random variable X has mean μ_X and variance σ_X^2 and the independent random variable Y has mean μ_Y and variance σ_Y^2. Find the following in terms of μ_X, μ_Y, σ_X^2 and σ_Y^2:

(a) $E(X + Y)$ (b) $E(2X - 3Y)$ (c) $Var(X + Y)$

(d) $Var(2X - 3Y)$ (e) $E(X + \frac{1}{2}Y)$ (f) $Var(X + \frac{1}{2}Y)$

(g) $E(X - Y)$ (h) $Var(X - Y)$

(i) $E[(X - Y)^2]$ (*Hint*: use (g) and (h))

(j) $E(2XY)$ (*Hint*: use (i)).

What can you say about $E(XY)$ if X and Y are independent?

5 The random variable X has mean 2 and variance 5 and the independent random variable Y has mean 3 and variance 4. Find the following:

(a) $E(X - Y + 1)$ (b) $Var(X - Y + 1)$ (c) $E\left(\dfrac{X + Y}{2}\right)$

(d) $Var\left(\dfrac{X + Y}{2}\right)$ (e) $E(5X + 4Y)$ (f) $Var(5X + 4Y)$

(g) $E(3Y - 2X)$ (h) $Var(3Y - 2X)$ (i) $E(X^2)$

(j) $E(X^2 + Y^2)$ (k) $E[(X - Y)(X + Y)]$ (l) $E[(X + Y)^2]$

6 The random variables X_1 and X_2 represent the two scores when two fair dice are thrown so $E(X_1) = E(X_2) = 3.5$ and $Var(X_1) = Var(X_2) = \frac{35}{12}$.

(a) A game is played where the two scores are added together and the random variable $S = X_1 + X_2$ represents this score. Find the mean and variance of S.

(b) On one occasion the second die was lost and the game was played by doubling the score on the first die. Find the mean and variance of the final score this time.

7 The discrete random variable X has the probability distribution specified in the following table:

x	-1	0	1	2
$P(X = x)$	0.25	0.10	0.45	0.20

(a) Find $P(-1 \leqslant X < 1)$.

(b) Find $E(2X + 3)$. [L]

8 X is a random variable having probability density function f where:

$$f(x) = \tfrac{1}{h} \qquad 0 < x < h$$

$$f(x) = 0 \qquad \text{otherwise.}$$

Given that $Y = X(h - X)$, find $E(Y)$.

Find also the probability that Y is greater than $\frac{3h^2}{16}$. [L]

9 The discrete random variable R has probability function p(r) defined by:

$$p(0) = p(6) = \tfrac{1}{16}, \ p(1) = p(4) = \tfrac{1}{4}$$

$$p(3) = \tfrac{3}{8}, \ p(r) = 0 \text{ elsewhere.}$$

Find $E(R)$ and $Var(R)$.

Find the mean and the variance of

(a) $2R - 5$

(b) $R_1 - R_2$, where R_1 and R_2 are independent observations of R. [L]

6.5 Cumulative distribution function

In chapter 3 cumulative frequency polygons were discussed and here the same idea is extended to probability distributions. The cumulative distribution function is defined as follows:

■ The **cumulative distribution function** $F(x_0)$ of the random variable X is:

$$F(x_0) = P(X \leqslant x_0)$$

If X has a discrete distribution then $F(x_0)$ is simply given by:

$$F(x_0) = \sum_{x \leqslant x_0} p(x)$$

but it is in connection with continuous random variables that the cumulative distribution function (c.d.f.) is most useful.

If X has a continuous distribution with probability density function (p.d.f.) $f(x)$, then the c.d.f. $F(x_0)$ is given by:

$$F(x_0) = \int_{-\infty}^{x_0} f(x)\,dx$$

Notice the use of the notation $F(x)$ (i.e. capital "F") for the c.d.f. but $f(x)$ (i.e. small "f") for the p.d.f. There is an important connection between these two functions:

■ If X is a continuous random variable with c.d.f. $F(x)$ and p.d.f. $f(x)$

$$f(x) = \frac{d}{dx} F(x)$$

This result depends upon the relationship between integration and differentiation.

The c.d.f. is obtained by *integrating* the p.d.f.
so the p.d.f. can be obtained by *differentiating* the c.d.f.

Care should be taken when forming the c.d.f. that the correct limits are applied in the integration.

In example 5 on page 144 the random variable X was used with the following probability density function $f(x)$:

$$f(x) = \begin{cases} \frac{1}{2}x & 0 \leqslant x \leqslant 2 \\ 0 & \text{otherwise.} \end{cases}$$

You can find the cumulative distribution function as follows. From the definition:

$$F(x_0) = P(X \leqslant x_0)$$
$$= \int_{-\infty}^{x_0} f(x)\,dx$$

but over the interval $(-\infty,0)$ $f(x)$ is zero, so $F(x_0)$ will also be zero for this interval. The interval of interest is $[0,2]$ and here $f(x)$ is given by $\frac{1}{2}x$, so the cumulative distribution function is given by:

$$F(x_0) = P(X \leqslant x_0)$$
$$= \int_0^{x_0} \tfrac{1}{2}x\,dx$$
$$= \left[\tfrac{1}{2}\tfrac{x^2}{2} \right]_0^{x_0}$$
$$= \tfrac{x_0^2}{4}$$

You need to be able to define $F(x_0)$ over the whole range $(-\infty, \infty)$ and, since $F(x_0)$ will be equal to 1 for any value of x_0 greater than 2, you can write $F(x_0)$ as follows:

$$F(x_0) = \begin{cases} 0 & x_0 < 0 \\ \frac{x_0^2}{4} & 0 \leqslant x_0 \leqslant 2 \\ 1 & x_0 > 2 \end{cases}$$

Example 7

The continuous random variable X takes values in the range $[0,2]$ and

$$P(X \leqslant x_0) = \frac{3x_0}{4} - \frac{x_0^3}{16} \qquad (0 \leqslant x_0 \leqslant 2)$$

(a) Find the probability density function $f(x)$.

(b) Sketch $f(x)$ and the cumulative distribution function.

(a) Differentiating $P(X \leqslant x_0) = F(x_0)$ gives:

$$\tfrac{3}{4} - \tfrac{3}{16}x_0^2$$

$$\therefore \qquad f(x) = \begin{cases} \tfrac{3}{4} - \tfrac{3}{16}x^2 & 0 \leqslant x \leqslant 2 \\ 0 & \text{otherwise.} \end{cases}$$

(b)

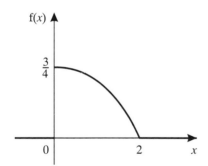
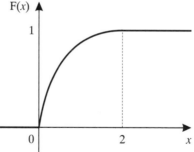

It is worth remembering that $F(x)$, the cumulative distribution function will always satisfy the following properties:

■ If $F(x)$ is the **c.d.f.** of a continuous random variable X:

(i) $0 \leqslant F(x) \leqslant 1$

(ii) The gradient of $F(x)$ is never negative.

The cumulative distribution function is particularly useful for finding medians and quartiles of continuous random variables in the same way that a cumulative frequency polygon was useful when dealing with data in chapter 3. The c.d.f. is also a powerful tool for finding the distributions of certain combinations of random variables but that is beyond the scope of this book.

6.6 Mode and median for continuous random variables

The concepts of mode and median for a sample of data were discussed in chapter 4 and the ideas introduced there are easily extended to continuous random variables. The probability density function shows how the probability is distributed and the **mode** is the value of the random variable X where it is most dense (note *mo*de for *mo*st dense). A sketch of the p.d.f. is often helpful as sometimes the mode occurs at a stationary point but not always!

Consider the following random variables X and Y with p.d.f.s $f_1(x)$ and $f_2(y)$ respectively:

$$f_1(x) = \begin{cases} 12x^2(1 - x) & 0 \leqslant x \leqslant 1 \\ 0 & \text{otherwise} \end{cases} \qquad f_2(x) = \begin{cases} 2y & 0 \leqslant y \leqslant 1 \\ 0 & \text{otherwise.} \end{cases}$$

The mode of X gives rise to the maximum point on the p.d.f. $f_1(x)$. So by differentiation:

$$\frac{d}{dx}(12x^2 - 12x^3) = 0$$

$\Rightarrow \qquad\qquad 12(2x - 3x^2) = 0$

i.e. $\qquad\qquad x(2 - 3x) = 0$

$\therefore \qquad\qquad\qquad x = \frac{2}{3}$

From the sketch above this clearly gives the maximum so the mode of X is $\frac{2}{3}$. The mode of Y does not occur at a stationary point so differentiating the p.d.f. is no help but from the sketch you can see that the mode of Y is 1. Sometimes a random variable may not have a mode and an example of such a distribution is discussed in chapter 8.

The cumulative distribution function (c.d.f.) is a useful tool for finding the **median** of a continuous random variable. The median value of the random variable X has 50% of the distribution below it and so a convenient way of finding the median, m, is to solve the equation $F(m) = \frac{1}{2}$.

■ If X is a continuous random variable with c.d.f. $F(x)$, the **median** value m of X is given by:

$$F(m) = \frac{1}{2}$$

You can also find the quartiles of a continuous random variable by solving the equation $F(p) = \frac{1}{4}$ to give the lower quartile, p, and $F(q) = \frac{3}{4}$ to find the upper quartile, q.

Example 8

The continuous random variable X has p.d.f. given by:

$$f(x) = \begin{cases} 4x - 4x^3 & 0 \leqslant x \leqslant 1 \\ 0 & \text{otherwise.} \end{cases}$$

(a) Find the mode of X.
(b) Find the c.d.f. of X.
(c) Find the $P(0.1 < X < 0.6)$.
(d) Find the median value of X.

A sketch of the p.d.f. is:

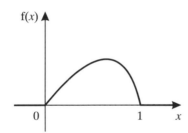

(a) The mode is clearly a stationary point, so set $\dfrac{d}{dx} f(x) = 0$

$\Rightarrow \qquad 4(1 - 3x^2) = 0$

$\Rightarrow \qquad\qquad x = \pm \frac{1}{\sqrt{3}}$ (but $-\frac{1}{\sqrt{3}}$ is outside the range)

∴ The mode of X is $\frac{1}{\sqrt{3}}$ or 0.577 (3 d.p.)

(b) The c.d.f. is given by:

$$F(x_0) = 4 \int_0^{x_0} (x - x^3) \, dx$$

$$= \left[2x^2 - x^4 \right]_0^{x_0}$$

$$= 2x_0^2 - x_0^4$$

So $\quad F(x) = \begin{cases} 0 & x < 0 \\ 2x^2 - x^4 & 0 \leqslant x \leqslant 1 \\ 1 & x > 1 \end{cases}$

(c) $P(0.1 < X < 0.6) = F(0.6) - F(0.1)$

$$= \{2 \times (0.6)^2 - (0.6)^4\} - \{2 \times (0.1)^2 - (0.1)^4\}$$

$$= 0.5705$$

(d) The median m is given by:

$$2m^2 - m^4 = 0.5$$

i.e. $\quad\quad\quad\quad 0 = 2m^4 - 4m^2 + 1$

i.e. $\quad\quad\quad\quad m^2 = \dfrac{4 \pm \sqrt{16 - 8}}{4}$

$$= 1 \pm \dfrac{\sqrt{2}}{2}$$

But to be in the range the $-$ve is needed:

$$m = \sqrt{1 - \dfrac{\sqrt{2}}{2}}$$

$\therefore \quad\quad\quad\quad = 0.541 (3 \text{ d.p.})$

Exercise 6E

1 The random variable X has p.d.f. $f(x)$ given by:

$$f(x) = \begin{cases} 1 - \frac{1}{2}x & 0 \leqslant x \leqslant 2 \\ 0 & \text{otherwise.} \end{cases}$$

(a) Sketch the p.d.f. of X. (b) Write down the mode of X.
(c) Find the c.d.f. of X. (d) Find the median value of X.

2 The random variable Y has p.d.f. $f(y)$ given by:

$$f(y) = \begin{cases} \frac{1}{2} - \frac{1}{9}y & 0 \leqslant y \leqslant 3 \\ 0 & \text{otherwise.} \end{cases}$$

(a) Sketch the p.d.f. of Y. (b) Write down the mode of Y.
(c) Find the c.d.f. of Y. (d) Find the median value of Y.

3 The random variable X has p.d.f. given by:

$$f(x) = \begin{cases} \frac{1}{4}x^3 & 0 \leqslant x \leqslant 2 \\ 0 & \text{otherwise.} \end{cases}$$

(a) Sketch the p.d.f. of X. (b) Write down the mode of X.
(c) Find the c.d.f. of X. (d) Find the median value of X.

4 The random variable X has p.d.f. given by:

$$f(x) = \begin{cases} \frac{3}{8}(x^2 + 1) & -1 \leqslant x \leqslant 1 \\ 0 & \text{otherwise.} \end{cases}$$

(a) Sketch the p.d.f. of X.
(b) What can you say about the mode of X?
(c) Write down the median value of X.
(d) Find the c.d.f. of X.

5 The random variable X has p.d.f. given by:

$$f(x) = \begin{cases} \frac{3}{32}(4 - x^2) & -2 \leqslant x \leqslant 2 \\ 0 & \text{otherwise.} \end{cases}$$

(a) Sketch the p.d.f. of X.
(b) Write down the mode and median of X.
(c) Find the c.d.f. of X.

6 The random variable X has p.d.f. given by:

$$f(x) = \begin{cases} \frac{3}{10}(3x - x^2) & 0 \leqslant x \leqslant 2 \\ 0 & \text{otherwise.} \end{cases}$$

(a) Sketch the p.d.f. of X. (b) Find the mode of X.
(c) Find the c.d.f. of X.
(d) Show that the median of X lies between 1.23 and 1.24.

7 The c.d.f. of a random variable X is given by:

$$F(x) = \begin{cases} 0 & x < 0 \\ 4x^3 - 3x^4 & 0 \leqslant x \leqslant 1 \\ 1 & x > 1. \end{cases}$$

(a) Find the p.d.f. of the random variable X.

(b) Find the mode of X.

(c) Find $P(0.2 < X < 0.5)$.

8 The c.d.f. of a random variable X is given by:

$$F(x) = \begin{cases} 0 & x < 1 \\ \frac{1}{8}(x^2 - 1) & 1 \leqslant x \leqslant 3 \\ 1 & x > 3. \end{cases}$$

(a) Find the p.d.f. of the random variable X.

(b) Find the mode of X.

(c) Find the median of X.

(d) Find the quartiles of X.

9 Some of the following are possible c.d.f.s and some are not. If the function is a valid c.d.f. find the p.d.f. and if not explain why?

(a) $F(x) = \begin{cases} 0 & x < 0 \\ 3x - 2x^2 & 0 \leqslant x \leqslant 1 \\ 1 & x > 1 \end{cases}$

(b) $F(x) = \begin{cases} 0 & x < 0 \\ \frac{1}{2}(7x - 3x^2) & 0 \leqslant x \leqslant 2 \\ 1 & x > 2 \end{cases}$

(c) $F(x) = \begin{cases} 0 & x < 0 \\ \frac{1}{2}(5x^3 - 3x^5) & 0 \leqslant x \leqslant 1 \\ 1 & x > 1 \end{cases}$

(d) $F(x) = \begin{cases} 0 & x < 2 \\ \frac{1}{8}(6x - x^2) & 2 \leqslant x \leqslant 4 \\ 1 & x > 4 \end{cases}$

10 The mode of a continuous random variable X is 1 and this is a stationary point. Given that X takes values over the range $[0,3]$ find possible expressions for:

(a) the c.d.f. of X (b) the p.d.f. of X.

11 The amount of vegetables eaten by a family in a week is a random variable W kg. The probability density function is given by:

$$f(w) = \begin{cases} \frac{20}{5^5} w^3(5-w) & 0 \leqslant w \leqslant 5 \\ 0 & \text{otherwise.} \end{cases}$$

(a) Find the cumulative distribution function of W.

(b) Find, to 3 decimal places, the probability that the family eats between 2 kg and 4 kg of vegetables in one week.

(c) Verify that the amount, m, of vegetables such that the family is equally likely to eat more or less than m in any week is about 3.431 kg.　　　　　　　　　　　　　　　[L]

12 A continuous random variable X has probability density function, f, defined by

$$f(x) = \tfrac{1}{4} \qquad 0 \leqslant x < 1$$
$$f(x) = \tfrac{x^3}{5} \qquad 1 \leqslant x \leqslant 2$$
$$f(x) = 0 \qquad \text{otherwise.}$$

Obtain the distribution function and hence, or otherwise, find, to 3 decimal places, the median and the interquartile range of the distribution.　　　　　　　　　　　　　　　[L]

SUMMARY OF KEY POINTS

Discrete random variable X

$$\sum_{\forall x} P(X = x) = 1$$

$$\mu = E(X) = \sum_{\forall x} x P(X = x)$$

$$\sigma^2 = E(X^2) - \mu^2 = \sum_{\forall x} x^2 P(X = x) - \mu^2$$

Continuous random variable X

$$\int_{-\infty}^{\infty} f(x)\, dx = 1$$

$$\mu = E(X) = \int_{-\infty}^{\infty} x f(x)\, dx$$

$$\sigma^2 = E(X^2) - \mu^2 = \int_{-\infty}^{\infty} x^2 f(x)\, dx - \mu^2$$

Properties of expected values and variance

$$E(aX + b) = aE(X) + b$$
$$\text{Var}(aX + b) = a^2\text{Var}(X)$$

$$E(aX \pm bY) = aE(X) \pm bE(Y)$$
$$\text{Var}(aX \pm bY) = a^2\text{Var}(X) + b^2\text{Var}(Y)$$

(if X and Y are independent)

Cumulative distribution function F(x)

$$0 \leqslant F(x) \leqslant 1$$

For the *discrete* random variable X is:

$$F(x_0) = P(X \leqslant x_0) = \sum_{x \leqslant x_0} p(x)$$

For the *continuous* random variable X is:

$$F(x_0) = P(X \leqslant x_0) = \int_{-\infty}^{x_0} f(x)\,dx$$

$$\frac{d}{dx}F(x) = f(x)$$

median m satisfies $F(m) = 0.5$

Discrete distributions

In this chapter you will meet three important discrete distributions and look at practical situations where they can be used as suitable models to describe real-world situations.

7.1 Discrete uniform distribution

In chapter 6 you considered the probability distribution for the score S on a single roll of a fair die, namely:

s:	1	2	3	4	5	6
$P(S = s)$:	$\frac{1}{6}$	$\frac{1}{6}$	$\frac{1}{6}$	$\frac{1}{6}$	$\frac{1}{6}$	$\frac{1}{6}$

This is an example of a **discrete uniform distribution** over the set $\{1, 2, 3, 4, 5, 6\}$.

This distribution is easily generalised so that if the discrete random variable X is defined over the set of distinct values $\{x_1, x_2, x_3, \ldots x_n\}$, and each value is equally likely, then X has a discrete uniform distribution and

$$P(X = x_r) = \frac{1}{n} \qquad r = 1, 2, 3 \ldots n$$

Conditions for a discrete uniform distribution:

- The discrete random variable X is defined over a set of n distinct values.
- Each value is equally likely.
- $X =$ the value of the next outcome.

This distribution, despite its simplicity, arises in a number of instances but care should be taken to ensure that the above conditions are applicable. For example, a table of random digits is designed so that each digit is equally likely. So, if the random variable R represents the value of the next digit in the table, then R will have a discrete uniform distribution over the set $\{0, 1, 2, 3, \ldots 9\}$ and R should be a good model for such a table.

Consider the following example. A bag contains five coins one 50p, one 10p, one 20p, one 2p and one 5p. You place your hand in the bag and pick out the first coin you feel. The random variable V represents the value of that coin. You could try and model V as a discrete uniform distribution over the set $\{2, 5, 10, 20, 50\}$. Is this a suitable model, as a 50p coin is much larger than a 5p one? It is not clear that the probability of selecting the 50p coin is the same as that for the 5p coin. You could use the discrete uniform distribution as a preliminary model, collect some experimental data and test how well this data fits the model. If the model does not provide a particularly good fit then the model can be refined, perhaps by making the probability proportional to the surface area of the coins.

In general, the mean and variance of the discrete uniform random variable X which is defined over the set $\{1, 2, 3, \ldots n\}$ can be found using the results:

$$\sum_{r=1}^{n} r = \frac{n(n+1)}{2} \quad \text{and} \quad \sum_{r=1}^{n} r^2 = \frac{n}{6}(n+1)(2n+1)$$

as follows:

$$E(X) = \sum_{r=1}^{n} r P(X = r)$$

$$= \sum_{r=1}^{n} r \times \frac{1}{n}$$

$$= \frac{1}{n} \sum_{r=1}^{n} r \qquad \text{since } n \text{ does not depend on } r$$

$$= \frac{1}{n} \times \frac{n(n+1)}{2}$$

i.e. $\qquad \mu = E(X) = \frac{n+1}{2}$

This result is, of course, obvious by the symmetry of the distribution.

$$\mathrm{Var}(X) = \sum_{r=1}^{n} r^2 \mathrm{P}(X = r) - \mu^2$$

$$= \frac{1}{n} \sum_{r=1}^{n} r^2 - \frac{(n+1)^2}{4}$$

$$= \frac{1}{n} \times \frac{n}{6}(n+1)(2n+1) - \frac{(n+1)^2}{4}$$

$$= \frac{(n+1)}{12}[2(2n+1) - 3(n+1)]$$

i.e. $\qquad \sigma^2 = \mathrm{Var}(X) = \dfrac{(n+1)(n-1)}{12}$

Example 1

Digits are selected at random from a table of random digits.

(a) Write down the mean and standard deviation of the value of a single digit.

(b) Find the probability that a particular digit lies within one standard deviation of the mean.

Let R represent a random variable having a discrete uniform distribution over the set $\{0, 1, 2, \ldots 9\}$. This should model the value of a random digit.

Let X represent a random variable having a discrete uniform distribution over the set $\{1, 2, 3, \ldots 10\}$. Since the probability functions for X and R are both equal to $\frac{1}{10}$ there is a simple relationship between X and R, namely $X = R + 1$. You can use the general formulae derived above for X with $n = 10$.

(a) $\therefore$ $\mathrm{E}(R) = \mathrm{E}(X - 1)$

$\qquad\qquad = \mathrm{E}(X) - 1$

$\qquad\qquad = \dfrac{10 + 1}{2} - 1$

$\qquad\qquad = 4.5$

and

$$\begin{aligned} \text{Var}(R) &= \text{Var}(X - 1) \\ &= \text{Var}(X) \\ &= \frac{11 \times 9}{12} \\ &= \frac{33}{4} \\ &= 8.25 \end{aligned}$$

So the standard deviation is:

$$\begin{aligned} \sigma &= \sqrt{8.25} \\ &= 2.87 \ (3 \ \text{s.f.}) \end{aligned}$$

(b) Using the value of σ in (a), the required probability is:

$$\begin{aligned} \text{P}(1.62\ldots < R < 7.37\ldots) &= \text{P}(2 \leqslant R \leqslant 7) \\ &= \frac{6}{10} \end{aligned}$$

Exercise 7A

1 A fair die is thrown once and the random variable X represents the value on the uppermost face.
   (a) Find the mean and variance of X.
   (b) Calculate the probability that X is within one standard deviation of the mean.

2 Repeat question 1 for an icosohedral die (20 faces) with the numbers 1 to 20 on the faces.

3 A card is selected at random from a pack of 10 cards containing the even numbers 2, 4, 6,... 20 and the random variable X represents the number on the card.
   (a) Find $\text{P}(X \geqslant 15)$.
   (b) Find the mean and variance of X.

4 Repeat question 3 for the odd numbers 1, 3, 5,... 19.

5 A straight line is drawn on a piece of paper. The line is divided into quarters and the segments are numbered 1, 2, 3 and 4. In a certain party game a person is blind folded and asked to mark a point on the line and the number of the segment in which their point lies is recorded. A discrete uniform distribution over the set {1, 2, 3, 4} is suggested as a model for this distribution. Comment on this suggestion.

6 A dart board consists of a circle divided into 20 equal-sized sectors marked with the numbers 1, 2,... 20. A dart is thrown to land in the sector marked 20. If the dart misses the board it is thrown again. A discrete uniform distribution over the set $\{1, 2, \ldots 20\}$ is suggested as a model to describe the number of the sector in which the dart lands. Comment on this suggestion.

7 In a T.V. game a contestant is asked to choose one of five plain brown envelopes. One envelope contains a blank piece of paper, one a £5 note, one a £10 note, one a £20 note and the last one contains a £50 note. Discuss whether a discrete uniform distribution could be used to model this situation.

8 Given that X is the number showing when a fair die is thrown, name the distribution of X, and write down its probability function.
Determine the values of $E(X)$ and $Var(X)$.   [L]

7.2 The binomial theorem

Before the next distribution is introduced a small detour into pure mathematics is required to consider the expansion of expressions of the form $(p+q)^n$.

The expansion:

$$(p+q)^2 = p^2 + 2pq + q^2$$

should be familiar to you and you should be able to multiply this by $(p+q)$ to obtain:

$$(p+q)^3 = p^3 + 3p^2q + 3pq^2 + q^3$$

Clearly to keep multiplying in this way is very laborious and a better way of obtaining these **binomial expansions** is needed.

Consider the expansion:

$$(p+q)^3 = (p+q)(p+q)(p+q) = p^3 + 3p^2q + 3pq^2 + q^3$$
$$\quad\quad\quad\quad\ A \quad\ \ B \quad\ \ C$$

Notice that each term of the expansion on the right is "cubic". This is because to work out $(p+q)^3$ you need to pick a term from bracket A, a term from bracket B and a term from bracket C so that eventually all possible arrangements are considered. [You might like to think how many arrangements there are? Remember two terms, p and q, to the power 3 gives 8 arrangements.] Your final expansion should consist of all *types* of cubic terms. These can be simply and systematically written down by starting with p^3q^0 and then reducing the power of p and raising the power of q until p^0q^3 is reached. Remembering that this expansion generates *all possible arrangements* the final step is to find the coefficients of each term. For example, the p^2q term could arise as these arrangements – pqp or qpp or ppq – that is in three ways. As on page 118, this calculation could be written as:

$$\frac{3!}{2!\,1!} = 3$$

In the same way, you should now be able to write down any binomial expansion, for example, consider $(p+q)^5$.

The first stage is to write down the terms:

$$p^5 \quad p^4q \quad p^3q^2 \quad p^2q^3 \quad pq^4 \quad q^5$$

Now the term p^4q could arise in:

$$\frac{5!}{4!\,1!} = 5 \text{ ways} \qquad \text{(as could } pq^4\text{)}$$

and the term p^3q^2 could arise in:

$$\frac{5!}{3!\,2!} = 10 \text{ ways} \qquad \text{(as could } p^2q^3\text{)}$$

So:

$$(p+q)^5 = p^5 + 5p^4q + 10p^3q^2 + 10p^2q^3 + 5pq^4 + q^5$$

Notice that $1+5+10+10+5+1 = 32 = 2^5$ so all possible arrangements of p and q are included.

A general term for this expansion can be written as:

$$\frac{5!}{r!(5-r)!}p^r q^{(5-r)} \qquad r = 0, 1, \ldots 5.$$

Notice that the coefficient is simply the number of combinations of r objects from 5, which in chapter 5 was written as $\binom{5}{r}$.

Example 2
Find the term in the expansion of $(p+q)^{12}$ with p^7.

The required term will be of the form Kp^7q^5.
The coefficient will be:

$$\frac{12!}{7!\,5!} = 792$$

So the term is $792p^7q^5$.

Exercise 7B

1 Find the binomial expansion of $(p+q)^4$.
2 Find the binomial expansion of $(p+q)^6$.
3 In the expansion of $(p+q)^{10}$ find the terms in (a) p^3, (b) p^6, (c) p^8.
4 In the expansion of $(p+q)^{12}$ find the terms in (a) p^4, (b) p^8, (c) p^{10}.
5 Part of the expansion of $(p+q)^{15}$ is:
$$\ldots Ap^{13}q^x + Bp^{12}q^y + Cp^{11}q^z \ldots$$
   Find the values of A, B, C, x, y and z.
6 Part of the expansion of $(p+q)^{13}$ is:
$$\ldots Ap^xq^{10} + Bp^yq^9 + Cp^zq^8 \ldots$$
   Find the values of A, B, C, x, y and z.
7 Find the coefficient of the term p^7q^{13} in the expansion of $(p+q)^{20}$.
8 The term $Ap^{15}q^x$ arises in the expansion of $(p+q)^{20}$. Find the values of A and x.
9 Find the values of the following terms in the expansion of $(\frac{1}{3}+\frac{2}{3})^{10}$:
   (a) $\binom{10}{7}(\frac{1}{3})^7(\frac{2}{3})^3$ (b) $\binom{10}{5}(\frac{1}{3})^5(\frac{2}{3})^5$ (c) $\binom{10}{6}(\frac{1}{3})^6(\frac{2}{3})^4$.
10 Find the values of A, B, C, x, y and z and evaluate the following terms in the expansion of $(\frac{1}{4}+\frac{3}{4})^8$:
   (a) $A(\frac{1}{4})^5(\frac{3}{4})^x$ (b) $B(\frac{1}{4})^3(\frac{3}{4})^y$ (c) $C(\frac{1}{4})^z(\frac{3}{4})^2$.

7.3 Binomial distribution

A fair cubical die is rolled four times and the random variable X represents the number of sixes obtained. What can be said about the probability distribution of X?

Notice that there are four **trials** and each trial consists of rolling the die once. Each trial has only *two* **outcomes**: if a six is obtained then the outcome is a **success** whereas *any other* outcome is a **failure**. It is also reasonable to assume that the *trials are* **independent** since the outcome of the first trial does not affect the second or subsequent trials. Since the same die is used in each trial it is reasonable to assume that the **probability of a six** (i.e. success) **at each trial is constant** and as the die is fair the probability is equal to $\frac{1}{6}$.

If a success is represented by s and a failure by f, then the sequence *ssss* occurs with probability

$$\tfrac{1}{6} \times \tfrac{1}{6} \times \tfrac{1}{6} \times \tfrac{1}{6}$$

or

$$P(X = 4) = \left(\tfrac{1}{6}\right)^4$$

and the sequence *ffff* occurs with probability

$$\tfrac{5}{6} \times \tfrac{5}{6} \times \tfrac{5}{6} \times \tfrac{5}{6}$$

or

$$P(X = 0) = \left(\tfrac{5}{6}\right)^4$$

Notice that because the trials are independent you can multiply to find the probability of success on the 1st trial *and* 2nd trial *and* 3rd trial *and* 4th trial.

Consider now the situation where there are two successes and two failures. The sequence *ssff* occurs with probability

$$\tfrac{1}{6} \times \tfrac{1}{6} \times \tfrac{5}{6} \times \tfrac{5}{6}$$

but the event $\{X = 2\}$ includes all possible sequences of two s and two f. The number of possible arrangements in situations like this is given by:

$$\frac{4!}{2!\,2!} \qquad \text{or} \qquad \binom{4}{2} = 6$$

So:

$$P(X = 2) = 6 \times \left(\tfrac{1}{6}\right)^2 \times \left(\tfrac{5}{6}\right)^2$$

In a similar way you can see that:

$$P(X = 1) = \binom{4}{1} \tfrac{1}{6} \times \tfrac{5}{6} \times \tfrac{5}{6} \times \tfrac{5}{6}$$

$$= 4 \times \tfrac{1}{6} \times \left(\tfrac{5}{6}\right)^3$$

and $$P(X = 3) = 4 \times \left(\tfrac{1}{6}\right)^3 \left(\tfrac{5}{6}\right)$$

So the distribution of X is:

x:	4	3	2	1	0
$P(X = x)$:	$\left(\tfrac{1}{6}\right)^4$	$4\left(\tfrac{1}{6}\right)^3\left(\tfrac{5}{6}\right)$	$6\left(\tfrac{1}{6}\right)^2\left(\tfrac{5}{6}\right)^2$	$4\left(\tfrac{1}{6}\right)\left(\tfrac{5}{6}\right)^3$	$\left(\tfrac{5}{6}\right)^4$

Since X is a probability distribution then:

$$\sum_{x=0}^{4} p(x) = 1$$

and this could be verified but if you look at the binomial expansion of $(p+q)^4$ (see question 1 in exercise 7B):

$$(p+q)^4 = p^4 + 4p^3q + 6p^2q^2 + 4pq^3 + q^4$$

you can see that the probabilities in the distribution of X are simply terms in a binomial expansion with $p = \frac{1}{6}$ and $q = \frac{5}{6}$. It is then easy to see that:

$$(\tfrac{1}{6} + \tfrac{5}{6})^4 = 1^4 = 1$$

It is *this* relationship between the *probabilities* and the *binomial expansion* that gives rise to the term **binomial distribution** to describe this important discrete distribution.

It is important that you know the conditions under which a binomial distribution may provide a good model. These are summarised as follows:

Conditions for a binomial distribution:
■ There must be a **fixed number** (n) of trials.
■ The trials must be **independent**.
■ The trials have only **two outcomes**: success or failure.
■ The **probability of success** (p) is **constant** for each trial.

If these conditions are satisfied then the random variable X representing the number of successes in the n trials has a **binomial distribution** and the **probability function** is:

$$P(X = r) = \binom{n}{r} p^r (1-p)^{n-r} \qquad r = 0, 1, 2, \ldots n$$

The binomial distribution is a very important discrete probability distribution and there are many areas where it can be applied. In order to use it in a particular situation you need to ensure that the above conditions are satisfied and find values for n and p. The binomial distribution is actually a whole family of distributions each member being determined by the particular values of n and p. Notice that n and p are sometimes referred to as the **parameters** of the binomial distribution. If the random variable X has a binomial distribution with parameters n and p this can be written as $X \sim B(n, p)$.

Example 3

Only 75% of sunflower seeds from a particular supplier produce flowers when planted. If 10 of the seeds are planted find the probability of obtaining 8 or more flowers.

Let the random variable X represent the number of seeds that produce a flower. Then model X with a binomial distribution so that $X \sim B(10, 0.75)$

$$P(X \geqslant 8) = \binom{10}{8}(0.75)^8(0.25)^2 + \binom{10}{9}(0.75)^9(0.25) + \binom{10}{10}(0.75)^{10}$$

$$= 45(0.75)^8(0.25)^2 + 10(0.75)^9(0.25) + (0.75)^{10}$$

$$= 0.28156\ldots + 0.1877\ldots + 0.05631\ldots$$

$$= 0.52559\ldots$$

$$= 0.5256 \text{ (4 d.p.)}$$

There are cumulative probability tables for the binomial distribution and these can sometimes be used to find approximate (4 d.p.) answers to problems. The tables are given for $X \sim B(n, p)$ for certain n and p and give the cumulative probabilities $P(X \leqslant r)$ for most values of r. So if $X \sim B(10, 0.3)$ then from tables $P(X \leqslant 6) = 0.9894$ or if $X \sim B(5, 0.15)$ then $P(X \leqslant 3) = 0.9978$. You could also use the tables to answer example 3 above. Define the random variable Y as the number of seeds that do *not* produce flowers then $Y \sim B(10, 0.25)$ and the problem is equivalent to finding $P(Y \leqslant 2)$. From tables this value is 0.5256 which agrees with the calculations above to 4 decimal places.

Although the tables give cumulative probabilities they can be used to find individual probabilities as well. Suppose $X \sim B(20, 0.35)$ and you wish to find $P(X = 9)$. This can be achieved as follows:

$$P(X = 9) = P(X \leqslant 9) - P(X \leqslant 8)$$

$$= 0.8782 - 0.7624$$

$$= 0.1158$$

Of course individual probabilities can be calculated quite easily from the probability function so in this case:

$$P(X = 9) = \binom{20}{9}(0.35)^9(0.65)^{11}$$

$$= 0.11584\ldots$$

$$= 0.1158 \text{ (4 d.p.)}$$

but sometimes the tables are more convenient and save time.

As previously mentioned, a binomial distribution can be used to model a wide variety of situations. The random variable needs to be carefully defined to ensure that the conditions for a binomial apply. Consider using the binomial distribution to model the behaviour of woodlice. An apparatus is set up in the shape of a letter "T", as shown in the diagram:

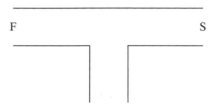

A substance that is attractive to woodlice is placed at one end of the apparatus near exit S. A woodlouse is released into the apparatus and the exit (F or S) from which it emerges is noted. If 20 different woodlice are used one at a time then the behaviour of the woodlice can be regarded as independent. It may be necessary to take some precautions in case, for example, the woodlice leave a trail behind them which a later woodlouse could follow.

If you assume that the woodlouse exits only via one of the two marked routes then S and F will provide you with your success and failure: a success will be when the woodlouse appears at exit S and a failure will be when it appears at F. What is the probability (p) of the woodlouse going towards the attracting substance? Does this depend upon the sex, species or size of the woodlouse? Is it a constant?

If the substance really is an attractor then p will be greater than $\frac{1}{2}$ but if the reactions of the woodlice to it are fairly neutral then you might expect the value of p to be close to $\frac{1}{2}$. Some big assumptions about the value of p will have to be made before a binomial distribution can be used but a value of $p = 0.5$ is probably a good starting point for a preliminary model.

If you define the random variable W to be the number of woodlice which leave at exit S then B(20, 0.5) might provide a reasonable model for W. If it turns out that this model provides a reasonable fit then this would have important implications about the attractiveness of the substance to the woodlice.

Example 4
Explain whether or not a binomial distribution can be used to model the following situations. In cases where it can be used, give a definition of the random variable and suggest suitable values for the parameters n and p.

(a) The number of throws of a die until a six is obtained.
(b) The number of girls in a family of 4 children.
(c) The number of red balls drawn when 3 balls are drawn from an urn which contains 15 white and 5 red balls.

(a) A binomial distribution requires a fixed number of trials, n. The number of times the die is thrown can not be fixed in this experiment and so a binomial distribution is of no use.

(b) There is a fixed number of children in the family, so $n = 4$ and the "trials" are "children". The trials can probably be assumed to be independent as if the first child is a girl, the gender of the other children should not be affected by this (identical twins could cause a problem though). There are only two possibilities for the outcomes of the trials and these can be defined in this example as success (a girl) and failure (a boy). It is probably reasonable to assume that p, the probability of a girl, is constant but what should that value be? An obvious solution is to use $p = 0.5$ but you could refer to national statistics which will give you the current proportion of girls which is just below 50%. So the random variable $G =$ the number of girls in a family of 4 children where $G \sim B(4, 0.5)$ should provide a suitable model in this case.

(c) Let the random variable R represent the number of red balls picked. The number of trials is fixed as 3 balls are to be picked, so $n = 3$. Also, each trial is either a success (red) or a failure (white) but the method of selecting the balls is all important here. If the balls are selected *without replacement* then the probability of a red ball is not constant. If the balls are selected *with replacement* then the probability of selecting a red ball is $\frac{1}{4}$, the trials are independent and $R \sim B(3, \frac{1}{4})$.

Exercise 7C

1 The random variable $X \sim B(8, \frac{1}{3})$, find:
   (a) $P(X = 2)$ (b) $P(X \leqslant 2)$ (c) $P(X \geqslant 2)$

2 The random variable $Y \sim B(6, \frac{1}{4})$, find:
   (a) $P(Y = 3)$ (b) $P(Y < 3)$ (c) $P(Y > 3)$

3 The random variable $T \sim B(12, 0.6)$, find:
   (a) $P(T = 6)$ (b) $P(T = 9)$ (c) $P(6 \leqslant T \leqslant 9)$

4 The random variable $U \sim B(16, 0.2)$, find:
   (a) $P(U = 4)$ (b) $P(U < 4)$ (c) $P(U > 4)$.

5 The random variable $W \sim$ B(10, 0.35), find:

(a) $P(W \leqslant 6)$ (b) $P(W \geqslant 5)$ (c) $P(W = 6)$

(d) $P(4 \leqslant W \leqslant 7)$

6 A fair cubical die is rolled 5 times and the number of sixes is counted. Find the probability of:

(a) no sixes   (b) at least one six   (c) no more than 4 sixes.

7 Four fair coins are tossed and the total number of heads showing is counted. Find the probability of:

(a) only one head   (b) at least one head

(c) the number of heads equalling the number of tails.

8 A balloon manufacturer claims that 95% of his balloons will not burst when blown up. If you have 20 of these balloons to blow up for a birthday party:

(a) what is the probability that none of them burst when blown up?

(b) Find the probability that exactly two balloons burst. There are 17 children coming to the party but you decide to blow up all 20 balloons as some spares might be helpful.

(c) What is the probability that there are enough balloons?

9 A student suggests using a binomial distribution to model the following situations. State any assumptions that must be made and give possible values for the parameters n and p.

(a) A sample of 20 bolts are checked for defects from each large batch produced. The process should produce about 1% of defects.

(b) Some traffic lights have three phases: stop 48% of the time, wait or get ready 4% of the time and go 48% of the time. Assuming that you only cross a traffic light when it is in the go position, model the number of times that you have to wait or stop on your way to school given that there are 6 sets of traffic lights.

(c) When Stephanie plays tennis with Timothy on average one in every 8 of her serves is an "ace". How many "aces" does Stephanie serve in the next 30 serves against Timothy?

10 State which of the following can be modelled with a binomial distribution and which can not. Reasons should be given.

(a) Given that 15% of people have blood that is Rhesus negative (Rh$^-$) model the number of pupils in a statistics class of 14 who are Rh$^-$.

(b) You are given a fair coin and told to keep tossing it until you obtain 4 heads in succession. Model the number of tosses you need.

(c) A certain car manufacturer produces 12% of new cars in the colour red, 8% blue, 15% white and the rest in other colours. You make a note of the colour of the first 15 new cars of this make. Model the number of red cars you observed.

11 A coin is biased so that a head is twice as likely to occur as is a tail. The coin is tossed repeatedly. Find the probability that:

(a) the first tail will occur on the fifth toss

(b) in the first seven tosses there will be exactly 2 tails.   [L]

12 Team A has probability $\frac{2}{3}$ of winning whenever it plays. Given that A plays 4 games, find the probability that A wins more than half of the games.   [L]

13 State the conditions under which the binomial distribution may be used. Illustrate your answer by referring to a specific example.

Records kept in a hospital show that 3 out of every 10 casualties who come to the casualty department have to wait more than half an hour before receiving medical attention. Find, to 3 decimal places, the probability that of the first 8 casualties who come to that casualty department: (a) none, (b) more than two will have to wait more than half an hour before receiving medical attention. Find also the most probable number of the 8 casualties that will have to wait more than half an hour.   [L]

14 A factory is considering two methods, I and II, of checking the quality of production of the batches of items it produces. Method I consists of taking a random sample of 10 items from a large batch and accepting the batch if there are no defectives and rejecting the batch if there are two or more defectives. If there is one defective in the sample, another random sample of 10 items is taken from the batch. The

batch is accepted if there are no defectives in this second sample and rejected otherwise.

Method II consists of taking a random sample of 20 items from a batch and accepting the batch if there is at most one defective in the sample. Otherwise the batch is rejected.

The factory knows that 1% of the items it produces are defective and wishes to use that method of checking the quality of production for which the probability of accepting a batch is the larger.

Decide whether the factory should use Method I or Method II. [L]

7.4 Mean and variance of a binomial distribution

Consider the random variable $X \sim B(n,p)$ and the random variables $Y_i(i = 1, 2, \ldots n)$ which represent the number of successes on the ith trial. The distribution of each of the Y_i will be the same, namely:

y:	0	1
$p(y)$:	$1-p$	p

It is easy to calculate:

$$E(Y_i) = 0 + 1 \times p = p$$

and

$$Var(Y_i) = 1^2 \times p - p^2 = p(1-p)$$

Now X is the total number of successes in the n trials and so:

$$X = Y_1 + Y_2 + \ldots + Y_n$$

In chapter 6 (page 148) you met some important properties of expected values and variances which you can apply here to obtain:

$$\begin{aligned}
E(X) &= E(Y_1) + E(Y_2) + \ldots + E(Y_n) \\
&= p + p + \ldots + p \\
&= np
\end{aligned}$$

$$\begin{aligned}
Var(X) &= Var(Y_1) + Var(Y_2) + \ldots + Var(Y_n) \quad (Y_i \text{ independent}) \\
&= p(1-p) + p(1-p) + \ldots + p(1-p) \\
&= np(1-p)
\end{aligned}$$

■ If $X \sim B(n, p)$ then:
$$\mu = E(X) = np$$
$$\sigma^2 = \text{Var}(X) = np(1 - p)$$

These results will be particularly useful in later work.

Example 5

A fair cubical die is thrown 36 times and the random variable X represents the number of sixes obtained.

(a) Find the mean and variance of X.
(b) Find $P(X < \mu - \sigma)$.

(a) The random variable $X \sim B(36, \frac{1}{6})$
$\therefore$
$$\mu = E(X)$$
$$= 36 \times \frac{1}{6}$$
$$= 6$$
$$\sigma^2 = \text{Var}(X)$$
$$= 36 \times \frac{1}{6} \times \frac{5}{6}$$
$$= 5$$

(b)

$$\begin{aligned}
P(X < \mu - \sigma) &= P(X < 6 - \sqrt{5}) \\
&= P(X < 3.763\ldots) \\
&= P(X \leqslant 3) \\
&= (\tfrac{5}{6})^{36} + 36(\tfrac{5}{6})^{35}\tfrac{1}{6} + 630(\tfrac{5}{6})^{34}(\tfrac{1}{6})^2 + 7140(\tfrac{5}{6})^{33}(\tfrac{1}{6})^3 \\
&= 0.0014\ldots + 0.0101\ldots + 0.0355\ldots + 0.0805\ldots \\
&= 0.128 \text{ (3 d.p.)}
\end{aligned}$$

Exercise 7D

1 (a) Find the mean and variance of the random variable $X \sim B(12, 0.25)$.
   (b) Find $P(\mu - \sigma < X < \mu + \sigma)$.
2 (a) Find the mean and variance of the random variable $Y \sim B(9, \frac{1}{3})$.
   (b) Find $P(\mu - \sigma < Y \leqslant \mu)$.
3 It is estimated that 1 in 20 people are left-handed.
   (a) What size sample should be taken to ensure that the expected number of left-handed people in the sample is 3?

(b) What is the standard deviation of the number of left-handed people in this case?

4 An experiment is conducted with a fair die to examine the number of sixes that occur. It is required to have the standard deviation smaller than 1. What is the largest number of throws that can be made?

5 The random variable X is distributed B(n, p). For a fixed value of n find the value of p which maximises the variance of X.

6 State clearly conditions under which it is appropriate to assume that a random variable has a binomial distribution.
A door-to-door canvasser tries to persuade people to have a certain type of double-glazing installed. The probability that his canvassing at a house is successful is 0.05. Use tables of cumulative binomial probabilities, or otherwise, to find, to 4 decimal places, the probability that he will have at least 2 successes out of the first 10 houses he canvasses.
Find the number of houses he should canvass per day in order to average 3 successes per day.
Calculate the least number of houses that he must canvass in order that the probability of his getting at least one success exceeds 0.99.
[L]

7.5 Poisson distribution

The exponential function e^x can be defined in a number of different ways and one, which is particularly helpful in statistics, is as a series expansion:

$$e^x = 1 + \frac{x}{1!} + \frac{x^2}{2!} + \frac{x^3}{3!} + \ldots + \frac{x^r}{r!} + \ldots$$

The series is infinite but most calculators have the facility to evaluate the exponential function to a reasonable degree of accuracy. So, for example, a calculator might give:

$$e^{0.5} = 1.648721271 \quad \text{and} \quad e^{-2} = 0.1353352832$$

See what your calculator shows for various value of x.

The definition above of e^x can be used to generate a probability distribution with parameter λ. Consider the series expansion for e^λ and remember that $\lambda^0 = 1$:

$$e^\lambda = \lambda^0 + \frac{\lambda^1}{1!} + \frac{\lambda^2}{2!} + \frac{\lambda^3}{3!} + \ldots + \frac{\lambda^r}{r!} + \ldots$$

Dividing both sides by e^λ gives:

$$1 = e^{-\lambda}\lambda^0 + \frac{e^{-\lambda}\lambda^1}{1!} + \frac{e^{-\lambda}\lambda^2}{2!} + \frac{e^{-\lambda}\lambda^3}{3!} + \ldots + \frac{e^{-\lambda}\lambda^r}{r!} + \ldots$$

Notice that the sum of the terms on the right-hand side equals 1 so you could use these values as probabilities to define a probability distribution. Let X be the random variable, then X will take values in the set $\{0, 1, 2, 3, \ldots\}$ so the probability distribution is:

x:	0	1	2	3	$\ldots$	r	$\ldots$
$p(X = x)$:	$e^{-\lambda}$	$\dfrac{e^{-\lambda}\lambda}{1!}$	$\dfrac{e^{-\lambda}\lambda^2}{2!}$	$\dfrac{e^{-\lambda}\lambda^3}{3!}$	$\ldots$	$\dfrac{e^{-\lambda}\lambda^r}{r!}$	$\ldots$

and the probability function is:

$$P(X = r) = \frac{e^{-\lambda}\lambda^r}{r!} \qquad \text{where } r = 0, 1, 2, \ldots$$

Notice, once again, that this gives a *family* of distributions depending upon the value of the parameter λ. (The *binomial* distributions were dependent upon the two parameters n and p).

You now have a probability distribution but is it useful as a model in any particular situations and if so under what conditions? This is a particularly useful distribution known as the **Poisson distribution** and is named after the French mathematician Siméon Poisson. As with the binomial distribution there are certain conditions which must be satisfied if a Poisson distribution is to provide a suitable model in a particular situation. The Poisson distribution, as described above, can be *derived* from these conditions but that requires a level of mathematics beyond the scope of this course; however it is important that you have a feel for these conditions so that you can decide when a Poisson distribution might be an appropriate model.

Conditions for a Poisson Distribution:
X is the number of occurrences of a particular event in an interval of fixed length in space or time. The events occur:

- **independently** of each other
- **singly** in continuous space or time

■ at a **constant rate** in the sense that the mean number in an interval is proportional to the length of the interval.
[Such events are sometimes called *random* or *rare* events.]

For example, a Poisson distribution should provide a good model for the number of radioactive particles being emitted by a certain source during a 5 minute period or the number of red cars passing your school or college gates in a 10 minute period. In both of these cases it is reasonable to assume that the events (radioactive particles or red cars) occur independently and singly (ignore the possibility of a car carrier with several red cars on board!) and at a constant rate in the sense that it is reasonable to assume that the events occur at a certain rate per minute.

Before you can use a Poisson distribution as a model though you need to know more about the parameter λ. It can be shown, but again the level of mathematics is a little beyond this course, that if the random variable X has a Poisson distribution with parameter λ then the mean and variance of X are both equal to λ.

■ **Mean and variance of the Poisson distribution**
   If X has a Poisson distribution with parameter λ then:
$$\mu = \text{E}(X) = \lambda$$
$$\sigma^2 = \text{Var}(X) = \lambda$$

This important property of λ completes the definition of the Poisson distribution as a model to describe the occurrences of particular events that satisfy the above conditions.

■ **Poisson distribution**
   If X is the number of events that occur at random in a certain interval and λ is the *average* or *mean* number of events that occur in the interval then X has a Poisson distribution with parameter λ and probability function:

$$\text{P}(X = r) = \frac{e^{-\lambda}\lambda^r}{r!} \qquad r = 0, 1, 2, 3, \ldots$$

X has a Poisson distribution with parameter λ is written as:

$$X \sim \text{Po}(\lambda)$$

Example 6

The number of telephone calls received at an exchange during a weekday morning follows a Poisson distribution with a mean of 6 calls per five minute period. Find the probability that:

(a) there are no calls in the next five minutes
(b) 3 calls are received in the next five minutes

(c) fewer than 2 calls are received between 11:00 and 11:05
(d) more than 2 calls are received between 11:30 and 11:35.

$\lambda = 6$ (= the mean number of calls in a five minute interval).

X = the number of calls received in a five minute period.

$$\therefore \qquad\qquad X \sim \text{Po}(6)$$

(a) $\qquad P(X = 0) = e^{-6} = 0.0025$ (4 d.p.)

(b) $\qquad P(X = 3) = \dfrac{e^{-6} \times 6^3}{3!} = 0.0892$ (4 d.p.)

(c) $\qquad \begin{aligned} P(X < 2) &= P(X = 0) + P(X = 1) \\ &= e^{-6} + e^{-6} \times 6 \\ &= e^{-6}(1 + 6) \\ &= 0.0174 \text{ (4 d.p.)} \end{aligned}$

(d) $\qquad \begin{aligned} P(X > 2) &= 1 - P(X \leqslant 2) \\ &= 1 - [P(X = 0) + P(X = 1) + P(X = 2)] \\ &= 1 - e^{-6}(1 + 6 + 18) \\ &= 1 - 25 \times e^{-6} \\ &= 0.9380 \text{ (4 d.p.)} \end{aligned}$

As with the binomial distribution there are tables of cumulative Poisson probabilities and these are particularly useful for calculations like those in part (d) of the above example. The tables give $P(X \leqslant r)$ for values of r and particular values of λ, the mean of the distribution. So to complete part (d) of example 6, use $\lambda = 6$ and look up $P(X \leqslant 2)$ in the tables. This gives 0.0620 and subtracting this from 1 gives 0.9380, which matches the above working.

The tables are particularly useful if you need to work backwards. For example, if $X \sim \text{Po}(6.5)$ then to find the value of r so that $P(X \leqslant r) \geqslant 0.95$ is fairly straightforward from tables. From the tables:

$$P(X \leqslant 10) = 0.9332 \qquad \text{and} \qquad P(X \leqslant 11) = 0.9661$$

so that the value of r is 11. (Remember that the Poisson distribution is a *discrete* distribution taking whole numbers so the value of r must be an integer.)

Sometimes you may be given a rate of occurrence (for example, telephone calls arrive at a rate of 1.2 per minute) and have to calculate the value of λ appropriate to the interval you are using. Thus, for the above rate of 1.2 calls per minute you could calculate probabilities for the next four minute period by using $\lambda = 4 \times 1.2 = 4.8$.

Example 7

Some river water contains on average 500 bacteria per litre. A large bucket of the water is collected and after it has been well stirred a $1\,cm^3$ sample is examined.

(a) Find the probability of there being no bacteria in this sample.
(b) Find the probability of there being at least 4 bacteria in the sample.

Let λ be the average number of bacteria in $1\,cm^3$ of the water then:

$$\lambda = \tfrac{500}{1000} = 0.5$$

Let X be the number of bacteria in $1\,cm^3$ of the water.

Given that the water was well stirred before the sample was taken the bacteria should occur singly and independently so the Poisson distribution should provide a good model where $X \sim Po(0.5)$.

(a) $P(X = 0) = e^{-0.5} = 0.6065$ (4 d.p.)

(b) $P(X \geqslant 4) = 1 - P(X \leqslant 3)$
$\qquad\qquad\quad = 1 - 0.9982$ (from tables)
$\qquad\qquad\quad = 0.0018$ (4 d.p.)

Exercise 7E

1 If $X \sim Po(2.5)$, find:
   (a) $P(X = 1)$ (b) $P(X > 2)$ (c) $P(X \leqslant 5)$
   (d) $P(3 \leqslant X \leqslant 5)$

2 The random variable Y has a Poisson distribution with mean 4.5, find:
   (a) $P(Y = 2)$ (b) $P(Y \leqslant 1)$ (c) $P(Y > 4)$
   (d) $P(2 \leqslant Y \leqslant 6)$

3 The random variable $Y \sim Po(1.6)$, find:
   (a) $P(Y = 0)$ (b) $P(Y > 1)$ (c) $P(Y \leqslant 2)$
   (d) $P(1 < Y \leqslant 3)$

4 The random variable $Y \sim Po(0.8)$, find:
   (a) $P(Y \leq 1)$ (b) $P(Y > 2)$ (c) $P(1 < Y < 3)$
   (d) $P(2 < Y \leq 4)$

5 The random variable $X \sim Po(8.0)$, find the values of a, b, c and d so that:
   (a) $P(X \leq a) = 0.3134$ (b) $P(X \leq b) = 0.7166$
   (c) $P(X < c) = 0.0996$ (d) $P(X > d) = 0.8088$

6 The random variable $X \sim Po(3.5)$, find the values of a, b, c and d so that:
   (a) $P(X \leq a) = 0.8576$ (b) $P(X > b) = 0.6792$
   (c) $P(X \leq c) \geq 0.95$ (d) $P(X > d) \leq 0.005$

7 The random variable $X \sim Po(5.5)$, find the values of a, b, c and d so that:
   (a) $P(X \leq a) \geq 0.90$ (b) $P(X \leq b) \geq 0.95$
   (c) $P(X > c) \geq 0.90$ (d) $P(X > d) \leq 0.005$

8 The number of accidents which occur on a particular stretch of road on a given day is modelled by a Poisson distribution with mean 1.25. Find the probability that on this road on a particular day:
   (a) no accidents occur   (b) at least two accidents occur.

9 A technician is responsible for a large number of machines. Minor adjustments have to be made to the machines and these occur at random and at a constant average rate of 7 per hour. Find the probability that:
   (a) in a particular hour the technician makes four or fewer adjustments
   (b) during a half-hour break no adjustments will be required.

10 A textile firm produces rolls of cloth but slight defects sometimes occur. The average number of defects per square metre is 2.5. Use a Poisson distribution to calculate the probability that:
   (a) a $1.5\,m^2$ portion of cloth bought to make a skirt contains no defects
   (b) a $4\,m^2$ portion of the cloth contains fewer than 5 defects.
   (c) State briefly what assumptions have to be made before the Poisson distribution can be accepted as a suitable model in this situation.

11 State which of the following could possibly be modelled by a Poisson distribution and which can not. Give reasons for your answers.

(a) The number of misprints on this page in the first draft of this book.

(b) The number of pigs in a particular square metre of their field 1 hour after their feed was placed in a central trough.

(c) The number of pigs in a particular square metre of their field 1 minute after their feed was placed in a central trough.

(d) The amount of salt, in mg, contained in $1\,cm^3$ of water taken from a bucket immediately after a teaspoon of salt was added.

(e) The number of marathon runners passing the finishing post between 20 and 21 minutes after the winner of the race.

12 The number of accidents per week at a certain road intersection has a Poisson distribution with parameter 2.5. Find the probability that

(a) exactly 5 accidents will occur in a week

(b) more than 14 accidents will occur in 4 weeks.   [L]

13 A shop sells a particular make of radio at a rate of 4 per week on average. The number sold in a week has a Poisson distribution.

(a) Find the probability that the shop sells at least 2 in a week.

(b) Find the smallest number that can be in stock at the beginning of a week in order to have at least a 99% chance of being able to meet all demands during that week.   [L]

14 The number of accidents per week at a factory is a Poisson random variable with parameter 2.

(a) Find the probability that in any week chosen at random exactly 1 accident occurs.

(b) The factory is observed for 100 weeks. Determine the expected number of weeks in which 5 or more accidents occur.   [L]

15 State the conditions under which a Poisson distribution is a suitable model to use in statistical work.

In a particular district it has been found, over a long period, that the number, X, of cases of measles reported per month has a Poisson distribution with parameter 1.5. Find, to 3 decimal places, the probability that in this district:

(a) in any given month, exactly 2 cases of measles will be reported

(b) in a period of 6 months, fewer than 10 cases of measles will be reported. [L]

16 During working hours an office switchboard receives telephone calls at random at an average rate of one call every 40 seconds.

(a) Find, to 3 decimal places, the probability that during a given one-minute period:

    (i) no call is received

    (ii) at least two calls are received

(b) Find, to 3 decimal places, the probability that no call is received between 10.30 a.m. and 10.31 a.m. and that at least two calls are received between 10.31 a.m. and 10.32 a.m. [L]

17 State conditions under which the Poisson distribution is a suitable model to use in statistical work.

The number of typing errors per 1000 words made by a typist has a Poisson distribution with mean 2.5.

(a) Find, to 3 decimal places, the probability that in an essay of 4000 words there will be at least 12 typing errors.

The typist types 3 essays, each of length 4000 words.

(b) Find the probability that each contains at least 12 typing errors. [L]

18 During office hours, telephone calls to a single telephone in an office come in at an average rate of 20 calls per hour. Assuming that a Poisson distribution is relevant, write down the probability function of X, the number of telephone calls arriving in each 5 minute period.

Find, to 3 decimal places, the probability that there will be

(a) fewer than 2 calls

(b) more than 3 calls in a 5 minute period. [L]

7.6 Poisson approximation to binomial

A garden centre claims that only 5% of its daffodil bulbs will not produce flowers next season. You buy 100 of these bulbs and the random variable X represents the number of bulbs that do not flower, a suitable model for X is B(100, 0.05). Evaluating these probabilities can be rather awkward without the aid of a calculator and sometimes it is helpful to use the fact that the Poisson distribution provides an approximation to the binomial. In this example the average number of bulbs that do not flower is 5 (using np) and the events (a bulb not flowering) occur singly, independently and at a rate of 5 per season, so the conditions for a Poisson distribution are satisfied apart from the obvious fact that the sample space is different. A Poisson random variable takes values over the set $\{0, 1, 2, \dots\}$ whereas our random variable X is defined over the set $\{0, 1, 2, \dots, 100\}$. Because the value of n is large and the probabilities for large values of X are very small the Poisson distribution with mean 5 should provide a reasonable approximation to B(100, 0.05). The table below shows that there is a reasonable match particularly to 2 d.p.

$P(X = r)$	$X \sim$B(100, 0.05)	$X \sim$Po(5)
$r = 0$	0.0059	0.0067
$r = 1$	0.0312	0.0337
$r = 2$	0.0812	0.0842
$r = 3$	0.1395	0.1404
$r = 4$	0.1781	0.1755
$r = 5$	0.1800	0.1755
$r = 6$	0.1500	0.1462

This use of the Poisson distribution as an approximation to a binomial distribution improves the larger the value of n is and the smaller the value of p.

So, in summary:

- **Poisson** as an *approximation* to the **binomial**
  If $X \sim$ B(n, p) and
  – n is large
  – p is small
  then X can be approximated by Po(np)

Example 8

The probability that a wrapped chocolate biscuit is double wrapped is 0.01. Use a suitable approximation to find the probability that of the next 60 biscuits that you unwrap:

(a) none are double wrapped
(b) at least 2 are double wrapped.

Let X = the number of biscuits that are double wrapped, then $X \sim$ B(60, 0.01). But n is quite large and p is small so $X \approx \sim$ Po(0.6). [$np = 60 \times 0.01 = 0.6$]

(a) $P(X = 0) \approx e^{-0.6} = 0.549$ (3 d.p.)

(b) $P(X \geqslant 2) = 1 - P(X \leqslant 1)$
$\approx 1 - e^{-0.6}[1 + 0.6]$
$= 1 - 0.8780\ldots$
$= 0.122$ (3 d.p.)

Notice that the answers using a binomial distribution in this case are (a) 0.547 and (b) 0.121.

Exercise 7F

1 In a certain manufacturing process the proportion of defective articles being produced is 2%. In a batch of 300 articles, find the probability that:
   (a) there are fewer than 2 defectives
   (b) there are exactly 4 defectives.

2 A medical practice screens a random sample of 250 of its patients for a certain condition which is present in 1.5% of the population. Find the probability that they obtained:
   (a) no patients with the condition
   (b) at least two patients with the condition.

3 An experiment involving two fair dice is carried out 180 times. The dice are placed in a container, shaken and the number of times a double six is obtained is recorded. Find the probability that the number of times a double six is obtained is:
   (a) once   (b) twice   (c) at least three.

4 It is claimed that 95% of the population in a certain village are right-handed. A random sample of 80 villagers are tested

to see if they are right or left-handed. Use a Poisson approximation to estimate the probability that the number who are right-handed is:

(a) 80   (b) 79   (c) at least 78.

5 In a computer simulation 500 dots were fired at a target and the probability of a dot hitting the target was 0.98. Find the probability that

(a) all the dots hit the target   (b) at least 495 hit the target.

6 State the conditions under which the Poisson distribution may be used as an approximation to the binomial distribution. Independently for each call into the telephone exchange of a large organisation, there is a probability of 0.002 that the call will be connected to a wrong extension. Find, to 3 significant figures, the probability that, on a given day, exactly one of the first 5 incoming calls will be wrongly connected.

Use a Poisson approximation to find, to 3 decimal places, the probability that, on a day when there are 1000 incoming calls, at least 3 of them are wrongly connected during that day. [L]

7 State the conditions under which the binomial distribution $B(n, p)$ may be approximated by a Poisson distribution and write down the mean of this Poisson distribution.

Samples of blood were taken from 250 children in a region in India. Of these children, 4 had blood type $A2B$. Write down an estimate of p, the proportion of all children in this region having blood type $A2B$.

Consider a group of n children from this region and let X be the number with blood type $A2B$. Assuming that X is distributed $B(n, p)$ and that p has the value estimated above, calculate, to 3 decimal places, the probability that the number of children of blood type $A2B$ in a group of 6 children from the region will be (a) zero, (b) more than one.

Use a Poisson approximation to calculate, to 4 decimal places, the probability that, in a group of 800 children from this region, there will be fewer than 3 children of blood type $A2B$. [L]

8 State the conditions under which a Poisson distribution may be used as an approximation to the binomial distribution $B(n, p)$.

Write down, in terms of n and p, the mean and the variance of the Poisson approximation.

Over a long period, a company finds that 2% of the gramophone records which it produces are faulty. A random sample of 15 records is taken from the production. Calculate, to 3 decimal places, the probability that there will be fewer than 2 faulty records in the sample.

Write down the mean number of faulty records in random samples of 15 taken from the production.

Using a Poisson approximation, or otherwise, find, to 3 decimal places, the probability that there will be at most 3 faulty records in a random sample of 100 records. [L]

7.7 Selecting the appropriate distribution

A difficulty that you may experience is in deciding whether a Poisson or a binomial distribution is appropriate in a particular situation. There are some key features which you should look for which may help. In order to use a binomial distribution there must be a *finite* value for n, the number of trials and therefore the maximum value for the random variable, and a value for p, the constant probability of success. A Poisson distribution, by contrast, has no (theoretical) limit to the maximum value of the random variable but there must be a value for λ the *average* number of successes.

Some situations involve a mixture of binomial and Poisson distributions with one distribution providing a parameter for the next as this final example illustrates.

Example 9
A piece of machinery breaks down on average once a fortnight but these breakdowns occur randomly throughout a week.

(a) Find the probability of a week with no breakdowns.

A week with no breakdowns is called a star week. Every 12 weeks the number of star weeks is recorded and a report is sent to the machine manufacturers.

(b) Find the probability that there are more than 10 star weeks in the next report.

(a) The *average* rate is 0.5 per week, so a Poisson distribution is required. Let $X =$ the number of breakdowns per week then $X \sim \text{Po}(0.5)$

$$P(X = 0) = e^{-0.5}$$
$$= 0.6065\ldots$$
$$= 0.607 \ (3 \text{ d.p.})$$

(b) Let $Y =$ the number of starred weeks in a period of 12 weeks. A value for n is 12 weeks and a value for p is your answer from part (a), so:

$$Y \sim \text{B}(12, 0.607)$$

$$P(Y > 10) = 12(0.607)^{11}(0.303) + (0.607)^{12}$$
$$= 0.01748\ldots$$
$$= 0.02 \ (2 \text{ d.p.})$$

Notice that if you had used a more accurate value for the probability in (a) in the binomial calculation of (b) you would have obtained the value 0.0217 ... but to 2 d.p. the answers agree.

There are some questions of this type in Review exercise 2.

SUMMARY OF KEY POINTS

1 Binomial distribution

$$X \sim B(n,p)$$

$$P(X = r) = \binom{n}{r} p^r (1-p)^{n-r} \qquad r = 0, 1, \ldots n$$

$$\mu = E(X) = np$$

$$\sigma^2 = \text{Var}(X) = np(1-p)$$

2 Poisson distribution

$$X \sim \text{Po}(\lambda)$$

$$P(X = r) = \frac{e^{-\lambda} \lambda^r}{r!}$$

$$\mu = E(X) = \lambda$$

$$\sigma^2 = \text{Var}(X) = \lambda$$

3 Poisson approximation to binomial

$$X \sim B(n,p)$$

if n is large

and p is small

then $X \approx \sim \text{Po}(np)$

Continuous distributions

8

In Chapter 6 you were introduced to **continuous random variables** and in particular to the concept of a **probability density function (p.d.f.)**. In this chapter you will meet two important continuous distributions and consider practical situations in which they can be used to model everyday situations. The second of these distributions is probably the most important distribution in statistics and without a knowledge of it and its properties you would not be able to progress to the next book on T2 or the rest of the London Modular Syllabus.

Before proceeding any further it is worth referring you back to section 6.3 on continuous random variables and in particular to the key points from that section.

■ **If X is a continuous random variable with p.d.f. $f(x)$**

(i) $$f(x) \geqslant 0 \forall x$$

(ii) $$\int_{-\infty}^{\infty} f(x)\, dx = 1$$

(iii) $$P(a < X < b) = \int_{a}^{b} f(x)\, dx$$

(iv) $$\mu = E(X) = \int_{-\infty}^{\infty} x f(x)\, dx$$

(v) $$\sigma^2 = \text{Var}(X) = \int_{-\infty}^{\infty} x^2 f(x)\, dx - \mu^2$$

(vi) Cumulative distribution function,

$$F(x_0) = P(X \leqslant x_0) = \int_{-\infty}^{x_o} f(x)\, dx.$$

With these in mind you can now proceed to deal with the new distributions.

8.1 Continuous uniform distribution

If you are asked "How tall are you?", you might respond "I am 6 feet 1 inch tall". By this you would *not* mean that you are exactly 6 feet 1 inch, or 73 inches, tall but that your height is between $72\frac{1}{2}$ inches and $73\frac{1}{2}$ inches and that it is equally likely to be anywhere in that range. What has happened is that your height is recorded to the nearest inch and the difference between your true height and your recorded height is a quantity that is equally likely to take any value between −0.5 inch and +0.5 inch. If all the students in your statistics group recorded their heights to the nearest inch then a reasonable model for the rounding errors produced is the continuous uniform distribution on the interval (−0.5, 0.5). If you let X represent the rounding errors then a sketch of the p.d.f. of X is as shown below.

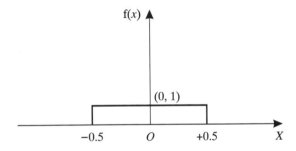

Note that the area under the p.d.f. is equal to unity and thus for this situation:

$$f(x) = 1 \qquad -0.5 \leqslant x \leqslant 0.5$$

It is useful to draw a sketch of any p.d.f. since it will often give you an insight into the shape of the distribution and perhaps more importantly the parameters of the distribution. For example, you can see from the above sketch, that the distribution is symmetrical about the zero, so the mean and median are both zero and that the distribution does not have a mode (see section 4.1, page 39).

Generalising the above for a random variable X, having a uniform distribution over the interval (α, β) gives

$$f(x) = \begin{cases} \dfrac{1}{\beta - \alpha} & \alpha < x < \beta \\ 0 & \text{otherwise.} \end{cases}$$

A sketch of the p.d.f. is as follows:

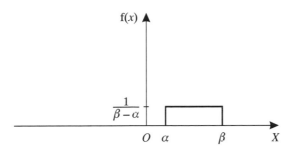

The geometry of the sketch shows that $f(x)$ is a valid p.d.f., since the area under the p.d.f. is given by:

$$\frac{1}{\beta - \alpha} \times (\beta - \alpha) = 1$$

Alternatively:

$$\int_{\alpha}^{\beta} \frac{1}{\beta - \alpha} \, dx = \left(\frac{x}{\beta - \alpha} \right)_{\alpha}^{\beta}$$

$$= \frac{\beta - \alpha}{\beta - \alpha}$$

$$= 1$$

By symmetry:

$$\text{the mean} = \text{median} = \frac{\alpha + \beta}{2}$$

but if you are unsure about these values, use the definitions given earlier in the book, together with your knowledge of calculus, to verify them.

The variance of the distribution is found using:

$$\text{Var}(X) = E(X^2) - \{E(X)\}^2$$

$$E(X^2) = \int_{\alpha}^{\beta} \frac{x^2}{(\beta - \alpha)} \, dx$$

$$-\frac{1}{\beta - \alpha} \left(\frac{x^3}{3} \right)_{\alpha}^{\beta}$$

$$= \frac{\beta^3 - \alpha^3}{3(\beta - \alpha)}$$

$$= \frac{\beta^2 + \alpha\beta + \alpha^2}{3}$$

$$\therefore \quad \text{Var}(X) = \tfrac{1}{3}(\beta^2 + \alpha\beta + \alpha^2) - \tfrac{1}{4}(\alpha + \beta)^2$$

$$= \tfrac{1}{12}\{4\beta^2 + 4\alpha\beta + 4\alpha^2 - 3\alpha^2 - 6\alpha\beta - 3\beta^2\}$$

$$= \tfrac{1}{12}\{\beta^2 - 2\alpha\beta + \alpha^2\}$$

$$= \tfrac{1}{12}(\beta - \alpha)^2$$

Sometimes it is advantageous to know the cumulative distribution function for a random variable and for X as defined above:

$$F(x_0) = P(X \leqslant x_0)$$

$$= \int_\alpha^{x_0} \frac{1}{\beta - \alpha}\,dx$$

$$= \left(\frac{x}{\beta - \alpha}\right)_\alpha^{x_0}$$

$$= \frac{x_0 - \alpha}{\beta - \alpha} \qquad \alpha < x_0 < \beta$$

Example 1

The continuous variable X is uniformly distributed over the interval (2,5). Find:

(a) $E(X)$ (b) $\text{Var}(X)$ (c) $P(X > 3.8)$.

A sketch of the p.d.f. of x is as shown below

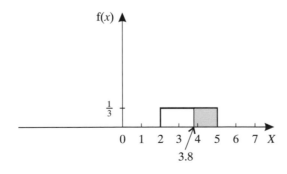

(a) $E(X) = 3.5$ by symmetry

or
$$E(X) = \int_2^5 x\tfrac{1}{3}\,dx$$

$$= \tfrac{1}{3}\left(\tfrac{x^2}{2}\right)_2^5$$

$$= \tfrac{1}{3}\left(\tfrac{25}{2} - \tfrac{4}{2}\right)$$

$$= \tfrac{1}{3} \times \tfrac{21}{2}$$

$$= \tfrac{7}{2}$$

$$= 3.5$$

(b)
$$Var(X) = E(X^2) - \{E(X)\}^2$$

$$= \tfrac{1}{12}(\beta - \alpha)^2$$

In this case $\beta = 5$ and $\alpha = 2$

$\therefore$
$$Var(X) = \tfrac{1}{12}(5-2)^2$$

$$= \tfrac{9}{12}$$

$$= \tfrac{3}{4}$$

Although the University of London Examinations & Assessment Council booklet contains the formulae for the mean and variance of the continuous uniform distribution – often known as the **rectangular distribution** (the reason for this being obvious from the above sketch) – it is important that you can obtain answers from first principles as well as from given formulae. Now show that $Var(X) = \tfrac{3}{4}$ using $Var(X) = E(X^2) - \{E(X)\}^2$.

(c)
$$P(X > 3.8) = \int_{3.8}^5 f(x)\,dx$$

$$= \int_{3.8}^5 \tfrac{1}{3}\,dx$$

$$= \tfrac{1}{3}(x)_{3.8}^5$$

$$= \frac{5 - 3.8}{3}$$

$$= \frac{1.2}{3}$$

$$= 0.4$$

or $P(X > 3.8) = 1 - F(3.8)$

$$= 1 - \left(\frac{3.8 - 2}{5 - 2}\right)$$

$$= 1 - \frac{1.8}{3}$$

$$= \frac{1.2}{3}$$

$$= 0.4$$

or $P(X > 3.8) =$ shaded area shown in sketch

$$= \tfrac{1}{3}(5 - 3.8)$$

$$= \frac{1.2}{3}$$

$$= 0.4$$

Example 2

A piece of string of length 8 cm is randomly cut into two pieces. Find the probability that the longer of the two pieces of string is at least 5 cm long.

Let X represent the distance of the cut from one end of the piece of string. Thus X has a uniform distribution over the interval (0,8) and the p.d.f. of X is illustrated below.

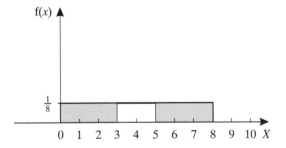

The longer piece of string is at least 5 cm long if $0 \leqslant X \leqslant 3$ or $5 \leqslant X \leqslant 8$. Since these intervals are mutually exclusive

$$P(0 \leqslant X \leqslant 3 \text{ or } 5 \leqslant X \leqslant 8 = P(0 \leqslant X \leqslant 3) + P(5 \leqslant X \leqslant 8)$$
$$= \frac{3-0}{8-0} + \frac{8-5}{8-0}$$
$$= \tfrac{3}{8} + \tfrac{3}{8}$$
$$= \tfrac{3}{4}$$

Exercise 8A

1 Find $E(X)$ and $Var(X)$ for the continuous random variable X having the following probability density functions:

(a)
$$f(x) = \begin{cases} \frac{1}{10} & 10 \leqslant x \leqslant 20 \\ 0 & \text{otherwise} \end{cases}$$

(b)
$$f(x) = \begin{cases} \frac{1}{6} & -3 \leqslant x \leqslant 3 \\ 0 & \text{otherwise} \end{cases}$$

(c)
$$f(x) = \begin{cases} \frac{1}{3} & -1 \leqslant x \leqslant 2 \\ 0 & \text{otherwise.} \end{cases}$$

2 For the random variable X, whose probability density function is shown below, find, using first principles, $E(X)$, $Var(X)$ and $P(X > 5.5)$.

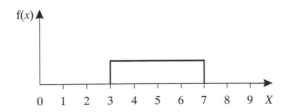

3 A clock stops at random. The random variable X is the hour as indicated by the hour hand.

   (a) Write down the probability distribution function which describes X.

   (b) Sketch the graph of its probability distribution function.

   (c) Find the probability that the hand is between 3 o'clock and 7 o'clock.

4 A uniform steel bar was loaded until it broke. The loaded length of bar was 240 mm.

   (a) Find the probability that the break did not lie in the middle third of the bar.

   (b) If x is the distance in from the left-hand end of the bar at which it broke, find $E(X)$ and $Var(X)$.

5 A continuous random variable Y is uniformly distributed. Given that $E(Y) = 3$ and $Var(Y) = 3$, find $P(Y < 2)$.

6 The continuous random variable X is uniformly distributed over the interval $(1,6)$.

   (a) Find $E(X)$ and $Var(X)$.

   (b) Write down the cumulative distribution function for X and use it to find $P(X < 4)$.

8.2 The normal distribution

If you sit in the lounge of a busy airport and watch people going about their business one of the features you will notice is the variation in the heights of these people. Some will be quite short, others very tall, but for both men and women you will find that most heights cluster about a central value, say 178 cm for the men and 163 cm for the women. If you were to measure the heights of a large sample of both men and women and then represent these heights by means of a histogram you might obtain histograms as follows.

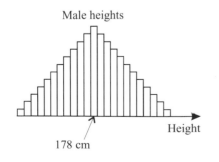

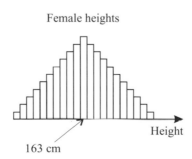

Notice that both distributions are approximately symmetrical and both have fewer and fewer observations as the distribution moves away from the central value. In this practical situation you would expect this. How many people have you seen over 213 cm tall or shorter than 122 cm?

Many other continuous random variables follow this pattern, for example, weight, time, distance, etc., and whilst a histogram is a useful method of representing these data it would also be useful for us to have a statistical distribution as a model for such variables. The distribution used is the **normal distribution**. Dating back to the seventeenth and eighteenth centuries the normal distribution is the most important distribution in statistics. Unfortunately it is a distribution which has a probability density function that is complicated and much of the mathematics associated with it is beyond the scope of this book. Nevertheless you need to be familiar with its p.d.f. which is defined as follows.

■ **A continuous random variable X has a normal distribution if it has a probability density function**

$$f(x) = \frac{1}{\sigma\sqrt{2\pi}}e^{-(x-\mu)^2/(2\sigma^2)} \qquad -\infty < x < \infty.$$

A sketch of $f(x)$ is shown below

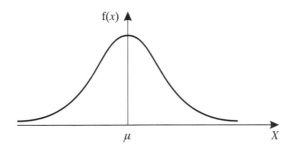

From this sketch the properties of a normal distribution can be summarised as:

■ The distribution is symmetrical about the mean μ.
■ The mode, median and mean are all equal, due to the symmetry of the distribution.
■ The range of X is from $-\infty$ to $+\infty$.
■ The horizontal axis is asymptotic to the curve as $x \to -\infty$ and $x \to +\infty$
■ The total area under the curve is unity.

It is beyond the scope of this book to show that the last property is true, but it is of paramount importance that you know that it is true.

As you can see from the p.d.f. of the normal distribution it is a two-parameter distribution, the parameters being μ and σ. You should recognise these from earlier parts of this book. Reference was made in Chapter 4 on page 56 to the fact that there is a link between μ and σ^2 and that it would be made in Chapter 8. The link is that they are the two parameters fundamental to the most important distribution in statistics. The practical implications of this link will be seen later in this chapter. You can see from the p.d.f. that the probability of X depends *only* on μ and σ^2, and rather than having to remember the p.d.f. of the normal distribution it will be sufficient for you to refer to the random variable X as having a normal distribution by using the notation:

$$X \sim \mathrm{N}(\mu, \sigma^2)$$

The first parameter in the brackets is the mean, μ, and the second one is the variance, σ^2. Proofs that $\mathrm{E}(X) = \mu$ and $\mathrm{Var}(X) = \sigma^2$ are beyond the scope of this book but it is important for you to remember them and to become competent in their use in the above notation. In practice these two parameters, μ and σ^2, determine the shape of a normal distribution as is illustrated below.

Let $X_1 \sim \mathrm{N}(\mu_1, \sigma^2)$ and $X_2 \sim \mathrm{N}(\mu_2, \sigma^2)$ $\qquad \mu_1 < \mu_2$

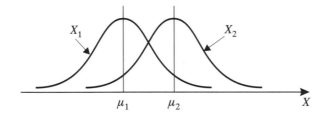

As can be seen, these two distributions have different location parameters but the same dispersion.

Let $Y_1 \sim \mathrm{N}(\mu, \sigma_1^2)$ and $Y_2 \sim \mathrm{N}(\mu, \sigma_2^2)$ $\qquad \sigma_1^2 < \sigma_2^2$

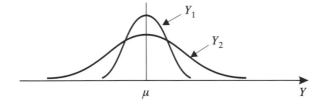

In this case the two distributions have the same location parameter but different dispersions.

Since the normal distribution is used to model continuous random variables, then if you need to evaluate probabilities associated with this distribution it is necessary to evaluate areas under the normal curve. Thus if $X \sim N(\mu, \sigma^2)$ then $P(a < X < b)$ is evaluated as the area under the normal curve between a and b. A sketch, as shown below, is helpful to illustrate the appropriate area.

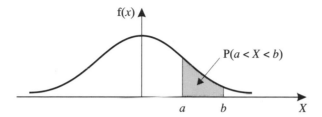

In theory, $P(a < X < b) = \int_a^b f(x) \, dx$, but unfortunately it cannot be evaluated using standard techniques of integration and in order to carry out such an evaluation you need to refer to statistical tables which have been derived for just that purpose.

8.3 The standard normal distribution

To evaluate probabilities associated with normal distributions the **standard normal distribution** is used which, as its name implies, has all the properties of a normal distribution but in addition it has a mean of zero and a standard deviation of 1. The **standard normal random variable** is denoted by Z where $Z \sim N(0, 1^2)$ and the important feature of this distribution is that *any normal distribution* can be mapped onto the standard normal distribution. Thus the normal distributions corresponding to the three random variables illustrated below can each be transformed into a standard normal distribution.

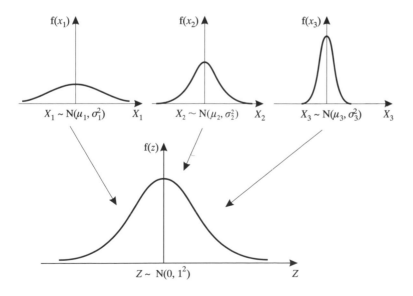

This transformation is achieved by subtracting the mean and dividing by the standard deviation. Hence:

$$Z = \frac{X - \mu}{\sigma} \qquad \text{where } X \sim N(\mu, \sigma^2) \text{ and } Z \sim N(0, 1^2).$$

The p.d.f. of Z is given by:

$$f(z) = \frac{1}{\sqrt{2\pi}} e^{-\frac{1}{2}z^2}$$

obtained by substituting $\mu = 0$ and $\sigma = 1$ in $f(x)$ as defined in the previous section.

Thus if $X \sim N(100, 15^2)$ then

$$Z = \frac{X - 100}{15} \sim N(0, 1^2)$$

Since *any* normal random variable can be transferred into a standard normal random variable then if probabilities for the standard normal variable can be found then this property can be used to evaluate probabilities associated with normal distributions.

If, for example, you wish to evaluate $P(12 < X < 16)$ where $X \sim N(10, 4^2)$ then using $Z = \frac{X-10}{4}$ gives:

$$P(12 < X < 16) = P\left(\frac{12 - 10}{4} < \frac{X - 10}{4} < \frac{16 - 10}{4}\right)$$
$$= P(0.5 < Z < 1.5)$$

Before evaluating such probabilities it is necessary to introduce the **cumulative distribution function (c.d.f.)** of the standard normal distribution which, by definition, is given by:

$$P(Z \leqslant z_0) = \Phi(z_0) = \frac{1}{\sqrt{2\pi}} \int_{-\infty}^{z_0} e^{\frac{1}{2}z^2} \, dz$$

Note that rather than using $F(z_0)$, the special symbol $\Phi(z_0)$ is used when referring to the c.d.f. of the standard normal distribution. So for the probability above:

$$P(12 < X < 16) = P(0.5 < Z < 1.5)$$
$$= \Phi(1.5) - \Phi(0.5)$$

When evaluating probabilities such as these you are strongly advised to draw appropriate diagrams to ensure that you are clear in your own mind exactly which areas under the normal curve you need to evaluate. An illustration is given below showing how $P(12 < X < 16)$, where $X \sim N(10.4^2)$ would be evaluated.

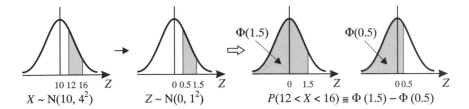

$$X \sim N(10, 4^2) \qquad Z \sim N(0, 1^2) \qquad P(12 < X < 16) \equiv \Phi(1.5) - \Phi(0.5)$$

Evaluation of $\Phi(z)$ is very difficult but, fortunately, values of $\Phi(z)$ have been extensively tabulated and you will find a number of different formats for these tabulations. The table 3 on page 247 of this book tabulates $\Phi(z)$ for values of z in the interval $(0.00, 4.00)$ giving values of $\Phi(z)$ in the interval $(0.5000, 1.0000)$. Thus if you now turn to page 247 and evaluate $P(12 < X < 16)$ you will find:

$$P(12 < X < 16) = P(0.5 < Z < 1.5)$$

$$= \Phi(1.5) - \Phi(0.5)$$

$$= 0.9332 - 0.6915$$

$$= 0.2417$$

Since the table only gives values of $\Phi(z)$ for z in the interval $(00.0, 4.00)$, to get values of $\Phi(z)$ in the interval $(-4.00, 0.00)$ you need to remember that any normal distribution is symmetrical about its mean and in particular the standard normal distribution is symmetrical about zero, i.e. $\Phi(0.00) = 0.500$. This will then enable you to find values such as $\Phi(-1.2)$ as illustrated below.

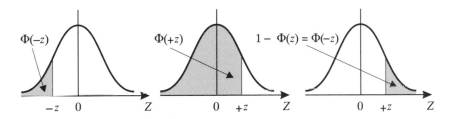

From this illustration you can see that:

$$\Phi(-z) = 1 - \Phi(z)$$

Hence:

$$\Phi(-1.2) = 1 - \Phi(1.2)$$

$$= 1 - 0.8849$$

$$= 0.1151$$

As with most techniques, the more you practice them the easier their use becomes and you *must* become familiar with the use of tables of $\Phi(z)$. **Good clear diagrams will always help**.

Example 3

The random variable $Z \sim N(0, 1^2)$. Find:

(a) $P(Z > 1.0)$ (b) $P(Z < -2.0)$ (c) $P(-1.5 < Z < 0.5)$

(a)

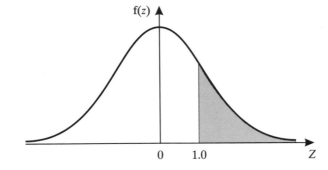

$$P(Z > 1.0) = 1 - \Phi(1.0)$$
$$= 1 - 0.8413$$
$$= 0.1587$$

(b)

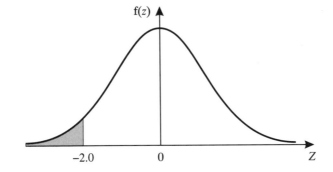

$$P(Z < -2.0) = \Phi(-2.0)$$
$$= 1 - \Phi(2.0)$$
$$= 1 - 0.9772$$
$$= 0.0228$$

(c)

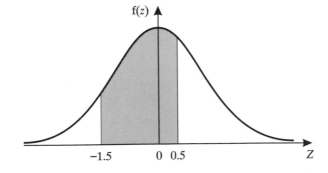

$$P(-1.5 < Z < 0.5) = \Phi(0.5) - \Phi(-1.5)$$
$$= \Phi(0.5) - \{1 - \Phi(1.5)\}$$
$$= 0.6915 - \{1 - 0.9332\}$$
$$= 0.6247$$

Example 4

The random variable $Y \sim N(56, 10^2)$. Find:
(a) $P(Y > 68)$ (b) $P(56 < Y < 65)$ (c) $P(42 < Y < 52)$

(a)

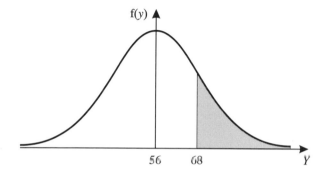

$$P(Y > 68) = P\left(\frac{Y - 56}{10} > \frac{68 - 56}{10}\right)$$
$$= P(Z > 1.2)$$
$$= 1 - \Phi(1.2)$$
$$= 1 - 0.8849$$
$$= 0.1151$$

(b)

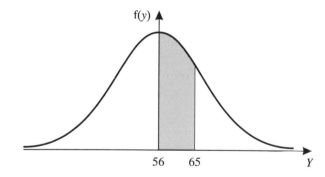

$$P(56 < Y < 65) = P\left(\frac{56 - 56}{10} < Z < \frac{65 - 56}{10}\right)$$
$$= P(0 < Z < 0.9)$$
$$= \Phi(0.9) - \Phi(0)$$
$$= 0.8159 - 0.5000$$
$$= 0.3159$$

(c)

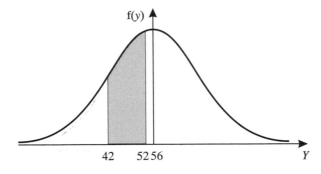

$$P(42 < Y < 52) = P\left(\frac{42 - 56}{10} < Z < \frac{52 - 56}{10}\right)$$

$$= P(-1.4 < Z < -0.4)$$

$$= \Phi(-0.4) - \Phi(-1.4)$$

$$= 1 - \Phi(0.4) - \{1 - \Phi(1.4)\}$$

$$= \Phi(1.4) - \Phi(0.4)$$

$$= 0.9192 - 0.6554$$

$$= 0.2638$$

Example 5

The random variable X is normally distributed with mean μ and variance σ^2. Given that

$$P(X > 58.39) = 0.0217 \qquad \text{and} \qquad P(X < 41.82) = 0.0287$$

find μ and σ.

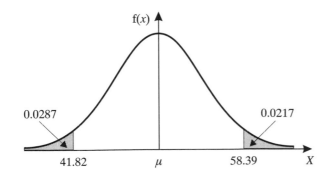

From the diagram you can see that:

$$P(X > 58.39) = P\left(Z > \frac{58.39 - \mu}{\sigma}\right)$$

$$= 0.0217$$

$$\therefore \qquad \Phi\left(\frac{58.39 - \mu}{\sigma}\right) = 1 - 0.217$$

$$= 0.9783$$

Thus from the tables:

$$\frac{58.39 - \mu}{\sigma} = 2.02$$

Similarly:

$$P(X < 41.82) = P\left(Z < \frac{41.82 - \mu}{\sigma}\right)$$

$$= 0.0287$$

$$\therefore \qquad \Phi\left(\frac{41.82 - \mu}{\sigma}\right) = 0.0287$$

$$\therefore \qquad \Phi\left\{-\left(\frac{41.82 - \mu}{\sigma}\right)\right\} = 1 - 0.0287$$

$$= 0.9713$$

$$\therefore \qquad -\left(\frac{41.82 - \mu}{\sigma}\right) = 1.90$$

Hence:

$$58.39 - \mu = 2.02\sigma$$
$$41.82 - \mu = -1.90\sigma$$

Solving gives:

$$\mu = 49.851 \qquad \sigma = 4.227$$

You will have realized that the values of z in the tables are given to two decimal places and that in the previous three examples this was adequate. Sometimes the value for z from your calculations may contain more than two decimal places. In such cases you should either round your value to two decimal places and use the table directly or you can **interpolate**. For example, if $z = 1.83$ then $\Phi(z) = 0.9664$ and if $z = 1.84$, $\Phi(z) = 0.9671$. If your value of z is 1.8372 then

$$\Phi(1.8372) = 0.9664 + \frac{72}{100}(0.9671 - 0.9664)$$

$$= 0.9669$$

Once you become experienced at evaluating areas under the normal curve you will soon appreciate that certain areas are commonly used and that sometimes a z value corresponding to a special standard probability is needed, consequently their z values have been tabulated more accurately. Table 4 on page 248 contains z values for the random variable $Z \sim N(0, 1)$ such that the random variable exceeds z with probability p. Thus:

$$P(Z > z) = 1 - \Phi(z) = p$$

From the table you will see that, for example:

$$P(Z > 1.9600) = 0.0250$$
$$P(Z > 1.6449) = 0.0500$$
$$P(Z > 3.0902) = 0.0010 \text{ etc.}$$

It is important to note that by symmetry if $P(Z > 1.9600) = 0.0250$ then $P(Z < -1.9600) = 0.0250$. As your statistical knowledge increases you will find that z-values such as 1.9600, 1.6449, etc. are values you will remember without needing to refer to the tables since they are values most commonly used by statisticians.

Example 6

The door frames used by a builder are of one standard height, 1.830 m. The heights of men are normally distributed with mean 1.730 m and standard deviation 0.064 m.
(a) Find the proportion of men that will be taller than the door frame.
(b) Find the frame height, such that one man in a thousand will be taller than the frame height.
The door frames are to be used in a department store. It is known that women outnumber men in the ratio 19:1 in the store and the proportion of women taller than the door frame is 0.00069.
(c) Find the proportion of people for whom a frame height of 1.830 m would be too low.　　　　　　　　　　　　　　　　　　　　[L]

(a) Let M represent the heights of men, such that
$M \sim N(1.73, 0.064^2)$.

$$\therefore \qquad P(M > 1.83) = P\left(Z > \frac{1.83 - 1.73}{0.064}\right)$$
$$= P(Z > 1.5625)$$

From tables, $\Phi(1.56) = 0.9406$ and $\Phi(1.57) = 0.9418$

$$\therefore \qquad \Phi(1.5625) = 0.9406 + \frac{25}{100}(0.9418 - 0.9406)$$
$$= 0.9409$$

Hence:

$$P(Z > 1.5625) = 1 - \Phi(1.5625)$$
$$= 1 - 0.9409$$
$$= 0.0591$$

(b) Let h represent the frame height, then $P(M > h) = 0.0010$.

$$\therefore \qquad P(M > h) = P\left(Z > \frac{h - 1.73}{0.064}\right)$$
$$= 0.0010$$

$$\therefore \qquad 1 - \Phi\left(\frac{h - 1.73}{0.064}\right) = 0.0010$$

As was stated earlier, 0.0010 is one of the values commonly used and can be found in Table 4 on page 248 corresponding to a z value of 3.0902.

Hence:

$$1 - \Phi(3.0902) = 0.0010$$

Thus:

$$\frac{h - 1.73}{0.064} = 3.0902$$
$$\therefore \qquad h = 1.9277728$$
i.e. $\qquad h = 1.93 \text{ to } 2 \text{ d.p.}$

(c) Since there are 19 women to every man in the store then the proportion of people for whom the frame height would be too low is given by:

$$\tfrac{19}{20}(0.00069) + \tfrac{1}{20}(0.0591) = 0.00361$$

Exercise 8B

1 Using normal distribution tables, find:
  (a) $P(Z < 1.78)$ (b) $P(Z < 2.5)$ (c) $P(Z < 0.28)$
  (d) $P(Z < 1.5)$ (e) $P(Z < 1.455)$ (f) $P(Z > 1.78)$
  (g) $P(Z > 2.5)$ (h) $P(Z > 0.28)$ (i) $P(Z > 1.5)$
  (j) $P(Z > 0.714)$

2 Using normal distribution tables, find:
  (a) $P(0.32 < Z < 1.38)$ (b) $P(1.25 < Z < 2.5)$
  (c) $P(-0.5 < Z < 0.5)$ (d) $P(-1.2 < Z < 2.1)$
  (e) $P(Z < 0.5 \text{ and } > 1.5)$ (f) $P(Z < -1.0 \text{ and } > 2.0)$

3   Find the value of z in each of the following:

(a) $\Phi(z) = 0.9495$ (b) $\Phi(z) = 0.5910$

(c) $\Phi(z) = 0.9660$ (d) $\Phi(-z) = 0.3783$

(e) $\Phi(-z) = 0.1056$ (f) $\Phi(-z) = 0.0244$

4   The random variable $Z \sim N(0, 1^2)$. Find:

(a) $P(Z > 1.25)$ (b) $P(Z < -1.0)$ (c) $P(-2.0 < Z < 1.0)$

5   For each of the following diagrams find the z value and hence the area of the shaded portion:

(a)

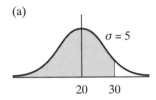

$\sigma = 5$

20   30

(b)

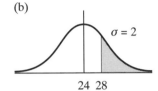

$\sigma = 2$

24 28

(c)

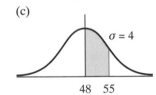

$\sigma = 4$

48   55

(d)

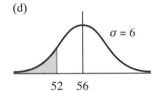

$\sigma = 6$

52   56

(e)

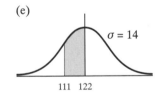

$\sigma = 14$

111   122

(f)

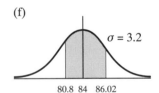

$\sigma = 3.2$

80.8 84   86.02

6   The random variable $A \sim N(28, 3^2)$. Find:

(a) $P(A < 32)$ (b) $P(A > 36)$ (c) $P(28 < A < 35)$

(d) $P(22 < A < 26)$ (e) $P(25 < A < 33)$

7   The random variable X has a normal distribution with mean 16 and variance 0.64. Find x, such that $P(X < x) = 0.025$. [L]

8   For each of the following diagrams find μ:

(a)

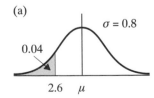

$\sigma = 0.8$

0.04

2.6 μ

(b)

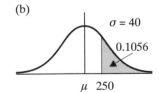

$\sigma = 40$

0.1056

μ 250

(c)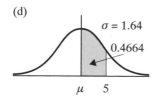

$\sigma = 15.79$

0.1271

μ 118

(d)

$\sigma = 1.64$

0.4664

μ 5

9 For each of the following diagrams find σ:

(a)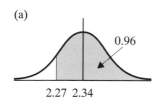

0.96

2.27 2.34

(b)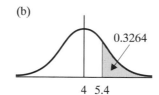

0.3264

4 5.4

(c)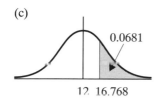

0.0681

12 16.768

(d)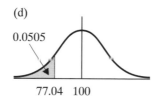

0.0505

77.04 100

10 For each of the following diagrams find μ and σ:

(a)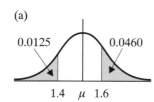

0.0125   0.0460

1.4 μ 1.6

(b)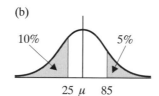

10%   5%

25 μ 85

11 The random variable M is normally distributed with mean μ and variance σ^2.
Given that $P(M > 34) = 0.0228$ and $P(M < 25) = 0.0062$ find μ and σ.

12 The weights of steel sheets produced by a plant are known to be normally distributed with mean 31.4 kg and standard deviation 2.4 kg. Find the percentage of sheets that weigh more than 35.6 kg.

13 A machine dispenses liquid into cartons in such a way that the amount of liquid dispensed on each occasion is normally distributed with standard deviation 20 ml and mean 266 ml. Cartons that weigh less than 260 ml have to be recycled. What proportion of cartons are recycled?

Cartons weighing more than 300 ml produce no profit. What percentage of cartons will this be?

14 Boxes of chocolate with mean weight 1 kg are produced. It is decided that all boxes weighing less than 990 g and more than 1050 g will be repacked. If the weight of the boxes is normally distributed with standard deviation 20 g, what proportion of the boxes are repacked?

15 Over a long period it has been found that the breaking strains of cables produced by a factory are normally distributed with mean 6000 N and standard deviation 150 N. Find, to 3 decimal places, the probability that a cable chosen at random from the production will have a breaking strain of more than 6200 N.   [L]

16 Records from a dental practice show that the probability of waiting to go into the surgery, for more than 20 minutes is 0.0239. If the waiting time is normally distributed with standard deviation 3.78 what is the mean waiting time?

17 Batteries for a radio have a mean life of 160 hours and a standard deviation of 30 hours. Assuming the battery life follows a normal distribution, calculate:
   (a) the proportion of batteries which have a life of between 150 hours and 180 hours
   (b) the range (symmetrical about the mean) within which 75% of batteries lie.

18 The thickness of some sheets of wood follows a normal distribution with mean μ and standard deviation σ. 96% of the sheets will go through an 8 mm gauge while only 1.7% will go through a 7 mm gauge. Find μ and σ.

8.4 Approximations using the Normal distribution

In Chapter 7 you were introduced to two important discrete probability distributions – the binomial distribution and the Poisson distribution. Let us consider the discrete random variable having a binomial distribution, such that $X \sim B(n, p)$, where n represents the fixed number of trials used and p the constant probability of success at any trial. If, for example, $n = 10$ and $p = 0.3$, then you can evaluate probabilities associated with $X \sim B(10, 0.3)$ either from tables or using the distribution itself. Thus:

$$P(X = 1) = \binom{10}{1}(0.3)^1(0.7)^9$$

$$= 0.1211 \qquad \text{using your calculator}$$

$$\text{or } P(X \leqslant 7) = 0.9984 \qquad \text{from tables.}$$

When n becomes large, say 75, tabular values are not available and calculations become tedious. In such situations it is possible to use the normal distribution to find approximate values for the binomial probabilities and, provided you keep to the guidelines associated with the normal approximation to the binomial, then the approximations are reasonably accurate.

It is important to remember that the binomial distribution is used with *discrete* random variables and the normal distribution with *continuous* random variables. Hence we are approximating a discrete variate by a continuous one and an allowance must be made for this using the $\frac{1}{2}$ **continuity correction**, as follows:

Let $X \sim B(100, 0.3)$, so that X can only take integer values $0, 1, ..., 100$, and in particular consider $x = 52$. Since X is discrete, $P(X = 52)$ can be found. However, when finding probabilities using continuous random variables it is not possible to find exact probabilities such as $P(X = 52)$, we have to find probabilities using the area under the p.d.f. between two given values. Referring back to the example on height at the beginning of section 8.1, a height of 73 inches was interpreted to range from $72\frac{1}{2}$ inches to $73\frac{1}{2}$ inches. Similarly, in situations where a discrete variable is being approximated by a continuous one, discrete values are converted into continuous ones by using the $\frac{1}{2}$ as illustrated with height. Hence, the name $\frac{1}{2}$ continuity correction. Thus, $P(X = 52)$ is approximated by $P(51\frac{1}{2} < Y < 52\frac{1}{2})$ where Y is a normal random variable. But what are the parameters of Y? In section 7.4 of Chapter 7, the mean and variance of X when $X \sim B(n, p)$ were derived as $E(X) = np$, $Var(X) = np(1 - p)$. Thus when approximating a binomial distribution by a normal distribution np and $np(1 - p)$ are used as the mean and variance for the normal distribution.

Thus, $X \sim B(n, p)$ is approximated by $Y \sim N(np, np(1 - p))$ and in particular, if $X \sim B(100, 0.3)$ then it is approximated using $Y \sim N(30, 21)$. In practice, another rule-of-thumb is needed for using the normal approximation to the binomial and the following is recommended:

$X \sim B(n, p)$ can be approximated by

$$Y \sim N(\mu, \sigma^2) \qquad \text{where } \mu = np, \sigma^2 = np(1-p)$$

provided that n is large and $np > 5$ and $n(1-p) > 5$.

Before evaluating a specific example it is essential that you understand how the $\frac{1}{2}$ continuity correction is applied. The diagram below should help you.

Hence we can approximate as follows:

$$P(X < 52) \simeq P(Y < 51\tfrac{1}{2})$$
$$P(X \leqslant 52) \simeq P(Y < 52\tfrac{1}{2})$$
$$P(X > 54) \simeq P(Y > 54\tfrac{1}{2})$$
$$P(X \geqslant 54) \simeq P(Y > 53\tfrac{1}{2})$$
$$P(52 < X < 54) \simeq P(52\tfrac{1}{2} < Y < 53\tfrac{1}{2})$$
$$P(52 \leqslant X < 54) \simeq P(51\tfrac{1}{2} < Y < 53\tfrac{1}{2})$$
$$P(52 \leqslant X \leqslant 54) \simeq P(51\tfrac{1}{2} < Y < 54\tfrac{1}{2})$$

Example 7
If $X \sim B(100, 0.3)$, find $P(33 \leqslant X < 37)$.

For the distribution of X,

$$E(X) = np$$
$$= 100 \times 0.3$$
$$= 30$$

and
$$Var(X) = np(1-p)$$
$$= 100 \times 0.3 \times 0.7$$
$$= 21.$$

Since $n = 100$ and both np and $n(1-p)$ exceed 5, you can use the normal approximation.

$\therefore \qquad P(33 \leqslant X < 37) \simeq P(32.5 < Y < 36.5) \quad \text{where } Y \sim N(30, 21)$

$$= P\left(\frac{32.5 - 30}{\sqrt{21}} < Z < \frac{36.5 - 30}{\sqrt{21}}\right)$$

$$= P(0.55 < Z < 1.42)$$

$$= \Phi(1.42) - \Phi(0.55)$$

$$= 0.9222 - 0.7088$$

$$= 0.2314$$

Example 8

If $X \sim B(100, 0.3)$, find $P(X = 33)$ using:
(a) the binomial distribution   (b) the normal approximation.

Calculate the error in approximating.

(a) $\quad P(X = 33) = \dbinom{100}{33}(0.3)^{33}(0.7)^{67}$

$$= 0.0685 \qquad \text{using a calculator.}$$

(b) $\quad P(X = 33) \simeq P(32\frac{1}{2} < Y < 33\frac{1}{2}) \qquad \text{where } Y \sim N(30, 21)$

$$= P(0.5455 < Z < 0.7638)$$

$$= \Phi(0.7638) - \Phi(0.5455)$$

$$= 0.7775 - 0.7073 \qquad \text{using interpolation}$$

$$= 0.0702$$

$$\text{Error} = 0.0702 - 0.0685$$

$$= 0.0017$$

In a similar way it is possible to approximate the Poisson distribution using the normal distribution. In section 7.5 in Chapter 7, a random variable X was defined to have a Poisson distribution with parameter λ if it had a p.d.f.

$$P(X = r) = \frac{e^{-\lambda}\lambda^r}{r!} \qquad r = 0, 1, 2, 3\ldots$$

The mean and variance of X were given as $E(X) = \lambda$ and $\text{Var}(X) = \lambda$. Cumulative Poisson probabilities have been tabulated for values of λ in the range $(0.5, 10)$ but if $\lambda > 10$ there are no tabular values and an approximation has to be used. Thus $X \sim \text{Po}(\lambda)$ can be approximated by $Y \sim N(\lambda, \lambda)$ and for values of

$\lambda > 10$ the approximation is very good. Again when using the normal approximation to the Poisson distribution the continuity correction must be incorporated.

Example 9

If $X \sim \text{Po}(22)$, find $P(X = 18)$ using:
(a) the Poisson distribution   (b)   the normal approximation.

(a)
$$X \sim \text{Po}(22) \Rightarrow P(X = r)$$
$$= \frac{e^{-22}22^r}{r!}$$

$\therefore$
$$P(X = 18) = \frac{e^{-22}22^{18}}{18!} = 0.0635$$

(b) $P(X = 18) \simeq P(17.5 < Y < 18.5)$ where $Y \sim \text{N}(22, 22)$
$$= P\left(\frac{17.5 - 22}{\sqrt{22}} < Z < \frac{18.5 - 22}{\sqrt{22}}\right)$$
$$= P(-0.9594 < Z < -0.7462)$$
$$= \Phi(0.9594) - \Phi(0.7462)$$
$$= 0.8313 - 0.7723$$
$$= 0.0590$$
$$\text{Error} = 0.0635 - 0.0590$$
$$= 0.0045$$

Example 10

A car hire firm has a large fleet of cars for hire by the day and it is found that the fleet suffers breakdowns at the rate of 21 per week. Assuming that breakdowns occur at a constant rate, at random in time and independently of one another, calculate the probability that in any one week more than 27 breakdowns occur.

Let X represent the number of breakdowns per week.

$\therefore$ $X \sim \text{Po}(21)$
$\therefore$ $P(X > 27) \simeq P(Y > 27.5)$ where $Y \sim \text{N}(21, 21)$
$$= P\left(Z > \frac{27.5 - 21}{\sqrt{21}}\right)$$
$$= P(Z > 1.4184)$$
$$= 1 - \Phi(1.4184)$$
$$= 1 - 0.9220$$
$$= 0.0780$$

Exercise 8C

1 Let $X \sim \mathrm{B}(n,p)$ and $Y \sim \mathrm{N}(np, np(1-p))$. For each of the following probabilities in X, write the corresponding probability in Y when using a normal approximation:
   (a) $\mathrm{P}(X < 26)$ (b) $\mathrm{P}(X \leqslant 41)$ (c) $\mathrm{P}(X > 10)$
   (d) $\mathrm{P}(X \geqslant 5)$ (c) $\mathrm{P}(2 \leqslant X < 10)$ (f) $\mathrm{P}(40 < X \leqslant 50)$

2 Let $X \sim \mathrm{Po}(\lambda)$ and $Y \sim \mathrm{N}(\lambda, \lambda)$. For each of the following probabilities in X, write the corresponding probability in Y when using a normal approximation.
   (a) $\mathrm{P}(X > 32)$ (b) $\mathrm{P}(X \leqslant 16)$ (c) $\mathrm{P}(X \geqslant 9)$
   (d) $\mathrm{P}(X < 48)$ (e) $\mathrm{P}(24 \leqslant X \leqslant 36)$ (f) $\mathrm{P}(4 < X < 10)$

3 Which of the following could reasonably be approximated by a normal distribution?
   (a) $X \sim \mathrm{B}(50, 0.3)$ (b) $Y \sim \mathrm{B}(12, 0.4)$ (c) $X \sim \mathrm{B}(15, 0.4)$
   (d) $Y \sim \mathrm{Po}(8)$ (c) $X \sim \mathrm{Po}(28)$

4 Use a normal approximation to find:
   (a) $\mathrm{P}(X < 44)$ if $X \sim \mathrm{B}(100, 0.5)$
   (b) $\mathrm{P}(X \geqslant 60)$ if $X \sim \mathrm{B}(80, 0.6)$
   (c) $\mathrm{P}(X = 35)$ if $X \sim \mathrm{B}(80, 0.4)$
   (d) $\mathrm{P}(20 < X \leqslant 25)$ if $X \sim \mathrm{B}(60, 0.3)$

5 Use a normal approximation to find:
   (a) $\mathrm{P}(Y < 4)$ if $Y \sim \mathrm{Po}(12)$
   (b) $\mathrm{P}(Y \geqslant 15)$ if $Y \sim \mathrm{Po}(22)$
   (c) $\mathrm{P}(Y = 36)$ if $Y \sim \mathrm{Po}(42)$
   (d) $\mathrm{P}(45 < Y \leqslant 65)$ if $Y \sim \mathrm{Po}(60)$

6 For $Y \sim \mathrm{B}(20, 0.4)$ find $\mathrm{P}(3 < Y < 13)$
   (a) using tables   (b) using a normal approximation.
   State the error in (b).

7 For $X \sim \mathrm{Po}(10)$ find $\mathrm{P}(6 < X < 16)$
   (a) using tables   (b) using a normal approximation.
   State the error in (b).

8 Explain briefly the circumstances under which a normal distribution may be used as an approximation to a binomial distribution.
   Write down the mean and the variance of the Normal approximation to the binomial distribution $\mathrm{B}(n,p)$.

In a multiple-choice examination, candidate Jones picks his answer to each question at random from the list of 3 answers provided, of which only one is correct. A candidate answering 18 or more questions correctly passes the examination.

(a) For a paper containing 45 questions, use a normal approximation to find, to 3 decimal places, the probability that Jones passes.

(b) It is required that the probability that Jones passes should be less than 0.005. Use a normal approximation to show that the paper should contain at most 31 questions. [L]

9 State the conditions under which a normal distribution may be used as an approximation to the binomial distribution $B(n,p)$, giving the parameters of the normal approximation.

In the production of compact discs at a certain factory, the proportion of faulty discs is known to be $\frac{1}{5}$. Each week the factory produces 2000 discs. Estimate, to 2 significant figures, the probability that there will be at most 349 faulty discs produced in one week.

It costs 60p to produce a disc. A faulty disc has to be discarded, while a non-faulty disc is sold for £9. Find the expected profit made by the factory per week. [L]

10 State the conditions under which a normal distribution may be used as an approximation to the distribution $B(n,p)$, and write down, in terms of n and p, the mean and the variance of this normal approximation.

(a) A large bag of seeds contains three varieties in the ratios $4:2:1$ and their germination rates are 50%, 60% and 80% respectively. Show that the probability that a seed chosen at random from the bag will germinate is $\frac{4}{7}$.

(b) Given that 150 seeds are chosen at random from the bag, estimate, to 3 decimal places, the probability that less than 90 of them will germinate. [L]

11 The disintegration of a radioactive specimen is known to be at the rate of 14 counts per sec. Using the normal approximation for a Poisson distribution determine the probability that in any given second the counts will be:

(a) 20, 21 or 22

(b) greater than 10

(c) above 12 but less than 16.

12 A marina hires out boats on a daily basis. The mean number of boats hired per day is 15. Using the normal approximation for a Poisson distribution, find, for a period of 100 days:

(a) how often 5 or less boats are hired

(b) how often exactly 10 boats are hired

(c) if the marina owns 20 boats, on how many days they will have to turn customers away.

13 Explain briefly the conditions under which a Poisson distribution may be approximated by a normal distribution. Give an example of the use of this approximation.

Street light failures in a town occur at an average rate of one every two days. Assuming that X, the number of street light failures per week, has a Poisson distribution, find to 3 decimal places, using the tables provided or otherwise, the probabilities that the number of street lights that will fail in a given week will be

(a) exactly 2

(b) less than 6.

(c) Using an appropriate distribution that approximates to that of X, find, to 3 decimal places, the probability that there will be fewer than 45 street light failures in 10 weeks.   [L]

8.5 Linear combinations of independent normal variables

Consider a carton containing twenty-four cans of baked beans. Each can will have been filled by a machine delivering a fixed quantity of beans, each can will be one of many produced to a given specification and the carton will also have been made, along with lots of others, to a given specification.

Let us consider the masses of the beans, the tins and their carton. A suitable model might be:

$$M = B_1 + B_2 + ... + B_{24} + T_1 + T_2 + ... + T_{24} + C$$

where M represents the total mass, B represents the mass of beans, T represents the mass of the tins and C represents the mass of the carton. It is very likely that the distributions of B, T and C will be known, but what is the distribution of M? Situations such as this are quite common and if we make the assumption that B, C and T each have normal distributions and that they are independent of one another then we can obtain the distribution of M.

To do this you need to know that if X is a random variable with p.d.f. $f(x)$ and Y is another random variable with p.d.f. $g(y)$ then:

$$E(X + Y) = E(X) + E(Y) \qquad \text{always}$$

and $\quad \text{Var}(X + Y) = \text{Var}(X) + \text{Var}(Y) \quad$ if X and Y are independent.

Proofs of the above relationships are not needed at this stage but you can make use of them.

With these in mind it can be shown that if $X_1 \sim N(\mu_1, \sigma_1^2)$, $X_2 \sim N(\mu_2, \sigma_2^2)$ and X_1 and X_2 are independent then:

$$(X_1 + X_2) \sim N(\mu_1 + \mu_2, \sigma_1^2 + \sigma_2^2)$$

and

$$(X_1 - X_2) \sim N(\mu_1 - \mu_2, \sigma_1^2 + \sigma_2^2)$$

Note that we always use $\sigma_1^2 + \sigma_2^2$ regardless of whether or not we are considering $(X_1 + X_2)$ or $(X_1 - X_2)$.

It was established in Chapter 6 that:

$$E(aX \pm bY) = aE(X) \pm bE(Y)$$

and

$$\text{Var}(aX \pm bY) = a^2\text{Var}(X) + b^2\text{Var}(Y)$$

If X and Y are independent.

Thus, in general, we can write:

$$aX_1 \pm bX_2 \sim N(a\mu_1, \pm b\mu_2, a^2\sigma_1^2 + b^2\sigma_2^2)$$

Although written for two random variables in this case, the general form can be extended to cover as many random variables as you want. Hence if we assume that $B \sim N(\mu_B, \sigma_B^2)$, $T \sim N(\mu_T, \sigma_T^2)$ and $C \sim N(\mu_C, \sigma_C^2)$ then if

$$M = B_1 + B_2 + ... + B_{24} + T_1 + T_2 + ... + T_{24} + C$$

as above then

$$M \sim N(24\mu_B + 24\mu_T + \mu_C, 24\sigma_B^2 + 24\sigma_T^2 + \sigma_C^2).$$

Example 11

If $X_1 \sim N(8, 3^2)$ and $X_2 \sim N(12, 4^2)$ find the distribution of Y where $Y = X_1 + X_2$.

From the above definitions

$$X_1 + X_2 \sim N(\mu_1 + \mu_2, \sigma_1^2 + \sigma_2^2)$$

$$\therefore \qquad Y = X_1 + X_2 \sim N(8 + 12, 3^2 + 4^2)$$

$$\therefore \qquad Y \sim N(20, 5^2)$$

Example 12

If X_1, X_2 and X_3 are independent normal random variables such that $X_1 \sim N(5, 2)$, $X_2 \sim N(13, 2)$ and $X_3 \sim N(10, 3)$ and Y is a random variable defined by $Y = X_1 - X_2 + 2X_3$, find the distribution of Y.

$$Y = X_1 - X_2 + 2X_3 \sim N(\mu_1 - \mu_2 + 2\mu_3, \sigma_1^2 + \sigma_2^2 + 4\sigma_3^2)$$

$$\therefore \qquad Y \sim N(5 - 13 + 20, 2 + 2 + 12)$$

$$\therefore \qquad Y \sim N(12, 16)$$

Example 13

Bottles of mineral water are delivered to shops in crates containing 12 bottles each. The weights of bottles are normally distributed with mean weight 2 kg and standard deviation 0.05 kg. The weights of empty crates are normally distributed with mean 2.5 kg and standard deviation 0.3 kg.

(a) Assuming that all random variables are independent, find the probability that a full crate will weigh between 26 kg and 27 kg.
(b) Two bottles are selected at random from a crate. Find the probability that they differ in weight by more than 0.1 kg.   [L]

(a) Let $W = X_1 + X_2 + \ldots + X_{12} + C$ where $X \sim N(2, 0.05^2)$ and $C \sim N(2.5, 0.3^2)$.

$$\therefore \qquad E(W) = 12E(X) + E(C)$$
$$= (12 \times 2) + 2.5$$
$$= 26.5$$
$$Var(W) = 12Var(X) + Var(C)$$
$$= (12 \times 0.05^2) + (0.3)^2$$
$$= 0.12$$

$\therefore \qquad P(26 < W < 27) = P\left(\dfrac{26 - 26.5}{\sqrt{0.12}} < Z < \dfrac{27 - 26.5}{\sqrt{0.12}}\right)$

$\qquad\qquad\qquad\qquad = P(-1.44 < Z < 1.44)$

$\qquad\qquad\qquad\qquad = \Phi(1.44) - \Phi(-1.44)$

$\qquad\qquad\qquad\qquad = 2\Phi(1.44) - 1$

$\qquad\qquad\qquad\qquad = 0.8502$

(b) $\qquad E(B_1 - B_2) = 0; Var(B_1 - B_2) = Var(B_1) + Var(B_2)$

$\qquad\qquad\qquad\qquad\qquad\qquad\quad = 0.05^2 + 0.05^2$

$\qquad\qquad\qquad\qquad\qquad\qquad\quad = 0.005$

$\therefore \qquad\qquad P(|B_1 - B_2| > 0.1) = 2P(B_1 - B_2 > 0.1)$

$\qquad\qquad\qquad\qquad\qquad\quad = 2P(Z > 1.41)$

$\qquad\qquad\qquad\qquad\qquad\quad = 2(1 - \Phi(1.41))$

$\qquad\qquad\qquad\qquad\qquad\quad = 0.1586$

Note that z values were rounded to 2 d.p. to avoid interpolation and ease the calculation. In general most people seem to prefer to interpolate – try the same calculation again using interpolation.

Exercise 8D

1 If $X \sim N(70, 4^2)$ and $Y \sim N(60, 3^2)$, find the distribution of W where:

   (a) $W = X + Y$ (b) $W = X - Y$

2 If $X \sim N(45, 5)$ and $Y \sim N(42, 3)$, find the distribution of M where:

   (a) $M = X + Y$ (b) $M = X - Y$

3 If $X \sim N(45, 6)$, $Y \sim N(54, 4)$ and $W \sim N(49, 8)$, find the distribution of A where $A = X + Y + W$.

4 X_1 and X_2 are independent normal random variables. $X_1 \sim N(50, 16)$ and $X_2 \sim N(40, 9)$. Find the distribution of Y where:

   (a) $Y = 2X_1$ (b) $Y = 3X_2$

   (c) $Y = 2X_1 + 3X_2$ (d) $Y = X_1 + 5X_2$

5   Y_1, Y_2 and Y_3 are independent normal random variables.
$Y_1 \sim N(7, 3)$, $Y_2 \sim N(10, 2)$ and $Y_3 \sim N(12, 4)$. Find the
distribution if Z where:

(a) $W = Y_1 + Y_2 + Y_3$ (b) $W = Y_3 - Y_1$
(c) $W = Y_1 + Y_2 + 3Y_3$ (d) $W = 2Y_1 + 2Y_3$
(e) $W = Y_1 - Y_2 + Y_3$

6   A, B and C are independent normal random variables.
$A \sim N(40, 5)$, $B \sim N(50, 7)$ and $C \sim N(70, 10)$. Find:

(a) $P(A + B > 95)$ (b) $P(A + B + C > 172)$
(c) $P(B + C < 116)$ (d) $P(A + B - C < 15)$
(e) $P(A + B - C < 10)$ (f) $P(88 < (A + B) < 95)$

7   The weights of bottles of wine are normally distributed with
mean weight 3 kg and standard deviation 0.05 kg. What is the
mean and standard deviation of 12 bottles of wine?

8   A battery under normal usage has a mean life of 160 hours,
with a standard deviation of 30 hours. Batteries are bought
in packs of four. A tourist has a camera which takes one
battery and he hopes that the pack of four will last for at
least 700 hours. What is the probability of this being the
case?

9   Bakewell tarts are sold in packs of six. The weight of each
tart is a normal variable with mean weight 25 g and standard
deviation 5 g. The weight of the packaging is also a normal
variable, with mean weight 40 g and standard deviation 6 g.
Find the following:

(a) the mean and standard deviation for six Bakewell tarts
(b) the mean and standard deviation for six Bakewell tarts
plus packaging
(c) the probability that the weight of one pack of tarts is less
than 170 g
(d) the mean and standard deviation for twenty packs of
tarts
(e) the probability that the weight of twenty packs of tarts is
less than 3.9 kg.

10 Cornflakes are packed in boxes and the boxes are then packed into cartons. Each carton contains 10 boxes. The weight of the boxes of cornflakes are normally distributed with mean weight 500 g and standard deviation 12 g. The empty cartons are also normally distributed with mean weight 2000 g and standard deviation 90 g. If all the random variables are independent, find the probability that a full carton will weigh between 6.75 kg and 7.25 kg.

11 A sweet manufacturer produces two varieties of fruit sweet, Xtras and Yummies. The weights, X and Y in grams, of randomly selected Xtras and Yummies are such that

$$X \sim N(30, 25) \text{ and } Y \sim N(32, 16)$$

(a) Find the probability that the weight of two randomly selected Yummies will differ by more than 5 g. One sweet of each variety is selected at random.

(b) Find the probability that the Yummy sweet weighs more than the Xtra.

A packet contains 6 Xtras and 4 Yummies.

(c) Find the probability that the average weight of the sweets in the packet lies between 28 g and 33 g.   [L]

12 If $X_1, X_2, ..., X_n$, are independent random variables, each with mean μ and variance σ^2, and the random variable Z is defined as $Z = X_1 + X_2 + ... + X_n$, show that $E(Z) = n\mu$ and $\text{Var}(Z) = n\sigma^2$.

A certain brand of biscuit is individually wrapped. The weight of a biscuit can be taken to be normally distributed with mean 75 g and standard deviation 5 g. The weight of an individual wrapping is normally distributed with mean 10 g and standard deviation 2 g. Six of these individually wrapped biscuits are then packed together. The weight of the packing material is a normal random variable with mean 40 g and standard deviation 3 g. Find, to 3 decimal places, the probability that the total weight of the packet lies between 535 g and 565 g.   [L]

SUMMARY OF KEY POINTS

1 A random variable X, having a uniform distribution over the interval (α, β) has p.d.f.

$$f(x) = \begin{cases} \dfrac{1}{\beta - \alpha} & \alpha < x < \beta \\ 0 & \text{otherwise.} \end{cases}$$

2 For a random variable X, having a uniform distribution

$$E(X) = \frac{\alpha + \beta}{2}$$

$$\text{Var}(X) = \tfrac{1}{12}(\beta - \alpha)^2.$$

3 A continuous random variable X has a normal distribution if it has a p.d.f.

$$f(x) = \frac{1}{\sigma \sqrt{2\pi}} e^{-(x-\mu)^2/(2\sigma^2)} \qquad -\infty < x < \infty$$

4 For a random variable X, having a normal distribution $E(X) = \mu$

$$\text{Var}(X) = \sigma^2.$$

5 For a random variable $X \sim N(\mu, \sigma^2)$

$$Z = \frac{X - \mu}{\sigma} \sim N(0, 1^2).$$

6 A random variable $X \sim B(n, p)$ can be approximated by $Y \sim N(\mu, \sigma^2)$ when $\mu = np$ and $\sigma^2 = np(1 - p)$ provided that n is large, $np > 5$ and $n(1 - p) > 5$.

7 A random variable $X \sim Po(\lambda)$ can be approximated by

$$Y \sim N(\lambda, \lambda) \qquad \text{for } \lambda > 10.$$

8 If X_1 and X_2 are independent random variables such that $X_1 \sim N(\mu_1, \sigma_1^2)$ and $X_2 \sim N(\mu_2, \sigma_2^2)$ then

$$X_1 \pm X_2 \sim N(\mu_1 \pm \mu_2, \sigma_1^2 + \sigma_2^2).$$

9 If X_1 and X_2 are defined as in 8 then

$$aX_1 \pm bX_2 \sim N(a\mu_1 \pm b\mu_2, a^2\sigma_1^2 + b^2\sigma_2^2)$$

Review exercise

2

1   The probability that a door-to-door salesman convinces a customer to buy is 0.7. Assuming sales are independent find the probability that the salesman makes a sale before reaching the fourth house.   [L]

2   Show that for any two events E and F:

$$P(E \cup F) = P(E) + P(F) - P(E \cap F).$$

Express in words the meaning of $P(E|F)$.   [L]

3   A child has a bag containing 12 sweets of which 3 are yellow, 5 are green and 4 are red. When the child wants to eat one of the sweets, a random selection is made from the bag and the chosen sweet is then eaten before the next random selection is made.

(a) Find the probability that the child does not select a yellow sweet in the first two selections.

(b) Find the probability that there is at least one yellow sweet in the first two selections.

(c) Find the probability that the fourth sweet selected is yellow, given that the first two sweets selected were red ones.   [L]

4   Students in a class were given two statistics problems to solve, the second of which was harder than the first. Within the class $\frac{5}{6}$ of the students got the first one correct and $\frac{7}{12}$ got the second one correct. Of those students who got the first problem correct, $\frac{3}{5}$ got the second one correct. One student was chosen at random from the class.

Let A be the event that the student got the first problem correct and B be the event that the student got the second one correct.

(a) Express in words the meaning of $A \cap B$ and of $A \cup B$.

(b) Find $P(A \cap B)$ and $P(A \cup B)$.

(c) Given that the student got the second problem right, find the probability that the first problem was solved correctly.

(d) Given that the student got the second problem wrong, find the probability that the first problem was solved correctly.

(e) Given that the student got the first problem wrong, find the probability that the student also got the second problem wrong.   [L]

5 When a person needs a minicab, she hires it from one of three firms X, Y and Z. Of her hirings 40% are from X, 50% are from Y and 10% are from Z. For cabs hired from X, 9% arrive late, the corresponding percentages for cabs hired from firms Y and Z being 6% and 20% respectively. Calculate the probability that the next cab she hires:

(a) will be from X and will not arrive late

(b) will arrive late.

Given that she calls for a minicab and that it arrives late, find, to 3 decimal places, the probability that it came from Y.

[L]

6 Express $P(E \cup F)$ in terms of $P(E)$ and $P(F)$ when the events E and F are (a) mutually exclusive, (b) independent.

(c) State in words the meaning of $P(G|H)$ for two events G and H.

(d) It is known that 0.3% of the population suffer from a certain kidney disease. A urine test for detecting the presence of the disease will show a positive reaction for 94% of people suffering from the disease, and for 1% of people who do not suffer from the disease. Find, to 3 significant figures, the probability that a randomly selected person who has the test will show a positive reaction.

Given that a randomly selected person who takes the urine test shows a negative reaction, find, to 2 significant figures, the probability that this person does, in fact, have the disease.

[L]

7 Define, in words or in symbols, the meaning of each of the following statements.

(a) Two events E and F are independent.

(b) Two events G and H are mutually exclusive.

Three events A, B and C are defined in the same sample space. The events A and C are mutually exclusive. The events A and B are independent. Given that:

$$P(A) = \tfrac{1}{3}, \ P(C) = \tfrac{1}{5}, \ P(A \cup B) = \tfrac{2}{3}$$

find:

$$P(A \cup C), \ P(B), \ P(A \cap B).$$

Given also that $P(B \cup C) = \tfrac{3}{5}$, determine whether or not B and C are independent. [L]

8 A chocolate factory produces two types of bar, 60% of its production being of type A and 40% of type B. Type A bars come in small and large sizes, 70% being small. Each size comes in milk and plain chocolate, 35% of each size being plain. Type B bars come in small and large sizes, 50% being small. Each size comes in milk and plain chocolate, 25% of each size being plain. By means of a probability tree diagram, or otherwise, find, to 3 significant figures, the probability that:

(a) a bar chosen at random from the production is small and of milk chocolate

(b) a small bar chosen at random from the production is of milk chocolate.

9 Given that E and F are independent events, $P(E) = \tfrac{1}{5}$ and $P(E \cap F) = \tfrac{1}{30}$, find $P(E|F)$, $P(F)$ and $P(E \cup F)$.

10 A dish D_1 contains 6 white, 3 green and 6 yellow sweets. Another dish D_2 contains 8 white, 5 green and 2 yellow sweets. Paula rolls a die and, if it shows 1 or 6, she takes 2 sweets at random from D_1, but if it shows 2, 3, 4 or 5, she takes 2 sweets at random from D_2. Find, to 2 decimal places, the probability that both sweets will be of the same colour when:

(a) sampling is with replacement

(b) sampling is without replacement.

11 A man has, by accident, mixed up two dud torch batteries with three new batteries of identical type. With a voltmeter he tests one battery after another until the two dud batteries are found. With the aid of a tree diagram, or otherwise, find the probability that he will require to test (a) 2 batteries, (b) 3 batteries, in order to be able to identify which two batteries are the dud ones.

12 Two coins are to be tossed one after the other. Find the probability that exactly one will show a head.
Let E denote the event that 'the first coin shows a head' and F denote the event that 'exactly one coin shows a head'. Investigate the independence of the two events E and F.

13 A student has 10 different mathematics books, 6 on pure mathematics and 4 on applied mathematics. Find the number of different ways in which the books can be arranged on a shelf given that:
(a) all the pure mathematics books are together and all the applied mathematics books are together
(b) all the pure mathematics books are together. [L]

14 Find the number of different arrangements that can be made using all eight letters of the word ROTATION.
Find the number of these arrangements in which the letters T are not consecutive. [L]

15 Six chairs are placed in a straight line. Find the number of different ways in which 6 students A, B, C, D, E and F may sit on these chairs so that:
(a) A and B sit next to each other
(b) C and D do not sit next to each other
(c) A and B sit next to each other and C and D do not sit next to each other. [L]

16 There are 7 staff and 6 students on the sports council of a college. A committee of 8 people from the 13 on the sports council is to be selected to organise a tennis competition. Find the number of different ways in which the committee can be selected:
(a) if all the 13 members are available
(b) if there must be more students than staff. [L]

17 (a) A discrete random variable X has the probability
function, p(x), given by:

$$p(x) = kx^2 \qquad x = 0, 1, 2, 3$$
$$p(x) = 0 \qquad \text{otherwise.}$$

Find the values of:

(i) k (ii) E(X)   (iii) Var(X).

(b) A continuous random variable X has the probability
density function, f(x), given by:

$$f(x) = kx^2 \qquad 0 \leqslant x \leqslant 3$$
$$f(x) = 0 \qquad \text{otherwise.}$$

Find the values of:

(i) k (ii) E(X)   (iii) Var(X).

(iv) the median of X, to 3 significant figures.   [L]

18 A random variable R takes the integer value r with
probability p(r) defined by:

$$p(r) = kr^2 \qquad\qquad r = 1, 2, 3$$
$$p(r) = k(7 - r)^2 \qquad r = 4, 5, 6$$
$$p(r) = 0 \qquad\qquad\quad \text{otherwise.}$$

Find the value of k and the mean and variance of the
probability distribution.

Determine the mean and the variance of:

(a) $4R - 2$

(b) $3R_1 - 2R_2$, where R_1 and R_2 are independent
observations of R.   [L]

19 The continuous random variable X has probability density
function:

$$f(x) = \begin{cases} \frac{1+x}{6} & 1 \leqslant x \leqslant 3 \\ 0 & \text{otherwise.} \end{cases}$$

(a) Sketch the probability density function of X.

(b) Calculate the mean of X.

(c) Specify fully the cumulative distribution function of X.

(d) Find m such that $P(X \leqslant m) = \frac{1}{2}$.   [L]

20 The continuous random variable X has probability density function given by:

$$f(x) = \begin{cases} k(1+x^2) & \text{for } 0 \leqslant x \leqslant 1 \\ 0 & \text{otherwise} \end{cases}$$

where k is a constant. Find the value of k and determine $E(X)$ and $\text{Var}(X)$.

A is the event $X > \frac{1}{2}$, B is the event $X > \frac{3}{4}$.

Find:

(a) $P(B)$ (b) $P(B|A)$

21 The probability density function $f(x)$ of a continuous random variable X is given by

$$f(x) = kx^2(2-x) \qquad \text{for } 0 \leqslant x \leqslant 2$$
$$f(x) = 0 \qquad \text{elsewhere}$$

where k is a constant.

(a) Evaluate k.

(b) Draw a sketch of $f(x)$, giving the x-coordinate of the maximum point.

(c) Calculate $P(1 \leqslant X \leqslant 2)$.

(d) Find the mean and variance of X.

22 The random variable X has the binomial distribution B(10, 0.35).

Find $P(X \leqslant 4)$.

The random variable Y has the Poisson distribution with mean 3.5.

Find $P(2 < Y \leqslant 5)$. [L]

23 The number, X, of breakdowns per day of the lifts in a large block of flats has a Poisson distribution with mean 0.2. Find, to 3 decimal places, the probability that on a particular day:

(a) there will be at least one breakdown

(b) there will be at most two breakdowns.

Find, to 3 decimal places, the probability that, during a 20 day period, there will be no lift breakdowns. [L]

24 Jane and Mary play five games. Independently for each game, Jane's probability of winning is $\frac{3}{4}$ in each of the first two games, and $\frac{2}{3}$ in each of the remaining three games. Find the probability that Jane will win exactly three of the five games. [L]

25 Rainfall records in a certain town show that it rains on average 2 days in every 5. Taking Monday as the first day of the week, find, to 3 significant figures, the probability that in a given week

(a) the first 3 days will be without rain and on the remaining days there will be rain

(b) rain will fall on exactly 4 days in the week

(c) Friday will be the first day on which it rains.

Find, to 3 decimal places, the probability that there will be rain in that town on exactly 160 days in a given year of 365 days. [L]

26 A process for making plate glass produces small bubbles (imperfections) scattered at random in the glass, at an average rate of four small bubbles per $10 \, \text{m}^2$.

Assuming a Poisson model for the number of small bubbles, determine, to 3 decimal places, the probability that a piece of glass $2.2 \, \text{m} \times 3.0 \, \text{m}$ will contain

(a) exactly two small bubbles

(b) at least one small bubble

(c) at most two small bubbles.

Show that the probability that five pieces of glass, each $2.5 \, \text{m} \times 2.0 \, \text{m}$, will all be free of small bubbles is e^{-10}.

Find, to 3 decimal places, the probability that five pieces of glass, each $2.5 \, \text{m} \times 2.0 \, \text{m}$, will contain a total of at least ten small bubbles. [L]

27 (a) The probability that a component intended for use in a computer passes a purity test is 0.038. In a batch of 10 randomly selected components find, to 3 decimal places, the probability that:

    (i) none of the components passes the test

    (ii) fewer than three components pass the test.

(b) Using a suitable approximation, estimate the probability that fewer than four components in a batch of 100 pass the test.   [L]

28 In the manufacture of a particular curtain material small faults occur at random at an average of 0.85 per $10\,m^2$.
(a) Find the probability that in a randomly selected $40\,m^2$ area of this material there are at most 2 faults.
This curtain material is going to be used in 10 of the rooms of a small block of furnished flats. Each room will require $40\,m^2$ of the material.
(b) Find the probability that for the first room to be furnished the material will contain at least 1 fault.
(c) Find the probability that in exactly half of these 10 rooms the material will contain exactly 3 faults.
The hooks on which these curtains are to hang are produced by a company which claims that only 2% of the hooks it produces are defective.
The owner of the block of flats buys 500 of the hooks which have been selected at random from the production.
(d) Using a suitable approximation find the probability that this sample contains between 8 and 12 defective hooks, inclusive.   [L]

29 All the letters in a particular office are typed either by Pat, a trainee typist, or by Lyn, who is a fully-trained typist. The probability that a letter typed by Pat will contain one or more errors is 0.3. Find the probability that a random sample of 4 letters typed by Pat will include exactly one letter free from error.
The probability that a letter typed by Lyn will contain one or more errors is 0.05. Use tables, or otherwise, to find, to 3 decimal places, the probability that in a random sample of 20 letters typed by Lyn, not more than 2 letters will contain one or more errors.
On any one day, 6% of the letters typed in the office are typed by Pat. One letter is chosen at random from those typed on that day. Show that the probability that it will contain one or more errors is 0.065.

Given that each of 2 letters chosen at random from the day's typing contains one or more errors, find, to 4 decimal places, the probability that one was typed by Pat and the other by Lyn. [L]

30 State, giving your reasons, the distribution which you would expect to be appropriate in describing:

(a) the number of heads in 10 throws of a penny

(b) the number of blemishes per m² of sheet metal.

A building has an automatic telephone exchange. The number X of wrong connections in any one day is a Poisson variable with parameter λ. Find, in terms of λ, the probability that in any one day there will be:

(c) exactly 3 wrong connections

(d) 3 or more wrong connections.

Evaluate, to 3 decimal places, these probabilities when $\lambda = 0.5$.

Find, to 3 decimal places, the largest value of λ for the probability of one or more wrong connections in any day to be at most $\frac{1}{6}$. [L]

31 A large store sells a certain size of nail either in a small packet at 50p per packet, or loose at £3 per kg. On any shopping day the number, X, of packets sold is a random variable where $X \sim B(8, 0.6)$, and the weight, Y kg, of nails sold loose is a continuous random variable with probability density function f(y) given by

$$f(y) = \frac{2(y-1)}{25} \qquad 1 \leqslant y \leqslant 6$$
$$f(y) = 0 \qquad\qquad \text{otherwise.}$$

Find, to 3 decimal places, the probability that, on any shopping day, the number of packets sold will be:

(a) more than one

(b) seven or fewer.

Find the probability that:

(c) the weight of nails sold loose on any shopping day will be between 4 kg and 5 kg,

(d) on any one shopping day the shop will sell exactly 2 packets of nails and less than 2 kg of nails sold loose, giving your answer to 2 significant figures.

(e) Calculate the expected money received on any shopping day from the sale of this size of nail in this store.   [L]

32 If the random variable X is distributed as N(5,4), find:

(a) $P(X > 0)$

(b) $P(|X - 5| > 3)$

33 By using a normal approximation for $X \sim$ B(80, 0.25) find:

(a) $P(X > 18)$ (b) $P(X < 25)$

(c) $P(X \geqslant 10)$ (d) $P(14 < X \leqslant 18)$

34 Climbing rope produced by a manufacturer is known to be such that one-metre lengths have breaking strengths that are normally distributed with mean 170.2 kg and standard deviation 10.5 kg. Find, to 3 decimal places, the probability that a one-metre length of rope chosen at random from those produced by the manufacturer will have a breaking strength of 175 kg to the nearest kg.   [L]

35 If the random variable $X \sim$ N(300, 25), find:

(a) $P(X < 312)$ (b) $P(305 < X < 312)$

36 If a coin is tossed 1600 times the most likely result is 800 heads. Using a normal approximation estimate how likely this is.

37 By using a normal approximation for $X \sim$ Po (36) find:

(a) $P(X = 36)$ (b) $P(X \geqslant 30)$

(c) $P(X < 40)$ (d) $P(32 < X \leqslant 39)$

38 The diameters of eggs of the little gull are approximately normally distributed with mean 4.11 cm and standard deviation 0.19 cm. Calculate the probability that an egg chosen at random has a diameter between 3.9 cm and 4.5 cm.   [L]

39 The continuous random variable Y has the rectangular distribution

$$f(y) = \begin{cases} \dfrac{1}{\pi} & \dfrac{-\pi}{2} \leqslant y \leqslant \dfrac{\pi}{2} \\ 0 & \text{otherwise.} \end{cases}$$

Find the mean and variance of Y [L]

40 A sample of 4000 people are to be given a certain drug during a trial. It is known that there is a probability of 0.005 that any person has an adverse reaction to the drug. Use a suitable approximation to find the probability that less than 10 have an adverse reaction.

41 During production in a cement plant, test cubes of cement are taken at regular intervals and their compressive strengths, in kg cm^{-2}, are determined. Analysis of data over a long time has shown that compressive strength is normally distributed with a mean of 468 kg cm^{-2} and a standard deviation of 16 kg cm^{-2}. Find, to 3 decimal places, the probability that a randomly chosen cube has a compressive strength:

(a) greater than 480 kg cm^{-2}

(b) between 450 kg cm^{-2} and 475 kg cm^{-2}.   [L]

42 Two gauges are used to test the thickness of panes of glass. Over a long period it is found that 1.25% of the panes pass through the 1.4 mm gauge but 95.4% pass through the 1.6 mm gauge. Assuming the thickness of the glass follows a normal distribution find its mean and standard deviation. Two panes are put together. Find the mean and standard deviation of the resulting thickness.

43 The continuous random variable X has a probability distribution function $f(x)$ as shown below.

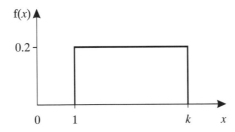

Find:

(a) value of k (b) $P(2.4 \leqslant X \leqslant 3)$ (c) $E(X)$ (d) $Var(X)$

44 The random variables X_1 and X_2 are both normally distributed such that $X_1 \sim N(\mu_1, \sigma_1^2)$ and $X_2 \sim N(\mu_2, \sigma_2^2)$.

Given that $\mu_1 < \mu_2$ and $\sigma_1^2 < \sigma_2^2$, sketch both distributions on the same diagram. The weights of vegetable marrows supplied to retailers by a wholesaler have a normal distribution with mean 1.5 kg and standard deviation 0.6 kg. The wholesaler supplies three sizes of marrow:

Size 1, under 0.9 kg

Size 2, from 0.9 kg to 2.4 kg

Size 3, over 2.4 kg.

Find, to 3 decimal places, the proportion of marrows in the three sizes.

Find, in kg to 1 decimal place, the weight exceeded on average by 5 marrows in every 200 supplied. The prices of the marrows are 16p for Size 1, 40p for Size 2 and 60p for Size 3. Calculate the expected total cost of 100 marrows chosen at random from those supplied.   [L]

45 In a factory, the packets of oats produced are supposed to contain 1 kg of oats each. Over a long period it has been found that the weights of the contents of the packets of oats produced in the factory are normally distributed with mean 1.02 kg and standard deviation 0.009 kg.

Find, to one decimal place, the percentage of packets in the production which have contents whose weights are not within 0.005 kg of the required 1 kg.   [L]

46 State the conditions which are necessary for the use of a binomial distribution. Give an example of the use of a normal approximation to a binomial distribution, giving the parameters of the two distributions and stating any conditions which have to be satisfied in order that the approximation may be used.

In a large restaurant one in four customers asks for iced water with a meal. Use normal distribution approximations to calculate:

(a) the probability, to 4 decimal places, that of the first 100 customers, fewer than 20 will ask for iced water with their meal

(b) the smallest value of n such that there is a probability of at least 0.98 that fewer than n of 1000 customers will ask for iced water.   [L]

47 Jam is packed in tins of nominal net weight 1 kg. The actual weight of jam delivered to a tin by the filling machine is normally distributed about the mean weight set on the machine with a standard deviation of 12 g. The average filling of jam is 1 kg.

(a) Find the probability that a tin chosen at random contains less than 985 g.

It is a legal requirement that no more than 1% of tins contain less than the nominal weight.

(b) Find the minimum setting of the filling machine which will meet this requirement.   [L]

48 Explain briefly the circumstances under which a normal distribution may be used as an approximation to a binomial distribution. Give an example of the use of this approximation.

A large mixture of marrow seeds consists of two strains A and B in the ratio 4 : 1. Seeds are chosen at random from the mixture and planted in rows with 10 seeds in each row. Assuming that all the seeds germinate, find the mean and the variance of the number per row of plants of strain B.

Find an approximate value for the probability that in a total of 50 rows there will be more than 110 plants of strain B.   [L]

49 The random variable X is distributed $N(\mu_1, \sigma_1^2)$ and the random variable Y is distributed $N(\mu_2, \sigma_2^2)$. X and Y are independent variables. State the form of the distribution of $(X + Y)$ and of $(X - Y)$ and give the mean and variance for each distribution.

A factory makes both rods and copper tubes. The internal diameter, X cm, of a copper tube is distributed $N(2.2, 0.0009)$.

(a) Find, to 3 significant figures, the proportion of tubes with internal diameter less than 2.14 cm.

The diameter, Y cm, of a rod is distributed $N(2.15, 0.0004)$.

(b) Find, to 3 decimal places, the proportion of rods with diameter greater than 2.1 cm and less than 2.2 cm.

(c) A rod and a tube are chosen at random. Find, to 3 decimal places, the probability that the rod will not pass through the tube.

(d) A rod and a tube are chosen at random. A second rod and a second tube are chosen at random and then a third rod and a third tube are chosen at random. Find, to 3 decimal places, the probability that each of two rods will pass through the tube which was selected at the same time and one will not. [L]

50 State the conditions under which a Poisson distribution with parameter μ can be approximated by a normal distribution. State the mean and variance of the approximate distribution. The average number of lorries pulling into a motorway service station is 3 every 5 minutes.

(a) Explain why a Poisson distribution is suitable to model the number of lorries pulling into the service station per minute.

(b) Find, to 3 decimal places, the probability that in 10 minutes more than 7 lorries will pull into that service station.

(c) Estimate, giving your answer to 2 significant figures, the probability that more than 45 lorries will pull in during any one hour. [L]

51 A machine produces sheets of glass of thickness X mm, where $X \sim N(\mu, \sigma^2)$. Over a long period of time it has been found that 2% of the sheets are less than 2 mm thick and 5% of the sheets are more than 3 mm thick. Find, to 2 decimal places, the values of μ and σ.

In the manufacture of a certain type of windscreen two of these sheets are taken at random and put together to form a sheet of double thickness. Find, to 2 decimal places, the mean and the standard deviation of the thickness, in mm, of these sheets of double thickness.

Find, to 2 decimal places, the probability that the thickness of a sheet of double thickness will lie between 4 mm and 6 mm.

Given that a sheet of double thickness is between 4 mm and 6 mm thick, find, to 2 decimal places, the probability that the two single sheets from which it is made are both between 2 mm and 3 mm thick. [L]

52 The random variable X is normally distributed with mean μ and variance σ^2.

Given that   P$(X > 58.37) = 0.02$

and P$(X < 40.85) = 0.01$

find μ and σ. [L]

53 A game contains 20 pieces, each of which has probability 0.08 of being defective.

(a) Suggest a suitable distribution to model the number of defective pieces in a game.

Let X represent the number of defective pieces in a game.

(b) Copy and complete the following probability distribution.

x	0	1	2	3	4	5	6 or more
P$(X = x)$	0.1887			0.1414	0.0523	0.0145	

(c) Estimate, giving your answer to 3 decimal places, the probability that a consignment of 10 000 such pieces contains:

(i) at most 750 defective pieces

(ii) between 750 and 850 (inclusive) defective pieces. [L]

54 State the condition under which a normal distribution may be used as an approximation to the Poisson distribution.

Write down the mean and the variance of the normal approximation to the Poisson distribution with mean λ.

Tomatoes from a particular nursery are packed in boxes and sent to a market. Assuming that the number of bad tomatoes in a box has Poisson distribution with mean 0.44, find, to 3 significant figures, the probability of there being (a) fewer than 2, (b) more than 2 bad tomatoes in a box when it is opened.

Use a normal approximation to find, to 3 decimal places, the probability that in 50 randomly chosen boxes there will be fewer than 20 bad tomatoes in total. [L]

55 A machine is producing a type of circular gasket. The specifications for the use of these gaskets in the manufacture of a certain make of engine are that the thickness should lie between 5.45 and 5.55 mm, and the diameter should lie between 8.45 and 8.54 mm. The machine is producing the gaskets so that their thicknesses are N(5.5, 0.0004), that is, Normally distributed with mean 5.5 mm and variance 0.0004 mm^2, and their diameters are independently distributed N(8.54, 0.0025).

Calculate, to one decimal place, the percentage of gaskets produced which will not meet:

(a) the specified thickness limits

(b) the specified diameter limits   [L]

Examination style paper

T1

1. The random variable $X \sim B(400, 0.02)$. Use a Poisson approximation to find $P(X = 7)$.

   (3 marks)

2. A committee of four people consisting of a chairperson, a secretary and two other members is to be selected from a group of 18 people.
   Find the number of possible choices for
   (a) the positions of chairperson and secretary
   (b) the full committee.

   (5 marks)

3. A running club records the number of kilometres, x, to the nearest kilometre, run in training by all of its 90 members. The results are summarized as follows

   $$\sum x = 2\,430 \qquad \sum x^2 = 67\,050$$

   (a) Calculate the mean μ and the standard deviation σ of the number of kilometres run by members of the club in training.
   A new member applies to join the club and she has run μ kilometres in training.
   (b) Explain how the mean and standard deviation will be affected if she were to join the club.

   (8 marks)

4. In a particular co-educational school 55% of the pupils are girls and 45% are boys. During a games afternoon 65% of the pupils play tennis whilst the remainder are engaged in other activities. Only 40% of the boys play tennis.
   A pupil is selected at random, find the probability that:
   (a) the pupil is a girl who plays tennis
   (b) the pupil is a boy who does not play tennis
   (c) the pupil is a girl *given that* the pupil plays tennis.

   (8 marks)

5. State conditions under which the Poisson distribution is a suitable model to use in statistical work.

   Flaws in a certain brand of rope occur at random and at an average of 0.70 per 100 metres. Assuming a Poisson distribution for the number of flaws, find the probability that in a 400 metre long piece of rope

   (*a*)   there will be at least one flaw

   (*b*)   there will be at most 2 flaws.

   Find the probability that in a batch of 5 pieces of rope, each of length 400 metres, all 5 pieces will contain fewer than 3 flaws.

   (11 marks)

6. The random variable X has probability density function given by

   $$f(x) = \begin{cases} 1 - \frac{1}{4}x & 1 \leqslant x \leqslant 3 \\ 0 & \text{otherwise.} \end{cases}$$

   (*a*) Sketch $f(x)$.

   (*b*) Find the mean μ of X.

   (*c*) Show that $P(X > \mu) = 0.462$ (3 d.p.)

   (*d*) Determine whether the median of X is greater or less than μ

   (13 marks)

7. Bottles of lemonade are delivered to shops in crates containing 12 bottles each. The weights of bottles are normally distributed with mean 2.4 kg and standard deviation 0.04 kg.

   The weights of empty crates are normally distributed with mean 2.7 kg and standard deviation 0.3 kg.

   (*a*) Assuming that all random variables are independent, find the probability that a full crate will weigh between 30 kg and 32 kg.

   (*b*) Two bottles are selected at random from a crate. Find the probability that they differ in weight by more than 0.15 kg.

   (15 marks)

8. A firm of accountants recorded the time, x minutes, to the nearest minute, taken to check the accounts of their clients. The values of x below are those recorded for a random sample of 45 clients.

37	33	36	31	31	36	31	30	45
51	31	47	40	40	50	43	41	46
55	42	30	34	41	41	30	51	36
36	42	46	34	38	33	42	37	39
32	34	43	46	34	34	56	32	30

   (*a*) For these data:

   (i)   construct a stem and leaf diagram

   (ii) find the median and quartiles

   (iii) draw a box plot.

   (*b*) Write down which of the mode, median and mean you would prefer to use as a representative for these data. Justify your choice.

   (17 marks)

9. A group of 100 students were each asked to shoot 3 arrows, one after the other, at a target and aim for a particular region in the centre of the target which consisted of 10% of the total area. The random variable X represents the number of times an individual hit the specified region with an arrow. A researcher attempts to model the random variable X with a binomial distribution.

(*a*) Show that, using this model, $P(X \geqslant 2) = 0.028$ and find the complete probability distribution of X.

The researcher's model leads him to expect about 3 (100×0.028) of the 100 students to hit the required region with 2 or more of their arrows.

(*b*) Write down the number of students who he would expect to hit the region with none of their arrows.

(*c*) (i) State the assumption that must be made about the probability p of a single arrow hitting the target.

  (ii) Comment on its realism.

The actual results for the 100 students were as follows

Number of darts in the region	0	1	2	3
Number of students	39	45	13	3

(*d*) Compare these results with your answers in (*b*) and comment on the assumption made in part (*c*).

The researcher decides to refine the model by assuming that the probability of hitting the region with each dart improves with practice. He assumes that the probability for the first dart hitting the region is $\frac{1}{10}$, for the second dart it is $\frac{1}{5}$ and for the third dart it is $\frac{2}{5}$.

(*e*) List the distribution for X using this model.

(*f*) Comment on whether this new model represents an improvement over the binomial model.

(20 marks)

Appendix

Table 1 Binomial cumulative distribution function

The tabulated value is $P(X \leqslant x)$, where X has a binomial distribution with index n and parameter p.

$p =$	0.05	0.10	0.15	0.20	0.25	0.30	0.35	0.40	0.45	0.50
$n = 5, x = 0$	0.7738	0.5905	0.4437	0.3277	0.2373	0.1681	0.1160	0.0778	0.0503	0.0312
1	0.9774	0.9185	0.8352	0.7373	0.6328	0.5282	0.4284	0.3370	0.2562	0.1875
2	0.9988	0.9914	0.9734	0.9421	0.8965	0.8369	0.7648	0.6826	0.5931	0.5000
3	1.0000	0.9995	0.9978	0.9933	0.9844	0.9692	0.9460	0.9130	0.8688	0.8125
4	1.0000	1.0000	0.9999	0.9997	0.9990	0.9976	0.9947	0.9898	0.9815	0.9688
$n = 10, x = 0$	0.5987	0.3487	0.1969	0.1074	0.0563	0.0282	0.0135	0.0060	0.0025	0.0010
1	0.9139	0.7361	0.5443	0.3758	0.2440	0.1493	0.0860	0.0464	0.0233	0.0107
2	0.9885	0.9298	0.8202	0.6778	0.5256	0.3828	0.2616	0.1673	0.0996	0.0547
3	0.9990	0.9872	0.9500	0.8791	0.7759	0.6496	0.5138	0.3823	0.2660	0.1719
4	0.9999	0.9984	0.9901	0.9672	0.9219	0.8497	0.7515	0.6331	0.5044	0.3770
5	1.0000	0.9999	0.9986	0.9936	0.9803	0.9527	0.9051	0.8338	0.7384	0.6230
6	1.0000	1.0000	0.9999	0.9991	0.9965	0.9894	0.9740	0.9452	0.8980	0.8281
7	1.0000	1.0000	1.0000	0.9999	0.9996	0.9984	0.9952	0.9877	0.9726	0.9453
8	1.0000	1.0000	1.0000	1.0000	1.0000	0.9999	0.9995	0.9983	0.9955	0.9893
9	1.0000	1.0000	1.0000	1.0000	1.0000	1.0000	1.0000	0.9999	0.9997	0.9990
$n = 20, x = 0$	0.3585	0.1216	0.0388	0.0115	0.0032	0.0008	0.0002	0.0000	0.0000	0.0000
1	0.7358	0.3917	0.1756	0.0692	0.0243	0.0076	0.0021	0.0005	0.0001	0.0000
2	0.9245	0.6769	0.4049	0.2061	0.0913	0.0355	0.0121	0.0036	0.0009	0.0002
3	0.9841	0.8670	0.6477	0.4114	0.2252	0.1071	0.0444	0.0160	0.0049	0.0013
4	0.9974	0.9568	0.8298	0.6296	0.4148	0.2375	0.1182	0.0510	0.0189	0.0059
5	0.9997	0.9887	0.9327	0.8042	0.6172	0.4164	0.2454	0.1256	0.0553	0.0207
6	1.0000	0.9976	0.9781	0.9133	0.7858	0.6080	0.4166	0.2500	0.1299	0.0577
7	1.0000	0.9996	0.9941	0.9679	0.8982	0.7723	0.6010	0.4159	0.2520	0.1316
8	1.0000	0.9999	0.9987	0.9900	0.9591	0.8867	0.7624	0.5956	0.4143	0.2517
9	1.0000	1.0000	0.9998	0.9974	0.9861	0.9520	0.8782	0.7553	0.5914	0.4119
10	1.0000	1.0000	1.0000	0.9994	0.9961	0.9829	0.9468	0.8725	0.7507	0.5881
11	1.0000	1.0000	1.0000	0.9999	0.9991	0.9949	0.9804	0.9435	0.8692	0.7483
12	1.0000	1.0000	1.0000	1.0000	0.9998	0.9987	0.9940	0.9790	0.9420	0.8684
13	1.0000	1.0000	1.0000	1.0000	1.0000	0.9997	0.9985	0.9935	0.9786	0.9423
14	1.0000	1.0000	1.0000	1.0000	1.0000	1.0000	0.9997	0.9984	0.9936	0.9793
15	1.0000	1.0000	1.0000	1.0000	1.0000	1.0000	1.0000	0.9997	0.9985	0.9941
16	1.0000	1.0000	1.0000	1.0000	1.0000	1.0000	1.0000	1.0000	0.9997	0.9987
17	1.0000	1.0000	1.0000	1.0000	1.0000	1.0000	1.0000	1.0000	1.0000	0.9998
18	1.0000	1.0000	1.0000	1.0000	1.0000	1.0000	1.0000	1.0000	1.0000	1.0000

Table 2 Poisson cumulative distribution function

The tabulated value is $P(X \leqslant x)$, where X has a Poisson distribution with parameter μ.

$\mu =$	0.5	1.0	1.5	2.0	2.5	3.0	3.5	4.0	4.5	5.0
$x = 0$	0.6065	0.3679	0.2231	0.1353	0.0821	0.0498	0.0302	0.0183	0.0111	0.0067
1	0.9098	0.7358	0.5578	0.4060	0.2873	0.1991	0.1359	0.0916	0.0611	0.0404
2	0.9856	0.9197	0.8088	0.6767	0.5438	0.4232	0.3208	0.2381	0.1736	0.1247
3	0.9982	0.9810	0.9344	0.8571	0.7576	0.6472	0.5366	0.4335	0.3423	0.2650
4	0.9998	0.9963	0.9814	0.9473	0.8912	0.8153	0.7254	0.6288	0.5321	0.4405
5	1.0000	0.9994	0.9955	0.9834	0.9580	0.9161	0.8576	0.7851	0.7029	0.6160
6	1.0000	0.9999	0.9991	0.9955	0.9858	0.9665	0.9347	0.8893	0.8311	0.7622
7	1.0000	1.0000	0.9998	0.9989	0.9958	0.9881	0.9733	0.9489	0.9134	0.8666
8	1.0000	1.0000	1.0000	0.9998	0.9989	0.9962	0.9901	0.9786	0.9597	0.9319
9	1.0000	1.0000	1.0000	1.0000	0.9997	0.9989	0.9967	0.9919	0.9829	0.9682
10	1.0000	1.0000	1.0000	1.0000	0.9999	0.9997	0.9990	0.9972	0.9933	0.9863
11	1.0000	1.0000	1.0000	1.0000	1.0000	0.9999	0.9997	0.9991	0.9976	0.9945
12	1.0000	1.0000	1.0000	1.0000	1.0000	1.0000	0.9999	0.9997	0.9992	0.9980
13	1.0000	1.0000	1.0000	1.0000	1.0000	1.0000	1.0000	0.9999	0.9997	0.9993
14	1.0000	1.0000	1.0000	1.0000	1.0000	1.0000	1.0000	1.0000	0.9999	0.9998
15	1.0000	1.0000	1.0000	1.0000	1.0000	1.0000	1.0000	1.0000	1.0000	0.9999
16	1.0000	1.0000	1.0000	1.0000	1.0000	1.0000	1.0000	1.0000	1.0000	1.0000
17	1.0000	1.0000	1.0000	1.0000	1.0000	1.0000	1.0000	1.0000	1.0000	1.0000
18	1.0000	1.0000	1.0000	1.0000	1.0000	1.0000	1.0000	1.0000	1.0000	1.0000
19	1.0000	1.0000	1.0000	1.0000	1.0000	1.0000	1.0000	1.0000	1.0000	1.0000
$\mu =$	5.5	6.0	6.5	7.0	7.5	8.0	8.5	9.0	9.5	10.0
$x = 0$	0.0041	0.0025	0.0015	0.0009	0.0006	0.0003	0.0002	0.0001	0.0001	0.0000
1	0.0266	0.0174	0.0113	0.0073	0.0047	0.0030	0.0019	0.0012	0.0008	0.0005
2	0.0884	0.0620	0.0430	0.0296	0.0203	0.0138	0.0093	0.0062	0.0042	0.0028
3	0.2017	0.1512	0.1118	0.0818	0.0591	0.0424	0.0301	0.0212	0.0149	0.0103
4	0.3575	0.2851	0.2237	0.1730	0.1321	0.0996	0.0744	0.0550	0.0403	0.0293
5	0.5289	0.4457	0.3690	0.3007	0.2414	0.1912	0.1496	0.1157	0.0885	0.0671
6	0.6860	0.6063	0.5265	0.4497	0.3782	0.3134	0.2562	0.2068	0.1649	0.1301
7	0.8095	0.7440	0.6728	0.5987	0.5246	0.4530	0.3856	0.3239	0.2687	0.2202
8	0.8944	0.8472	0.7916	0.7291	0.6620	0.5925	0.5231	0.4557	0.3918	0.3328
9	0.9462	0.9161	0.8774	0.8305	0.7764	0.7166	0.6530	0.5874	0.5218	0.4579
10	0.9747	0.9574	0.9332	0.9015	0.8622	0.8159	0.7634	0.7060	0.6453	0.5830
11	0.9890	0.9799	0.9661	0.9467	0.9208	0.8881	0.8487	0.8030	0.7520	0.6968
12	0.9955	0.9912	0.9840	0.9730	0.9573	0.9362	0.9091	0.8758	0.8364	0.7916
13	0.9983	0.9964	0.9929	0.9872	0.9784	0.9658	0.9486	0.9261	0.8981	0.8645
14	0.9994	0.9986	0.9970	0.9943	0.9897	0.9827	0.9726	0.9585	0.9400	0.9165
15	0.9998	0.9995	0.9988	0.9976	0.9954	0.9918	0.9862	0.9780	0.9665	0.9513
16	0.9999	0.9998	0.9996	0.9990	0.9980	0.9963	0.9934	0.9889	0.9823	0.9730
17	1.0000	0.9999	0.9998	0.9996	0.9992	0.9984	0.9970	0.9947	0.9911	0.9857
18	1.0000	1.0000	0.9999	0.9999	0.9997	0.9993	0.9987	0.9976	0.9957	0.9928
19	1.0000	1.0000	1.0000	1.0000	0.9999	0.9997	0.9995	0.9989	0.9980	0.9965
20	1.0000	1.0000	1.0000	1.0000	1.0000	0.9999	0.9998	0.9996	0.9991	0.9984
21	1.0000	1.0000	1.0000	1.0000	1.0000	1.0000	0.9999	0.9998	0.9996	0.9993
22	1.0000	1.0000	1.0000	1.0000	1.0000	1.0000	1.0000	0.9999	0.9999	0.9997

Table 3 The normal distribution function

The function tabulated below is $\Phi(z)$, defined as

$$\Phi(z) = \frac{1}{\sqrt{2\pi}} \int_{-\infty}^{z} e^{-\frac{1}{2}t^2} dt.$$

z	$\Phi(z)$	z	$\Phi(z)$	z	$\Phi(z)$	z	$\Phi(z)$	z	$\Phi(z)$
0.00	0.5000	0.50	0.6915	1.00	0.8413	1.50	0.9332	2.00	0.9772
0.01	0.5040	0.51	0.6950	1.01	0.8438	1.51	0.9345	2.02	0.9783
0.02	0.5080	0.52	0.6985	1.02	0.8461	1.52	0.9357	2.04	0.9793
0.03	0.5120	0.53	0.7019	1.03	0.8485	1.53	0.9370	2.06	0.9803
0.04	0.5160	0.54	0.7054	1.04	0.8508	1.54	0.9382	2.08	0.9812
0.05	0.5199	0.55	0.7088	1.05	0.8531	1.55	0.9394	2.10	0.9821
0.06	0.5239	0.56	0.7123	1.06	0.8554	1.56	0.9406	2.12	0.9830
0.07	0.5279	0.57	0.7157	1.07	0.8577	1.57	0.9418	2.14	0.9838
0.08	0.5319	0.58	0.7190	1.08	0.8599	1.58	0.9429	2.16	0.9846
0.09	0.5359	0.59	0.7224	1.09	0.8621	1.59	0.9441	2.18	0.9854
0.10	0.5398	0.60	0.7257	1.10	0.8643	1.60	0.9452	2.20	0.9861
0.11	0.5438	0.61	0.7291	1.11	0.8665	1.61	0.9463	2.22	0.9868
0.12	0.5478	0.62	0.7324	1.12	0.8686	1.62	0.9474	2.24	0.9875
0.13	0.5517	0.63	0.7357	1.13	0.8708	1.63	0.9484	2.26	0.9881
0.14	0.5557	0.64	0.7389	1.14	0.8729	1.64	0.9495	2.28	0.9887
0.15	0.5596	0.65	0.7422	1.15	0.8749	1.65	0.9505	2.30	0.9893
0.16	0.5636	0.66	0.7454	1.16	0.8770	1.66	0.9515	2.32	0.9898
0.17	0.5675	0.67	0.7486	1.17	0.8790	1.67	0.9525	2.34	0.9904
0.18	0.5714	0.68	0.7517	1.18	0.8810	1.68	0.9535	2.36	0.9909
0.19	0.5753	0.69	0.7549	1.19	0.8830	1.69	0.9545	2.38	0.9913
0.20	0.5793	0.70	0.7580	1.20	0.8849	1.70	0.9554	2.40	0.9918
0.21	0.5832	0.71	0.7611	1.21	0.8869	1.71	0.9564	2.42	0.9922
0.22	0.5871	0.72	0.7642	1.22	0.8888	1.72	0.9573	2.44	0.9927
0.23	0.5910	0.73	0.7673	1.23	0.8907	1.73	0.9582	2.46	0.9931
0.24	0.5948	0.74	0.7704	1.24	0.8925	1.74	0.9591	2.48	0.9934
0.25	0.5987	0.75	0.7734	1.25	0.8944	1.75	0.9599	2.50	0.9938
0.26	0.6026	0.76	0.7764	1.26	0.8962	1.76	0.9608	2.55	0.9946
0.27	0.6064	0.77	0.7794	1.27	0.8980	1.77	0.9616	2.60	0.9953
0.28	0.6103	0.78	0.7823	1.28	0.8997	1.78	0.9625	2.65	0.9960
0.29	0.6141	0.79	0.7852	1.29	0.9015	1.79	0.9633	2.70	0.9965
0.30	0.6179	0.80	0.7881	1.30	0.9032	1.80	0.9641	2.75	0.9970
0.31	0.6217	0.81	0.7910	1.31	0.9049	1.81	0.9649	2.80	0.9974
0.32	0.6255	0.82	0.7939	1.32	0.9066	1.82	0.9656	2.85	0.9978
0.33	0.6293	0.83	0.7967	1.33	0.9082	1.83	0.9664	2.90	0.9981
0.34	0.6331	0.84	0.7995	1.34	0.9099	1.84	0.9671	2.95	0.9984
0.35	0.6368	0.85	0.8023	1.35	0.9115	1.85	0.9678	3.00	0.9987
0.36	0.6406	0.86	0.8051	1.36	0.9131	1.86	0.9686	3.05	0.9989
0.37	0.6443	0.87	0.8078	1.37	0.9147	1.87	0.9693	3.10	0.9990
0.38	0.6480	0.88	0.8106	1.38	0.9162	1.88	0.9699	3.15	0.9992
0.39	0.6517	0.89	0.8133	1.39	0.9177	1.89	0.9706	3.20	0.9993
0.40	0.6554	0.90	0.8159	1.40	0.9192	1.90	0.9713	3.25	0.9994
0.41	0.6591	0.91	0.8186	1.41	0.9207	1.91	0.9719	3.30	0.9995
0.42	0.6628	0.92	0.8212	1.42	0.9222	1.92	0.9726	3.35	0.9996
0.43	0.6664	0.93	0.8238	1.43	0.9236	1.93	0.9732	3.40	0.9997
0.44	0.6700	0.94	0.8264	1.44	0.9251	1.94	0.9738	3.50	0.9998
0.45	0.6736	0.95	0.8289	1.45	0.9265	1.95	0.9744	3.60	0.9998
0.46	0.6772	0.96	0.8315	1.46	0.9279	1.96	0.9750	3.70	0.9999
0.47	0.6808	0.97	0.8340	1.47	0.9292	1.97	0.9756	3.80	0.9999
0.48	0.6844	0.98	0.8365	1.48	0.9306	1.98	0.9761	3.90	1.0000
0.49	0.6879	0.99	0.8389	1.49	0.9319	1.99	0.9767	4.00	1.0000
0.50	0.6915	1.00	0.8413	1.50	0.9332	2.00	0.9772		

Table 4 Percentage points of the normal distribution

The values z in the table are those which a random variable $Z \sim N(0, 1)$ exceeds with probability p; that is, $P(Z > z) = 1 - \Phi(z) = p$.

p	z	p	z
0.5000	0.0000	0.0500	1.6449
0.4000	0.2533	0.0250	1.9600
0.3000	0.5244	0.0100	2.3263
0.2000	0.8416	0.0050	2.5758
0.1500	1.0364	0.0010	3.0902
0.1000	1.2816	0.0005	3.2905

Answers

Exercise 2A

1. (a) quantitative and continuous
   (b) quantitative and discrete
   (c) qualitative
2. (a) described by numbers; rises in one penny steps
   (b) described by numbers; takes all possible values in a given range
   (c) cannot be described numerically
3. (a) examination marks, number of students, cost of lunch, etc.
   (b) time taken to do homework, classroom temperature, student weights, etc.
4. (a) continuous; age can take values between the integers
   (b) discrete; goes up in 1 year steps
5. (a) infinite
   (b) countably infinite
   (c) finite
6. (a) a book
   (b) a car
   (c) a patient
7. (a) a register of all students at the university
   (b) all L-registered cars recorded at the Driver and Vehicle Licensing Centre, Swansea
   (c) all registered professional golfers
8. A car could be the sampling unit. Because the population is to all purposes infinite a suitable sampling frame could be all cars passing a check point on a given road at a certain time.
9. Advantages: quick, cheap, does not destroy all batteries
   Disadvantages: may contain natural variations and bias due to smallness of samples.
10. This is an infinite population so you cannot measure each tree. Rates of growth may vary in different parts of the forest – each type of area must be identified and an appropriate sampling frame drawn up. Sampling units must be free from bias, etc.

Exercise 3A

1

Temp. (°C)	Tally	Frequency
18					3
19	⊦⊦⊦		6
20	⊦⊦⊦ ⊦⊦⊦ |||	13
21	⊦⊦⊦ ||||	9
22	⊦⊦⊦ ⊦⊦⊦	10
23						4
24	⊦⊦⊦		6
25	⊦⊦⊦	5
26				2
27					3

2

Rating	Tally	Frequency
A	~~IIII~~	5
B	~~IIII~~ ~~IIII~~ ~~IIII~~ II	17
C	~~IIII~~ ~~IIII~~ ~~IIII~~	14
D	~~IIII~~ IIII	9
E	~~IIII~~	5

3 Cumulative frequencies: 3, 9, 22, 31, 41, 45, 51, 56, 58, 61

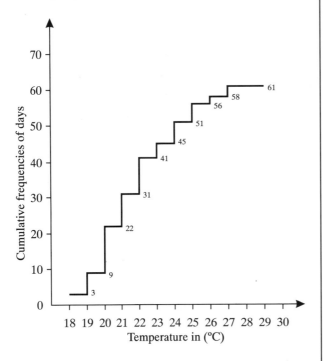

4 Cumulative frequencies: 3, 7, 9, 14, 17, 23, 26, 27, 30

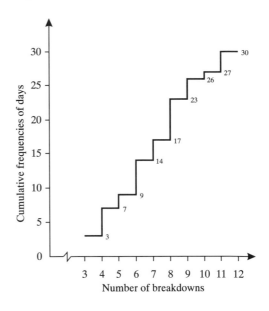

5 Cumulative frequencies: 4, 14, 30, 58, 92, 136, 168, 184, 194, 200

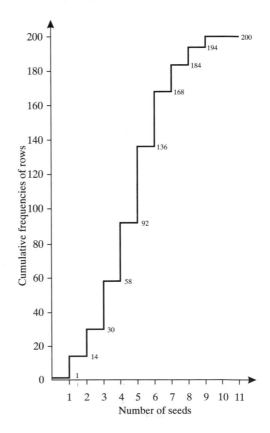

6

4	0 1 1 1 1 1 2 2 2 2 4 4 5 6 7 8 9
5	0 0 1 1 2 4 4 5 8 9 9
6	2 5 6 7 7 7 8 9 9 9
7	0 1 2 2 3 3 7 8 8
8	0 0 2 4 4 5 5 6 6 8 9 9 9

7

0	8 9 9
1	0 0 2 2 3 4 5 5 6 7 7 7 7 8 9 9 9 9
2	0 1 1 1 2 2 3 3 3 6 6 6 6 7 8 8 8
3	0 0 0 1 2 3 4 6 6 7
4	3 5

8 *Length in cm*   2 $\vert$ 2 means 2.2

2	2 5 5 7 7
3	1 2 2 4 5 5 5 7 8 8
4	3 3 7 7 8
5	1 1 2 2 2 2 2 6 8
6	1 1 2 4 4 4 6 6 7 8
7	1 2 3 5 5 5 5 6 6 7 8 8
8	1 3 3 4 6 6 8 8 9

9 *Playing times*   Rounding to two significant figures, for example, 2 $\vert$ 6 means 2.57

2	6
3	2 2 3 3 4 4 4
4	2 2 3 4 5 5
5	0 1 1 1 1 2 2 4
6	2 2 2 3 3 3 4 5
7	1 2 3 4 5
8	0 2 5 6
9	1

10

1	0 4 4 5 6 7 7 9 9
2	0 1 1 2 5 5 5 8 8 9 9 9
3	1 2 3 4 5 5 6 7 8 8 8 9
4	2 3 4 4 4 5 5 6 6 7 8 9 9
5	1 1 1 2 2 2 3 4 5 6 7 7 7 9

11

	1994			1993

```
              8 7 5 4 2 2 2 2 1 0 0 | 3 |
9 9 8 8 7 7 7 7 7 5 5 5 3 3 3 3 3 3 2 2 0 0 | 4 | 0 1 1 1 1 1 2 2 2 2 4 4 5 6 7 8 9
                    6 6 4 2 2 2 0 0 | 5 | 0 0 1 1 2 4 4 5 8 9 9
                  9 6 6 3 3 3 2 0 0 | 6 | 2 5 6 7 7 7 8 9 9 9
                      7 6 6 3 2 1 0 | 7 | 0 1 2 2 3 3 7 8 8
                                    | 8 | 0 0 2 4 4 5 5 6 6 8 9 9 9
```

Marks in 1994 are generally lower than in 1993.

12

	Girls			Boys

```
9 8 8 6 6 3 3 1 1 1 0 0 | 1 | 0 1 4 7 7 9
    9 9 8 7 7 6 5 5 4 3 1 | 2 | 0 0 0 2 2 4 5 6 6 8 8 8 9
        9 8 6 5 4 3 2 2 1 0 | 3 | 1 2 2 4 4 6 7 8 9
              8 4 4 3 2 1 0 | 4 | 0 1 1 2 2 2 2 4 6 7 8 9
```

Boys buy slightly more packets than girls.

Exercise 3B

1 (a) 5.5, 7.5; 6.5; 2   (b) −0.5, 2.5; 1; 3

   (c) 4.5, 14.5; 9.5; 10   (d) −8.5, −1.5; −5; 7

   (e) 1.45, 1.80, 1.625, 0.35

2

Classes	0–9	10–19	20–29	30–39	40–49	50–59	60–69	70–79
Frequency	10	4	5	12	7	5	5	2

3 Reveals patterns; allows summaries to be made. Some detail lost.

4

Class	60–64	65–69	70–74	75–79	80–84	85–89	90–94	95–99
Frequency	9	6	5	7	6	9	4	4

5

Mark	0–9	10–19	20–29	30–39	40–49	50–59	60–69	70–79
Frequency	10	4	5	12	7	5	5	2
Cumulative frequency	10	14	19	31	38	43	48	50

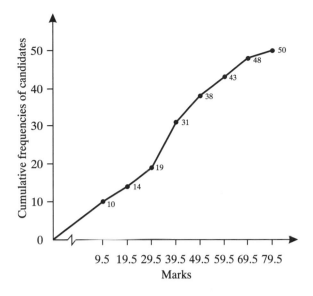

6

No. of pairs	30–39	40–49	50–59	60–69	70–79	80–89	90–99
No. of Fridays	1	5	9	17	12	3	5
Cumulative No. of Fridays	1	6	15	32	44	47	52

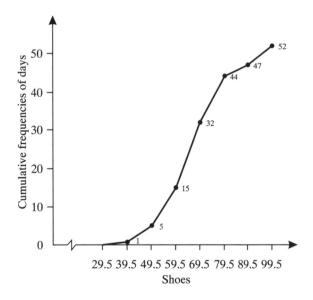

7

Time (hours)	650–659	660–669	670–679	680–689	690–699	700–709	710–719	720–729	730–739
Frequency	1	3	3	7	15	7	7	4	3
Cumulative frequency	1	4	7	14	29	36	43	47	50

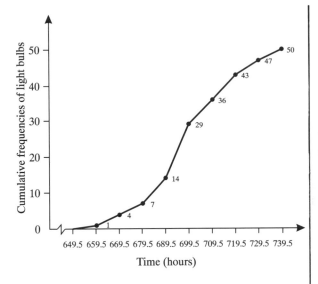

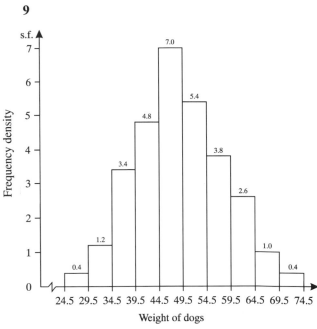

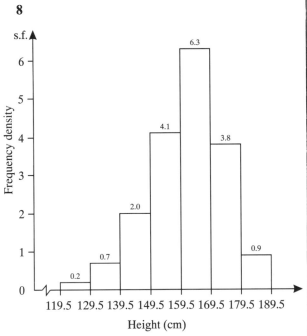

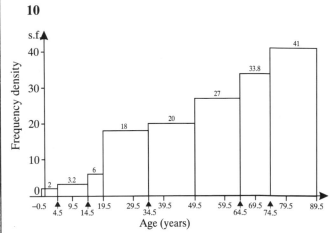

11

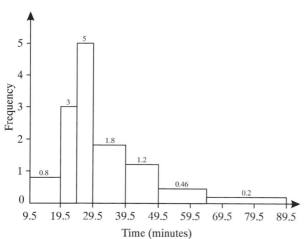

12

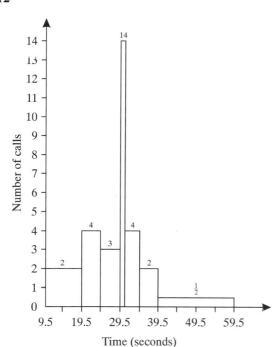

13

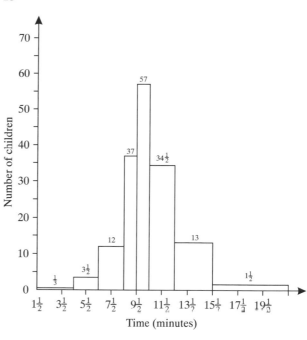

Exercise 4A

Answers using other recognized methods are
acceptable. They will be close to those given here.

1 (a) 8, 8   (b) 13, 13   (c) 15–19, 16.16
2 (a) 3, 8   (b) 4, 6   (c) 23.46, 41.75
3 (a) 20.5, 39.5   (b) 18.33, 24.7   (c) 2, 6
4 (a) 48, 60   (b) 13, 14   (c) 32.57, 47.5
5 (a) 8 cars   (b) 7 cars   (c) 3 cars
6 (a) 182.5   (b) 182.5, 177.5, 187.5
    (c) 180 cm
7 (a) 2   (b) 3   (c) 4, 4
8 (a) 21.49, 16.3, 26.97 (b) 33.76 (c) 20.21
9 (a) 107, 101.44   (b) 102.83, 111.17
    (c) 105.04
10 44, 35, 55
11 (a) 21.9 words/sentence   (b) 30.08
12 £13 094.60
13 3.34
14 5.689 peas/pod
15 39.37
16 630.95
17 (a) 29 commuters   (b) 8.541, 11.397

Exercise 4B

1 (a) 12, 5.5, 2.75   (b) 6, 2, 1   (c) 8, 4, 2

2 (a) 17   (b) (i) 9, 18 (ii) 9   (iii) 4.5

3 (a) 12.5, 5.749   (b) 3.52, 1.27
(c) 23.25, 5.449

4 (a) 17.6, 3.627   (b) 14.49, 1.353
(c) 21.46, 4.886

5 6, 3.667

6 54, 13.6

7 48.30, 14.838

8 147.94, 88.15

9 6.25, 1.333

10 548.25, 67.925

11 4.6, 2

12 (a)

```
      ┌────┬──────┬────┐
├─────┤    │      │    ├──────┤
      └────┴──────┴────┘
  1     15    28    37    48

0    10    20    30    40    50
```

(b) negative skew

13 5, 6, 6.6, positive skew

14 −1.1617, negative skew

Review exercise 1

1 (a)

g:	0	1	2	3	4	5	6	7	8
Frequency:	2	4	6	9	12	9	8	7	3
Cumulative frequency:	2	6	12	21	33	42	50	57	60

(b)

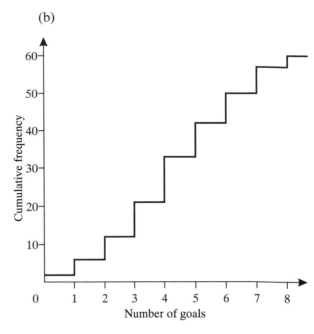

2 (a) continuous; rainfall can take any value.
(b) continuous; the growth rate can take any value.
(c) discrete; money goes up in 1 penny steps.
(d) continuous; temperature can take any value.

3 (i) It is more cost effective.
(ii) It may be a destructive test.

4 1.29 m

5

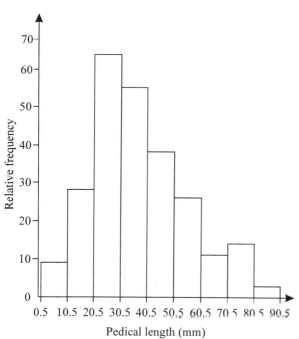

6 (a) and (d) are qualitative

(b), (c) and (e) are quantitative

7 (a) 60.5 kg (b) 68.5 kg (c) 4 kg (d) 77 kg

(e) 78.5 kg

8 (a) countably infinite

(b) finite

(c) finite

(d) countably infinite

9

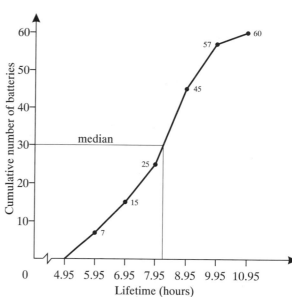

median 8.3 (8.2 to 8.4 acceptable).

10 58.37

11

```
0 | 5 5 7
1 | 1 2 2 3 5 9
2 | 3 3 3 4 5 5 5 6 6 9
3 | 2 3 3 4 4 4 5 5 5 6 6 7 7 9 9 9
4 | 0 1 1 2
```

median 32.5

12 (a) a single leaf

(b) all the leaves on one tree

13

```
                    AH1                    AH2
                              0    9
                        8 6 2    1    0 4 6 6 7 7 8 8 8 9 9
              8 6 5 5 4 3 3 1    2    2 3 3 3 4 5 5 5 6 6 8 9
    7 7 6 4 4 4 4 2 2 0 0 0    3    1 2 4 4 4 4 6 7 8
      8 7 4 4 4 2 1 1 1 0 0    4    0 0 4 4 5
                  9 6 4 0 0    5    0 1
                          2    6
```

Scores are not equally balanced.

Scores tend to be higher on AH1.

14 (a) 2 years

(b) 3.5, 2, 5

(c) 3.98

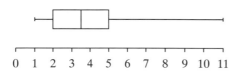

mode < median < mean

15 205.16 ml, 9.22 ml

16

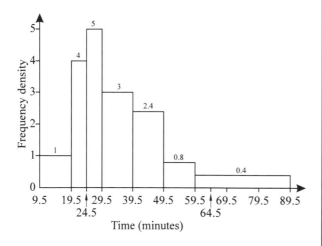

Positive skew

17 (a) a child

(b) all the children in the school

(c) all English school children

No. Does not allow for regional or age variations.

18

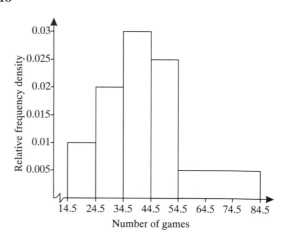

19 (a) 46.94, 35.44, 58.43

(b) 41.06, 55.89

(c) 25.03, 69.41

20 (a) Group B

(b) 4 years 8 months, 3 years 2 months

(c)

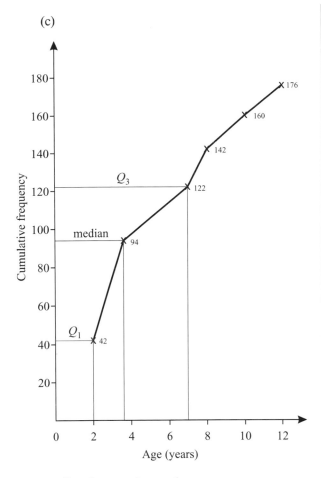

median 3 years 9 months

$Q_3 - Q_1 = (7.1 - 2.1) = 5$ years

Median is best (mean affected by long tail, and no spread measure associated with mode).

21 (a) 755.0 hours, 744.3 hours, 761.2 hours

    (b) mean 751.2,

        standard deviation 15.9, skew -0.7

    (c) negative skew.

22

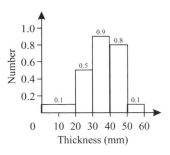

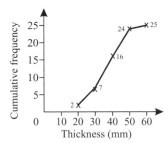

    37 mm, 25 mm, 0–2

23 117.73, 10.1698

24 (a)

4	1 2 3 4 4 6 7 7 8 8
5	0 2 2 2 3 4 6 7 8 8
6	0 2 3 3 6 6 7 7 8
7	0 0 2 2 4 4 6 7 8 8 8
8	0 1 2 5 5 6 6 7
9	3 3 4

    (b) 52 m, 66 m, 78 m

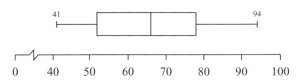

25 50.28 matches, 1.2942 matches

26

Census: complete enumeration of population

Survey: small portion of population used, chosen randomly

Examples: 10 year population census opinion polls

Census: very accurate since all included costly

Survey: cuts down time/organisation problems of accuracy, etc.

27 (a) 1.955 m, 0.0669 m

(b)

(c) 1.955 m, 1.916 m, 1.992 m, negative skew since $Q_2 - Q_1 > Q_3 - Q_2$

(d) 1.955, 0.0046.

28 (a)

```
0   2 3 3 3 4 4 4 5 5 5 5 5 5 6 6 7 8 8 8 9
1   0 0 0 2 3 3 3 3 4 4 4 4 5 7 7 9
2   1 2 2 3 3 3 3 4 6
3   3 4 4 6
4   1 3
```

(b) positive skew

(c) 14.76 minutes, 114.96 minutes

(d) reduced accuracy due to loss of detail

29 (a) £54.03, £90.31

(b) Distribution is skewed in favour of small orders but very large ones will distort the calculations.

(c) median and SIQR

30 (a) 9.56 m, 1.015 m

(b) 0.33, little evidence of normality

(c) 4.65 m – 14.61 m

(d) 4.30 m – 15.27 m, intervals not identical although close.

Exercise 5A

1 (a) $\frac{8}{15}$ (b) $\frac{1}{5}$ (c) $\frac{17}{30}$ (d) $\frac{3}{10}$

2 (a) $\frac{1}{52}$ (b) $\frac{4}{13}$ (c) $\frac{49}{52}$ (d) $\frac{3}{52}$

(e) Card is a diamond but not a queen.

(f) Card is not a diamond and not a queen.

3 0.35

4 (a) 0.1 (b) 0.2 (c) $\frac{1}{2}$ (d) 0.2

(e) 0.8 (f) $\frac{1}{2}$

5 (a) 0.10 (b) 0.25 (c) 0.50 (d) 0.25

(e) 0.85

6 (a) 0.2 (b) 0.4 (c) 0.4 (d) 0.2

7 (a) 0.10 (b) 0.05

8 (a) 0.45

9 (a) 0.05

10 (b) 0.009, 0.012, 0.0075 (d) 0.0285

Exercise 5B

1 (a) $\frac{1}{3}$ (b) $\frac{8}{15}$ (c) $\frac{2}{3}$

2 (a) 0.1 (b) 0.7

3 (a) (i) 0.175 (ii) $\frac{9}{20}$ (b) P(CnKof)

4 (a) 0.3 (b) $\frac{3}{4}$ (c) $\frac{3}{7}$ (d) $\frac{2}{3}$

5 (a) 0.46 (b) 0.652 (c) 0.348 (d) $\frac{4}{9}$

6 (a) 0.3375 (b) 0.2225 (c) 0.434

7 (a) $\frac{23}{30}$ (b) $\frac{4}{15}$ (c) $\frac{3}{4}$

8 (a) $\frac{1}{2}, \frac{1}{8}$ (b) $\frac{1}{4} = P(A)$

9 (a) 0.395 (b) 0.089 (c) 0.107

10 (a) 0.33 (b) $\frac{7}{11}$

11 $\frac{13}{25}, \frac{3}{4}$

12 (a) $\frac{7}{15}$ (b) $\frac{4}{15}$ (c) $\frac{4}{15}, \frac{119}{450}$

Exercise 5C

1 (a) 0.42 (b) 0.88

2 0.58

3 0.94

4 (a) $\frac{1}{6}, \frac{1}{9}, \frac{1}{6}, 0, 0, \frac{1}{36}$ (b) B (c) C

5 (a) $\frac{4}{15}$ (b) $\frac{2}{5}$ (c) $\frac{2}{3}$ (d) $\frac{3}{5}$

(e) $H =$ hard-back and $F =$ fiction

6 (a) 0.65 (b) 0.7 (c) 0.35

7 (a) 0.1 (b) 0.2 (c) 0.5

8 (a) $\frac{1}{2}$ (b) $\frac{1}{3}$ (c) $\frac{1}{2}$ (d) $\frac{2}{3}$ (e) $\frac{1}{3}$ (f) 0

(g) $\frac{1}{6}$ (h) R and Q'

10 (a) 0.2 (b) 0.03 (c) 0.32

11 (a) $\frac{10}{49}$ (b) $\frac{4}{21}$ $8 \to \frac{1}{7}$; $7,8,9 \to \frac{1}{7}$

12 (a) Independence (b) Mutually exclusive
  (c) Mutually exclusive (d) 0 (e) $\frac{1}{6}$

13 (a) $\frac{1}{8}$ (b) $\frac{3}{11}$

14 $\frac{15}{44}$; not; $\frac{1}{10}$

Exercise 5D

1 (a) $5! = 120$ (b) $^5P_3 = 60$

2 $6! = 720$

3 (a) $8! = 40\,320$ (b) $^8P_6 = 20\,160$

4 (a) $5! = 120$ (b) $\frac{2}{5}$ (c) $3 \times 4! = 72$

5 (a) 60 (b) $\frac{3}{5}$ (c) 24

6 (a) $\frac{1}{720}$ (b) $\frac{1}{7560}$

7 (a) $4\,989\,600$ (b) $453\,600$ (c) $90\,720$
  (d) $10\,800$

8 (a) 180 (b) $\frac{1}{180}$ (c) $\frac{4}{15}$

9 $\binom{8}{5} - 56$

10 $3 \times \binom{17}{10} = 58\,344$

11 12

12 (a) 30 (b) 42

13 (a) 182 (b) 41

14 (a) 11 (b) 192

15 (a) 40 (b) 385

Exercise 6A

1 (a) $\frac{1}{12}$ (b) $\frac{3}{4}$

2 (a) $\frac{3}{8}$ (b) $\frac{5}{8}$

3 (a) Yes; $x = \frac{1}{6}$ (b) Yes; $x = 0.2$ (c) No

4 $a = \frac{1}{2}$, $b = \frac{1}{6}$, $c = \frac{1}{3}$

5 $p(x = r) = \frac{r}{21}$; $r = 1, 2, \ldots 6$

6 (b)

S:	2	3	4	5	6	7	8
$p(s) \times \frac{1}{16}$:	1	2	3	4	3	2	1

  (d)

d:	0	1	2	3
$p(d)$:	$\frac{4}{16}$	$\frac{6}{16}$	$\frac{4}{16}$	$\frac{2}{16}$

7 (a)

x:	150	120	70	40
$p(x)$:	$\frac{1}{10}$	$\frac{3}{10}$	$\frac{3}{10}$	$\frac{3}{10}$

8 (b)

t:	1	2	3
$p(t)$:	$\frac{1}{2}$	$\frac{1}{4}$	$\frac{1}{4}$

  (c)

h:	0	1
$p(h)$:	$\frac{1}{8}$	$\frac{7}{8}$

9 (a) (i) Yes; discrete (ii) No; F not a number
  (iii) Yes; discrete
  (b) (i) No; E not a number
  (ii) Yes; continuous (iii) Yes; discrete
  (iv) Yes; continuous

10 (a) Continuous (b) Discrete (c) Discrete
  (d) Continuous

11 $\frac{1}{32}$

12 (a) 0.128 (c) 0.512

13 (a) $\frac{2}{15}$ (b) $\frac{2}{5}$

Exercise 6B

1 (a) $E(X) = \frac{11}{6}$ $\mathrm{Var}(X) = \frac{17}{36}$
  (b) $E(X) = 0$ $\mathrm{Var}(X) = 0.5$
  (c) $E(X) = -0.5$ $\mathrm{Var}(X) = 2.25$

2 $E(Y) = 3.5 + \mathrm{Var}(Y) = \frac{35}{12}$

3 (a)

s:	2	3	4	5	6	7	8	9	10	11	12
$p(s) \times \frac{1}{36}$:	1	2	3	4	5	6	5	4	3	2	1

  (b) $E(S) = 7$ (c) $\mathrm{Var}(S) = \frac{35}{6}$

4 (a)

d:	0	1	2	3	4	5
$p(d) \times \frac{1}{36}$:	6	10	8	6	4	2

  (b) $E(D) = \frac{35}{18}$ (c) $\mathrm{Var}(D) = \frac{665}{324}$

5 (a) $\frac{91}{6}$ (b) $\frac{140}{3}$

6 (a)

h:	0	1	2
$p(h)$:	$\frac{1}{4}$	$\frac{1}{2}$	$\frac{1}{4}$

  (b) $E(H) = 1$
  (c) $\mathrm{Var}(H) = \frac{1}{2}$

7 (b) $E(T) = \frac{7}{4}$ (c) $\mathrm{Var}(T) = \frac{11}{16}$ or 0.6875

8 87.5p

9 (a) 2 (b) $a = \frac{3}{8}$ $b = \frac{1}{4}$

10 (a) 1p $\to \frac{17}{40}$ 2p $\to -\frac{7}{20}$
  (b) Yes with 1p since expected value is positive.
  (c) It was making a loss because people saw that 1p was better.

11 (a) $\frac{20}{49}$ (b) $\frac{120}{49}$ (c) 2.5739

12 $\frac{11}{100}$ $E(X) = 0.21$ $\mathrm{Var}(X) = 0.2059$

13 (a) $\frac{1}{100}$ (b) 3.54; 0.4684

Exercise 6C

1 (a) 2 (b) $\frac{1}{3}$ (d) $\frac{4}{9}$
2 (a) $\frac{10}{9}$ (b) $\frac{26}{81}$ (c) $\frac{5}{12}$ (d) $\frac{128}{243}$
3 (a) $\frac{5}{16}$ (b) $\frac{3}{5}$
4 (b) 0 (d) 0.54
5 (a) $\frac{1}{4}$ (b) 1.6 (c) $\frac{1}{16}$
6 (a) No; f(−1) < 0 (b) No; Area > 1
   (c) Yes
7 (a) 2 (b) $\frac{3}{4}$
8 (b) £102.19 (c) £10.22 (d) £13.61
9 (a) $\frac{1}{2500}$ (b) $\frac{16}{3}$ (c) 2.21 (d) 0.9216; 0.0064
10 (a) 0 (b) $\frac{\pi^2}{12}$

Exercise 6D

1 (a) 7 (b) −4 (c) 81 (d) 81 (e) 13
   (f) 11 (g) 12 (h) 18
2 (a) 3μ (b) $2\mu + 3$ (c) $3 - 2\mu$ (d) $4\sigma^2$
   (e) $4\sigma^2$ (f) $\sigma^2 + \mu^2$ (g) $\sigma^2 + \mu^2 + \mu$
   (h) $\sigma^2 + \mu^2 - \mu - 2$
3 (a) $a = \frac{1}{5}$, $b = -4$ (b) $a = 3$, $b = 40$
   (c) $a = 2$, $b = 10$ (d) $a = 1$, $b = -15$
4 (a) $\mu_X + \mu_Y$ (b) $2\mu_X - 3\mu_Y$ (c) $\sigma_X^2 + \sigma_Y^2$
   (d) $4\sigma_X^2 + 9\sigma_Y^2$ (e) $\mu_X + \frac{1}{2}\mu_Y$
   (f) $\sigma_X^2 + \frac{1}{4}\sigma_Y^2$ (g) $\mu_X - \mu_Y$ (h) $\sigma_X^2 + \sigma_Y^2$
   (i) $\sigma_X^2 + \sigma_Y^2 + (\mu_X - \mu_Y)^2$
   (j) $2\mu_X\mu_Y$; $E(XY) = E(X).E(Y)$
5 (a) 0 (b) 9 (c) $\frac{5}{2}$ (d) $\frac{9}{4}$ (e) 22 (f) 189
   (g) 5 (h) 56 (i) 9 (j) 22 (k) −4 (l) 34
6 (a) $E(S) = 7$ $Var(S) = \frac{35}{6}$ (b) $\mu = 7$,
   $\sigma^2 = \frac{35}{3}$
7 (a) 0.35 (b) 4.2
8 $E(Y) = \frac{h^2}{6}; \frac{1}{2}$
9 $E(R) = \frac{11}{4}$ $Var(R) = \frac{37}{16}$
   (a) $E(2R - 5) = \frac{1}{2}$ $Var(2R - 5) = \frac{37}{4}$
   (b) $E(R_1 - R_2) = 0$ $Var(R_1 - R_2) = \frac{37}{8}$

Exercise 6E

1 (b) 0

(c)
$$F(x) = \begin{cases} 0 & x < 0 \\ x - \frac{1}{4}x^2 & 0 \leqslant x \leqslant 2 \\ 1 & x > 2 \end{cases}$$

(d) $2 - \sqrt{2}$
2 (b) 0
(c)
$$F(y) = \begin{cases} 0 & y < 0 \\ \frac{1}{2}y - \frac{y^2}{18} & 0 \leqslant y \leqslant 3 \\ 1 & y > 3 \end{cases}$$

(d) $\left(\dfrac{9 - 3\sqrt{5}}{2}\right)$

3 (b) 2
(c)
$$F(x) = \begin{cases} 0 & x < 0 \\ \frac{x^4}{16} & 0 \leqslant x \leqslant 2 \\ 1 & x > 2 \end{cases}$$

(d) 1.68
4 (b) Bimodal at −1 and 1 (c) 0
(d)
$$F(x) = \begin{cases} 0 & x < -1 \\ \frac{x^3}{8} + \frac{3}{8}x + \frac{1}{2} & - \leqslant x \leqslant 1 \\ 1 & x > 1 \end{cases}$$

5 (b) mode = median = 0
(c)
$$F(x) = \begin{cases} 0 & x < -2 \\ \frac{1}{2} + \frac{3x}{8} - \frac{x^3}{32} & -2 \leqslant x \leqslant 2 \\ 1 & x > 2 \end{cases}$$

6 (b) 1.5
(c)
$$F(x) = \begin{cases} 0 & x < 0 \\ \frac{x^2}{20}(9 - 2x) & 0 \leqslant x \leqslant 2 \\ 1 & x > 2 \end{cases}$$

7 (a)
$$f(x) = \begin{cases} 12x^2(1-x) & 0 \leqslant x \leqslant 1 \\ 0 & \text{otherwise.} \end{cases}$$

(b) $\frac{2}{3}$ (c) 0.2853

8 (a)
$$f(x) = \begin{cases} \frac{x}{4} & 1 \leqslant x \leqslant 3 \\ 0 & \text{otherwise.} \end{cases}$$

(b) 3   (c) $\sqrt{5}$ (d) $\sqrt{3}, \sqrt{7}$

9 (a) No $\because$ $F^1(1) < 0$
(b) No $\because$ $F^1(2) < 0$
(c) Yes

$$f(x) = \begin{cases} \frac{15}{2}x^2(1-x^2) & 0 \leqslant x \leqslant 1 \\ 0 & \text{otherwise.} \end{cases}$$

(d) No $\because$ $F^1(4) < 0$

10 Possible expressions are for:
(a) $F(x) = \frac{(x-1)^3 + 1}{9}$ (b) $f(x) = \frac{(x-1)^3}{3}$

11 (a)
$$F(w) = \begin{cases} 0 & w < 0 \\ \frac{w^4}{5^5}(25 - 4w) & 0 \leqslant w \leqslant 5 \\ 1 & w > 5 \end{cases}$$

(b) 0.650

12
$$F(x) = \begin{cases} 0 & x < 0 \\ \frac{x}{4} & 0 \leqslant x \leqslant 1 \\ \frac{1}{5} + \frac{x^4}{20} & 1 \leqslant x \leqslant 2 \\ 1 & x > 2 \end{cases}$$

median 1.565

I.Q.R. 0.821

Exercise 7A

1 (a) 3.5; $\frac{35}{12}$ (b) $\frac{2}{3}$
2 (a) 10.5; $\frac{399}{12}$ (b) 0.6
3 (a) $\frac{3}{10}$ (b) 11; 33
4 (a) $\frac{3}{10}$ (b) 10; 33
5 Possibly but may cluster towards the centre.
6 Assumes dart aimed at random. Depends on skill of thrower.
7 Yes
8 $P(X = r) = \frac{1}{6}$, $r = 1, \ldots 6$; $3\frac{1}{2}$, $\frac{35}{12}$

Exercise 7B

1 $p^4 + 4p^3q + 6p^2q^2 + 4pq^3 + q^4$
2 $p^6 + 6p^5q + 15p^4q^2 + 20p^3q^3 + 15p^2q^4 + 6pq^5 + q^6$
3 (a) $120p^3q^7$ (b) $210p^6q^4$ (c) $45p^8q^2$
4 (a) $495p^4q^8$ (b) $495p^8q^4$ (c) $66p^{10}q^2$
5 $A = 105$, $x = 2$; $B = 455$, $y = 3$; $C = 1365$, $z = 4$
6 $A = 286$, $x = 3$; $B = 715$, $y = 4$; $C = 1287, z = 5$
7 77 520
8 $A = 15\,504$, $x = 5$
9 (a) 0.0163   (b) 0.1366   (c) 0.0569
10 (a) $A = 56$, $x = 3$; 0.0231
(b) $B = 56$, $y = 5$; 0.2076
(c) $C = 28$, $z = 6$; 0.0038

Exercise 7C

1 (a) 0.2731   (b) 0.4682   (c) 0.8049
2 (a) 0.1318   (b) 0.8306   (c) 0.0376
3 (a) 0.1766   (b) 0.1419   (c) 0.7583
4 (a) 0.2001   (b) 0.5981   (c) 0.2018
5 (a) 0.9740   (b) 0.2485   (c) 0.0689
(d) 0.4814
6 (a) 0.4019   (b) 0.5981   (c) 0.9999
7 (a) 0.25   (b) $\frac{15}{16}$ (c) $\frac{3}{8}$
8 (a) 0.3585   (b) 0.1887   (c) 0.9841
9 (a) Bolts independent, $n = 20$, $p = 0.01$
(b) Lights independent, $n = 6$, $p = 0.52$
(c) Serves independent, prob. of ace constant, $n = 30$, $p = \frac{1}{8}$
10 (a) Yes; $B(14, 0.15)$ (b) No; n not fixed
(c) Yes; $B(15, 0.12)$
11 (a) $\frac{16}{243}$ (b) 0.307
12 $\frac{48}{81}$
13 (a) 0.058   (b) 0.448
14 Method I: 0.987, Method II: 0.983
$\therefore$ Use Method I.

Exercise 7D

1 (a) $\mu = 3$; $\sigma^2 = 2.25$ (b) 0.6840
2 (a) $\mu = 3$; $\sigma^2 = 2$ (b) 0.5072
3 (a) $n = 60$ (b) $\sigma = 1.69$
4 $n \leqslant 7$
5 $p = \frac{1}{2}$
6 0.086; 60; 90

Exercise 7E

1 (a) 0.2052 (b) 0.4562 (c) 0.9580
   (d) 0.4142
2 (a) 0.1125 (b) 0.0611 (c) 0.4679
   (d) 0.7700
3 (a) 0.2019 (b) 0.4751 (c) 0.7834
   (d) 0.3963
4 (a) 0.8088 (b) 0.0474 (c) 0.1438
   (d) 0.0460
5 (a) 6 (b) 9 (c) 5 (d) 5
6 (a) 5 (b) 2 (c) $\geqslant 7$ (d) $\geqslant 9$
7 (a) $\geqslant 9$ (b) $\geqslant 10$ (c) $\leqslant 2$ (d) $\geqslant 12$
8 (a) 0.2865 (b) 0.3554
9 (a) 0.1730 (b) 0.0302
10 (a) 0.0235 (b) 0.0293
   (c) defects occur randomly
11 (a) Yes – if they occur randomly
   (b) Yes – pigs randomly dispersed
   (c) No – pigs clustered
   (d) No – salt needs to diffuse
   (e) Yes but possible clustering.
12 (a) 0.067 (b) 0.083
13 (a) 0.905 (b) 9
14 (a) 0.2707 (b) 5.3
15 (a) 0.251 (b) 0.587
16 (a) (i) 0.223 (ii) 0.442 (b) 0.099
17 (a) 0.303 (b) 0.028
18 (a) 0.504 (b) 0.088

Exercise 7F

1 (a) 0.0174 (b) 0.1339
2 (a) 0.0235 (b) 0.8883

3 (a) 0.0337 (b) 0.0843 (c) 0.8753
4 (a) 0.0183 (b) 0.0733 (c) 0.2381
5 (a) 4.5×10^{-5} (b) 0.0671
6 0.00992; 0.323
7 0.016; (a) 0.908 (b) 0.004; 0.0003
8 np, np; 0.965; 0.3; 0.857

Exercise 8A

1 (a) 15, $8\frac{1}{3}$ (b) 0, 3 (c) 0.5, $\frac{3}{4}$
2 5, $\frac{4}{3}$ 0.375
3 (a) $\frac{1}{12}$ O $< x \leqslant 12$

   (b)

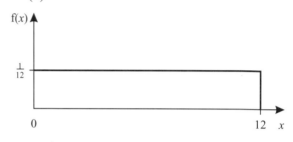

   (c) $\frac{1}{3}$
4 (a) $\frac{2}{3}$
   (b) 120 mm, 4800 mm^2
5 $\frac{1}{3}$
6 (a) $3\frac{1}{2}$, 2.083
   (b) $P(X \leq x_0) = \frac{x_0 - 1}{5}$ $\leq x_0 \leq 6$, 0.6

Exercise 8B

1 (a) 0.9625 (b) 0.9938 (c) 0.6103
   (d) 0.9332 (e) 0.9272 (f) 0.0375
   (g) 0.0062 (h) 0.3897 (i) 0.0668
   (j) 0.2377
2 (a) 0.2907 (b) 0.0994 (c) 0.383
   (d) 0.867 (e) 0.7583 (f) 0.1815
3 (a) 1.64 (b) 0.23 (c) 1.825 (d) 0.31
   (e) 1.25 (f) 1.97
4 (a) 0.1056 (b) 0.1587 (c) 0.8188
5 (a) 2, 0.9772 (b) 2, 0.0228 (c) 1.75, 0.4599
   (d) $-\frac{2}{3}$, 0.2525 (e) -0.786, 0.2840
   (f) -1, 0.631, 0.5773

6 (a) 0.9088   (b) 0.0037   (c) 0.49
   (d) 0.2297   (e) 0.7935

7 14.432

8 (a) 4   (b) 200   (c) 100   (d) 2

9 (a) 0.04   (b) 3.11   (c) 3.2   (d) 14

10 (a) $\mu = 1.5142$, $\sigma = 0.05096$
    (b) $\mu = 51.3$, $\sigma = 20.5$

11 $\mu = 30$, $\sigma = 2$

12 4.01%

13 38.2%, 4.46%

14 31.47%

15 0.091

16 12.52 minutes

17 (a) 37.8%   (b) 125.5 hours to 194.5 hours

18 $\mu = 7.548$, $\sigma = 0.258$

Exercise 8C

1 (a) $P(Y < 25.5)$ (b) $P(Y < 41.5)$
   (c) $P(Y > 10.5)$ (d) $P(Y > 4.5)$
   (e) $P(1.5 < Y < 9.5)$ (f) $P(40.5 < Y < 50.5)$

2 (a) $P(Y > 32.5)$ (b) $(Y < 16.5)$
   (c) $P(Y > 8.5)$ (d) $P(Y < 47.5)$
   (e) $P(23.5 < Y < 36.5)$ (f) $P(4.5 < Y < 9.5)$

3 (a), (c) and (e)

4 (a) 0.097   (b) 0.004   (c) 0.072   (d) 0.223

5 (a) 0.007   (b) 0.946   (c) 0.042   (d) 0.7305

6 (a) 0.961   (b) 0.960 error 0.001

7 (a) 0.8212   (b) 0.8248 error 0.0036

8 n large, $np > 5$, $n(1 - p) > 5$
   mean $= np$, variance $= np(1 - p)$
   (a) 0.215

9 (a) 0.0024, £13 200

10 (a) n large, $np > 5$, $n(1 - p) > 5$
    mean $= np$, variance $= np(1 - p)$
    (b) 0.734

11 (a) 0.059   (b) 0.825   (c) 0.314

12 (a) $0.007 \times 100 = 1$ day
    (b) $0.0448 \times 100 = 4$ days
    (c) $0.778 \times 100 = 8$ days

13 (a) 0.185   (b) 0.858   (c) 0.946

Exercise 8D

1 (a) $N(130, 5^2)$ (b) $N(10, 5^2)$

2 (a) $N(87, 8)$ (b) $N(3, 8)$

3 $N(148, 18)$

4 (a) $N(100, 64)$ (b) $N(120, 81)$
   (c) $N(220, 145)$ (d) $N(250, 241)$

5 (a) $N(29, 9)$ (b) $N(5, 7)$ (c) $N(53, 41)$
   (d) $N(38, 28)$ (e) $N(9, 9)$

6 (a) 0.0744   (b) 0.0053   (c) 0.166
   (d) 0.142/3   (e) 0.0165   (f) 0.6441

7 mean $= 36$, standard deviation $= 0.173$

8 0.1587

9 (a) mean $= 150$ g, standard deviation $= 12.25$
   (b) mean $= 190$ g, standard deviation $= 13.64$
   (c) 0.0708
   (d) mean $= 3800$ g, standard deviation $= 60.99$
   (e) 0.9495

10 0.9894

11 (a) 0.3788   (b) 0.6226   (c) 0.9059

12 $E(Z) = E(X)_1) + E(X_2) + ... + E(X_n) =$
    $\mu + \mu + ... + \mu = n\mu$
    $Var(Z) = Var(X_1) + Var(X_2) + ... +$
    $Var(X_n) = \sigma^2 + \sigma^2 + ... + \sigma^2 = n\sigma^2$ 0.732

Review exercise 2

1 0.973

3 (a) $\frac{6}{11}$ (b) $\frac{5}{11}$ (c) $\frac{3}{10}$

4 (b) $\frac{1}{2}$; $\frac{11}{12}$ (c) $\frac{6}{7}$ (d) $\frac{4}{5}$ (e) $\frac{1}{2}$

5 (a) 0.364   (b) 0.086; 0.349

6 (a) $P(E \cup F) = P(E) + P(F)$
   (b) $P(E \cup F) = P(E) + P(F) - P(E)P(F)$
   (c) $P(G/H)$ is the conditional probability of G
      given H
   (d) 0.0128;   0.00018

7 (a) $P(E \cap F) = P(E).P(F)$
   (b) $P(G \cap H) = 0$; $\frac{8}{15}$; $\frac{1}{2}$; $\frac{1}{6}$; Yes

8 (a) 0.423   (b) 0.682

9 $\frac{1}{5}$; $\frac{1}{6}$; $\frac{1}{3}$

10 (a) 0.40   (b) 0.35

11 (a) $\frac{1}{10}$ (b) $\frac{3}{10}$

12 $\frac{1}{2}$; Independent

13 (a) 34560 (b) 86400

14 10 080; 7560

15 (a) 240 (b) 480 (c) 144

16 (a) 1287 (b) 231

17 (a) (i) $\frac{1}{14}$ (ii) $\frac{18}{7}$ (iii) $\frac{19}{49}$
   (b) (i) $\frac{1}{9}$ (ii) $\frac{9}{4}$ (iii) $\frac{27}{80}$ (iv) 2.38

18 $\frac{1}{28}$; $\mu = \frac{7}{2}$; $\sigma^2 = 1.25$; (a) 12; 20 (b) 3.5; 16.25

19 (b) $2\frac{1}{9}$

   (c)
$$F(x) = \begin{cases} 0 & x < 1 \\ \frac{1}{12}(x^2 + 2x - 3) & 1 \leqslant x < 3 \\ 1 & x \geqslant 3 \end{cases}$$

   (d) 2.16

20 $k = \frac{3}{4}$ $\mu = \frac{9}{16}$ $\sigma^2 = \frac{107}{1280}$ $P(B) = \frac{85}{256}$; $\frac{85}{152}$

21 (a) $\frac{3}{4}$ (b) $\frac{4}{3}$ (c) $\frac{11}{16}$ (d) $\frac{6}{5}, \frac{4}{25}$

22 0.7515; 0.5368

23 (a) 0.181 (b) 0.999 (c) 0.018

24 $\frac{67}{216}$

25 (a) 0.00553 (b) 0.194 (c) 0.0518; 0.014

26 (a) 0.249 (b) 0.929 (c) 0.508; 0.542

27 (a) (i) 0.679 (ii) 0.995 (b) 0.473

28 (a) 0.34 (b) 0.976 (c) 0.0366
   (d) 0.57–0.58

29 0.0756; 0.925; 0.04005

30 (a) binomial (b) Poisson
   (c) 0.013 (d) 0.014; 0.182

31 (a) 0.991 (b) 0.983 (c) $\frac{7}{25}$ (d) 0.0017
   (e) £15.40

32 (a) 0.9938 (b) 0.1336

33 (a) 0.6506 (b) 0.8774
   (c) 0.9966 (d) 0.2716

34 0.0345

35 (a) 0.9918 (b) 0.1505

36 0.02

37 (a) 0.0664 (b) 0.8606
   (c) 0.7201 (d) 0.4402

38 0.845

39 (a) 0 (b) $\frac{\pi^2}{12}$

40 0.0093

41 (a) 0.227 (b) 0.539

42 1.5142 mm, 0.05096 mm
   3.0284 mm, 0.07207

43 (a) 6 (b) 0.12 (c) 3.5 (d) $\frac{25}{12}$

44

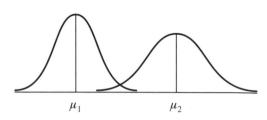

   0.159, 0.7745, 0.067
   2.7
   £37.53

45 4.5%

46 Fixed number of trials, independent, only two outcomes, probability of success is constant.
   (a) 0.1020 (b) 279

47 (a) 0.1056 (b) 1.028

48 n large, $np > 5$, $np(1 - p) > 5$; $\mu = 2, \sigma^2 = 1.6$;
   0.12
   0.147

49 $N(\mu_1 + \mu_2, \sigma_1^2 + \sigma_2^2)$, $N(\mu_1 - \mu_2, \sigma_1^2 + \sigma_2^2)$
   (a) 0.0228 (b) 0.988
   (c) 0.083 (d) 0.209

50 μ is large, mean μ, variance μ
   (a) random arrival of lorries, independent arrivals, arrive singly, average number of arrivals α to the period.
   (b) 0.256 (b) 0.057

51 0.27, 2.56
   5.11, 0.38
   0.99
   0.87

52 50.154, 4

53 (a) B(20, 0.08) (b) 0.3282, 0.2711, 0.0038
   (c) (i) 0.034 (ii) 0.937

54 λ large, mean λ, variance λ
     0.9273, 0.0103, 0.297

55   (a) 1.24%   (b) 53.6%

Examination style paper T1

1   0.1395

2   (a) 306   (b) 36 720

3   (a) $\mu = 27$, $\rho = 4$ (b) μ : no change;
     σ : reduced.

4   (a) 0.47   (b) 0.27   (c) 0.72

5   (a) 0.9392   (b) 0.4695   (c) 0.023

6   (b) $\frac{11}{6}$ (c) 0.462   (d) greater

7   (a) 0.935   (b) 0.008

8   (a) (ii) $Q_1 = 33$ $Q_2 = 37$ $Q_3 = 43$
     (b) median

9   (b) 73   (c) (i) p constant (iii) not realistic
     (d) −   (e) 0.432, 0.444, 0.116, 0.008
     (f) better.

List of symbols and notation

The following symbols and notation are used in the London modular mathematics examinations:

$\{ \quad \}$	the set of
$\mathrm{n}(A)$	the number of elements in the set A
$\{x: \quad \}$	the set of all x such that
$\in$	is an element of
$\notin$	is not an element of
$\emptyset$	the empty (null) set
$\mathscr{E}$	the universal set
$\cup$	union
$\cap$	intersection
$\subset$	is a subset of
A'	the complement of the set A
PQ	operation Q followed by operation P
$\mathrm{f}: A \rightarrow B$	f is a function under which each element of set A has an image in set B
$\mathrm{f}: x \mapsto y$	f is a function under which x is mapped to y
$\mathrm{f}(x)$	the image of x under the function f
f^{-1}	the inverse relation of the function f
fg	the function f of the function g

	open interval on the number line
	closed interval on the number line

$\mathbb{N}$	the set of positive integers and zero, $\{0, 1, 2, 3, \ldots\}$
$\mathbb{Z}$	the set of integers, $\{0, \pm 1, \pm 2, \pm 3, \ldots\}$
$\mathbb{Z}^+$	the set of positive integers, $\{1, 2, 3, \ldots\}$
$\mathbb{Q}$	the set of rational numbers
$\mathbb{Q}^+$	the set of positive rational numbers, $\{x: x \in \mathbb{Q}, x > 0\}$
$\mathbb{R}$	the set of real numbers
$\mathbb{R}^+$	the set of positive real numbers, $\{x: x \in \mathbb{R}, x > 0\}$
$\mathbb{R}_0^+$	the set of positive real numbers and zero, $\{x: x \in \mathbb{R}, x \geqslant 0\}$
$\mathbb{C}$	the set of complex numbers

$\sqrt{}$	the positive square root
$[a, b]$	the interval $\{x: a \leqslant x \leqslant b\}$
$(a, b]$	the interval $\{x: a < x \leqslant b\}$
(a, b)	the interval $\{x: a < x < b\}$

$\lvert x\rvert$	the modulus of $x = \begin{cases} x \text{ for } x \geqslant 0 \\ -x \text{ for } x < 0 \end{cases}, x \in \mathbb{R}$
$\approx$	is approximately equal to
A^{-1}	the inverse of the non-singular matrix A
A^{T}	the transpose of the matrix A
$\det A$	the determinant of the square matrix A
$\displaystyle\sum_{r=1}^{n} f(r)$	$f(1) + f(2) + \ldots + f(n)$
$\displaystyle\prod_{r=1}^{n} f(r)$	$f(1)f(2)\ldots f(n)$
$\binom{n}{r}$	the binomial coefficient $\dfrac{n!}{r!(n-r)!}$ for $n \in \mathbb{Z}^{+}$ $\dfrac{n(n-1)\ldots(n-r+1)}{r!}$ for $n \in \mathbb{Q}$
$\exp x$	e^{x}
$\ln x$	the natural logarithm of $x, \log_{e} x$
$\lg x$	the common logarithm of $x, \log_{10} x$
arcsin	the inverse function of sin with range $[-\pi/2, \pi/2]$
arccos	the inverse function of cos with range $[0, \pi]$
arctan	the inverse function of tan with range $(-\pi/2, \pi/2)$
arsinh	the inverse function of sinh with range $\mathbb{R}$
arcosh	the inverse function of cosh with range $\mathbb{R}_{0}^{+}$
artanh	the inverse function of tanh with range $\mathbb{R}$
$f'(x), f''(x), f'''(x)$	the first, second and third derivatives of $f(x)$ with respect to x
$f^{(r)}(x)$	the rth derivative of $f(x)$ with respect to x
$\dot{x}, \ddot{x}, \ldots$	the first, second, ... derivatives of x with respect to t
z	a complex number, $z = x + iy = r(\cos\theta + i\sin\theta) = re^{i\theta}$
Re z	the real part of z, Re $z = x = r\cos\theta$
Im z	the imaginary part of z, Im $z = y = r\sin\theta$
z^{*}	the conjugate of $z, z^{*} = x - iy = r(\cos\theta - i\sin\theta) = re^{-i\theta}$
$\lvert z\rvert$	the modulus of $z, \lvert z\rvert = \sqrt{(x^{2}+y^{2})} - r$
$\arg z$	the principal value of the argument of z, $\arg z = \theta$, where $\left.\begin{array}{l}\sin\theta = y/r\\\cos\theta = x/r\end{array}\right\} -\pi < \theta \leqslant \pi$
$\mathbf{a}$	the vector $\mathbf{a}$
$\overrightarrow{AB}$	the vector represented in magnitude and direction by the directed line segment AB
$\hat{\mathbf{a}}$	a unit vector in the direction of $\mathbf{a}$
$\mathbf{i,j,k}$	unit vectors in the directions of the cartesian coordinate axes
$\lvert\mathbf{a}\rvert$	the magnitude of $\mathbf{a}$
$\lvert\overrightarrow{AB}\rvert$	the magnitude of $\overrightarrow{AB}$
$\mathbf{a.b}$	the scalar product of $\mathbf{a}$ and $\mathbf{b}$
$\mathbf{a}\times\mathbf{b}$	the vector product of $\mathbf{a}$ and $\mathbf{b}$

A'	the complement of the event A
$P(A)$	probability of the event A
$P(A\|B)$	probability of the event A conditional on the event B
$E(X)$	the mean (expectation, expected value) of the random variable X
X, Y, R, etc.	random variables
x, y, r, etc.	values of the random variables X, Y, R, etc.
$x_1, x_2 \ldots$	observations
$f_1, f_2, \ldots$	frequencies with which the observations $x_1, x_2, \ldots$ occur
$p(x)$	probability function $P(X = x)$ of the discrete random variable X
$p_1, p_2, \ldots$	probabilities of the values $x_1, x_2, \ldots$ of the discrete random variable X
$f(x), g(x), \ldots$	the value of the probability density function of a continuous random variable X
$F(x), G(x), \ldots$	the value of the (cumulative) distribution function $P(X \leqslant x)$ of a continuous random variable X
$\text{Var}(X)$	variance of the random variable X
$B(n, p)$	binomial distribution with parameters n and p
$N(\mu, \sigma^2)$	normal distribution with mean μ and variance σ^2
μ	population mean
σ^2	population variance
σ	population standard deviation
$\bar{x}$	sample mean
s^2	unbiased estimate of population variance from a sample,

$$s^2 = \frac{1}{n-1}\sum(x - \bar{x})^2$$

ϕ	probability density function of the standardised normal variable with distribution $N(0, 1)$
Φ	corresponding cumulative distribution function
α, β	regression coefficients
ρ	product-moment correlation coefficient for a population
r	product-moment correlation coefficient for a sample
$\sim p$	not p
$p \Rightarrow q$	p implies q (if p then q)
$p \Leftrightarrow q$	p implies and is implied by q (p is equivalent to q)

Index